THE FUNDAMENTALS OF
X-RAY AND RADIUM PHYSICS

SEVENTH EDITION

THE FUNDAMENTALS OF X-RAY AND RADIUM PHYSICS

By

JOSEPH SELMAN, M.D.

Clinical Professor of Radiology
University of Texas Health Center at Tyler

Director, School of Radiologic Technology
Tyler Junior College

Attending Staff in Radiation Oncology
East Texas Cancer Center, Tyler

Attending Radiologist
Mother Frances Hospital

Attending Radiologist
Medical Center Hospital
Tyler, Texas

CHARLES C THOMAS • PUBLISHER
Springfield • Illinois • U.S.A.

Published and Distributed Throughout the World by

CHARLES C THOMAS • PUBLISHER
2600 South First Street
Springfield, Illinois 62717

ISBN 0-398-05065-1
Library of Congress Catalog Card Number: 84-16401

Printed in the United States of America
SC-OK-3

Library of Congress Cataloging in Publication Data

Selman, Joseph.
　The fundamentals of X-ray and radium physics, 7th. Edition

　Bibliography: p.
　Includes index.
　1. X-rays.　2. Radium.　3. Radiography.　I. Title.
[DNLM: 1. Health Physics.　2. Radiation, Ionizing.
3. Radium.　WN 110 S468f]
QC481.S457　　1985　　　　537.5'35　　　　84-16401
ISBN 0-398-05065-1

Dedicated to my wife

PREFACE TO SEVENTH EDITION

A number of important advances in radiographic equipment and procedures have taken place since publication of the previous edition six years ago. Outstanding among these has been digital radiography. While these should all be of interest to the student radiographer, they do not greatly affect the fundamental principles of radiography and so will not be dealt with in detail, if at all.

The main purpose of the present revision is to clarify important concepts, based on further experiences of the author in an ongoing and active teaching program. This aspect of the new edition includes many areas of revision of text and figures. Those figures that may have undergone loss of clarity as the result of numerous reproductions have been redrawn.

Updated and new material has also been included, whenever this is relevant to basic radiographic principles. Greater emphasis has been placed on solid state rectifier diodes as well as the pulse concept of rectification. Valve tube rectifiers have been replaced by solid state diodes in all illustrations.

For some years the author has insisted on a precise meaning of penetrating ability of an x-ray beam, and this has been clarified by text and figure. In addition, penetrating ability has been more directly related to photon energy. At the same time, x-ray wavelength has been de-emphasized in favor of photon energy. Increased attention is given to megavoltage over orthovoltage radiation in the section on radiotherapy.

Data for backup timing in radiographic equipment with automatic (phototimed) exposure control have been added. This has assumed increased importance as the result of increasing use of automatic exposure systems.

A description of an exciting new type of high-speed film emulsion, with virtually no loss of recorded detail (Eastman Kodak Company), has been included, together with a discussion of the crossover phenomenon in film-screen systems using two screens and double-emulsion films prevailing in general radiography. The numerical designation of screen speed with different film-screen combinations can be confusing because these numbers are based on par speed being 50, whereas the present trend is to assign an arbitrary speed of 100 to par speed screens. Emphasis is placed, where it should be, on the speed of particular screen-film combinations which differs according to the speed of the screens *and* films.

The most extensive revision involves standardization of terminology related to radiographic quality. The term "recorded detail" is used as an all-inclusive designation for sharpness, definition, and detail, although there are slight differences in connotation among them. Penumbra, while still used, is de-emphasized in favor of blur in referring to image unsharpness. In general, an attempt has been made to simplify and emphasize certain terminology and avoid excessive use of synonyms. Figures depicting these factors have been redrawn.

A new section has been added to explain air gap technic and its applications in the removal of scattered radiation. This has been related to magnification radiography.

The preferred term "beam-limiting device," recommended by federal agencies, has been introduced, although its equivalent "collimator" is retained because of its simplicity.

Compensation filters receive more attention in view of the new lead-incorporated plastic, which makes it possible to insert such filters in the beam of modern radiographic equipment. A description and illustration of the trough filter is included.

A new section has been added to explain, as simply as possible, the elements of computed tomography. This includes basic principles, types of equipment, and image reconstruction, with appropriate figures.

New information has been included in the last chapter dealing with the calculation of organ doses in radiography. Beam filtration for patient protection has also been updated to conform to latest recommendations.

The author wishes to thank again those individuals who were so cooperative in furnishing technical information. These have all been mentioned in previous editions.

Appreciation is also due our artist, A. Howard Marlin, for his superb rendition of new and revised figures. These contribute so much to the clarification of material in the text.

The author wishes particularly to thank Mr. Payne Thomas and his editorial staff for their cooperation and patience.

J.S.

PREFACE TO SIXTH EDITION

AFTER A FOUR-YEAR INTERVAL, revision time has come around again. While the physical basis of radiologic technology has not undergone any revolutionary changes, certain new information is of sufficient importance to be incorporated in the curriculum. In addition, it has been felt that some well-established concepts could benefit from more detailed discussion.

Of special importance has been the development of new types of intensifying screens, both as modifications of existing phosphors, and in the form of completely novel rare earth phosphors. This subject is explored in depth. Furthermore, greater attention has been given to the basic phenomena of luminescence of phosphors to elucidate the fundamental nature of intensifying screen behavior.

Because of growing interest in the accurate measurement of focal spot size, especially in angiography with magnification, the problems of focal spot evaluation have been presented in some detail. In connection with focal spot measurement, it was felt that a simplified description of modulation transfer function would be of interest.

Direct magnification, having escaped from the realm of "trick radiography," has become an integral part of modern small vessel angiography. Therefore, the basic principles governing this special field of radiography have been explored, and important references noted.

The advent of a practical 350-kV unit for chest radiography using a field emission tube has contributed significantly to improved image quality in this area. A section has been devoted to the practical aspects of such high kilovoltage radiography, with emphasis on depth resolution.

In the last few years the Bureau of Radiological Health has reported on its studies of population exposure to x rays in radiography.

These have been of sufficient importance to contribute to the updating of the chapter on Protection in Radiology.

As in earlier editions, there has been a significant rewriting of the text in an effort to simplify even further the explanation of fundamental concepts. In some instances there has been an accompanying revision of illustrations. A number of entirely new figures have also been added.

The most recently revised definition of the roentgen, as well as the proposed new International System of Units (SI), is included to keep the technologist and student abreast of changes in terminology.

Again, the author wishes to thank the previously mentioned individuals and manufacturers who have been so cooperative in supplying pertinent material. To this list should be added 3M Company; Nuclear Associates, Inc.; and Treck Photographic, Inc.

Our artist, A. Howard Marlin, has again carried off the task of revising old figures and preparing new ones in his characteristically competent style.

Finally, the author wishes to express his gratitude to Mr. Payne Thomas and the editorial staff of Charles C Thomas, Publisher, for their encouragement, kindness, and patience during the vicissitudes of revision.

J.S.

PREFACE TO FIFTH EDITION

IN THE SEVEN YEARS since publication of the Fourth Edition, important changes have taken place in the design of x-ray equipment, although fundamental concepts have undergone relatively little revision. Accordingly, new material has been introduced covering such subjects as solid state rectifiers; newer mobile apparatus, including battery powered and capacitor-discharge units; field emission tubes; special tubes for mammography, using molybdenum targets and filters; xeroradiography; and saturable reactor for control of filament current.

Many of the illustrations have been revised or completely redrawn, and corresponding changes have been made in the descriptive legends.

Despite the many changes, the format has been kept essentially intact. However, certain areas have been expanded; for example, improvements in x-ray tube design; tomography; radiographic quality; radionuclides and nuclear medicine; irradiation therapy; and health physics.

Throughout the book, many sections have been rewritten on the basis of the author's further teaching experience, with a view toward improving the explanation of fundamental principles and the description of devices and equipment. Wherever possible, the aim has been in the direction of greater simplification. The material has been generally updated on the basis of the most reliable data available at the time of revision.

Credit is again due to the previously mentioned sources. Additionally, we would like to thank the Field Emission Corporation, the Machlett Laboratories, the Dunlee Corporation, the Xerox Corporation, and the CGR Medical Corporation for their kindness in supplying important material relative to their products.

The author again wishes to express his gratitude to Charles C

Thomas, Publisher, for providing the opportunity of preparing this new edition.

J.S.

PREFACE TO FOURTH EDITION

IN ORDER TO KEEP ABREAST of new developments in the field of radiologic physics, especially those concerning the radiologic technologist and the radiology resident, a number of significant changes have been introduced into this, the Fourth Edition. Only the more important ones will be mentioned here.

Again, the format will be retained intact, all changes being made within its framework. Outdated material, such as mechanical rectification, has been deleted.

The concept of electrical field and the relationship between static electricity, electric discharge, and current electricity have been given greater emphasis. The factors in series and parallel circuits, often difficult for the student technologist, have been discussed more fully with the aid of numerical examples.

X-ray quantity and quality have been described in greater depth, and more attention given to half value layer, including a summary of the methods of measuring it. The determination of tumor exposure and absorbed dose is explained more completely and is based on the latest method of converting the data in published depth dose tables so that they become applicable to any particular therapy unit. In accordance with recent changes in terminology proposed by the International Commission on Radiation Units and Measurements (ICRU), the Capital R now designates the exposure in roentgens. The exposure rate is indicated as R/min or R/sec.

Due to lack of clarity, generally, concerning saturation current as it applies to the modern diagnostic x-ray tube, this subject is covered more fully than before.

In view of the wide use of automatic processing of x-ray films, mainly as the result of improvement in quality and reduction in cost, more space has been devoted to the principles and construction of this type of equipment. In addition, the basic theory of photographic image formation is presented in greater detail for those students who seek a deeper understanding of this subject.

The chapters on radiographic quality and its control have been rearranged and largely rewritten. Radiographic grids are discussed in greater depth, the latest methods of designating grid quality presented, and newer terminology used throughout in accordance with the recommendations of the ICRU.

Under special procedures, bright fluoroscopy (image intensification) have been emphasized because of its wide acceptance by radiologists. Stereoscopic viewing of radiographs has been presented in a much more fundamental manner than before.

A completely new chapter on radioactive isotopes has been added. It is not meant to replace standard textbooks devoted exclusively to this subject, but rather to provide a well-rounded background for the medical use of radioisotopes for the general radiologic technologist. The chapter on health physics has been expanded to include the more commonly used radioisotopes.

It must be pointed out, that insofar as possible, the latest terminology is used throughout this book, conforming to the recommendations of the ICRU, and the International Union of Pure and Applied Chemistry and its twin in Physics. For example, the form "x ray" refers to the noun, whereas "x-ray" designates the adjective; thus, x rays, but x-ray physics. The form ^{131}I instead of I^{131} exemplifies the designation of radioisotopes. Attempts at international standardization of scientific terms are highly commendable in this age of automatic retrieval of information by means of computers.

The author again acknowledges with thanks the cooperation of a number of commercial suppliers in furnishing important data about their products. In addition to those mentioned in earlier editions are: Picker X-Ray Corporation; Liebel-Flarsheim Company; United States Radium Corporation; General Aniline and Film Corporation; and Smit-Roentgen Company.

Grateful recognition is due Charles C Thomas, Publisher, for interest in the preparation of the Fourth Edition, and for the excellence in publication of previous editions.

J.S.

PREFACE TO THIRD EDITION

ONLY FOUR YEARS have passed since the publication of the Second Edition, but a number of changes, some major and some minor, are considered to be of sufficient importance to warrant a fairly thorough revision. This is dictated in part by changing concepts, and in part by the author's further experience with students of widely different degrees of ability and educational background.

The format and figures have been kept essentially intact, although some figures have been revised and several new ones added. Every effort has been made to retain the simplicity of the first two editions. A decimal system of numbering the illustrations has been introduced, a practice which is gaining acceptance in scientific books.

One of the major changes in the present edition is in the chapters on the electric current, electromagnetism, and electric generators and motors. Whereas the conventional direction was emphasized previously, this has now been relegated to history, and all the directional rules have been altered to conform to the flow of electrons. This step was taken only after considerable deliberation, but was finally adopted in compliance with the vast majority of present-day physics textbooks. For the same reason, the term *condenser* has been changed to *capacitor.*

The theory of magnetism has been brought up to date, with the introduction of the concept of atomic magnets and magnetic domains. Otherwise, the same simple approach to magnetic phenomena has been retained.

There have been no radical innovations in the field of x-ray equipment generally, but certain theoretical aspects of this subject have been rewritten in an effort to improve their comprehensibility.

The sections on radiation dosage have been completely revised and expanded, although the student should be encouraged to read more advanced material on this subject, especially during his second year. The modern concept of absorbed dose and its unit, the rad, have been described in some detail. Filtration and radiation quality have received increased attention.

In the sections on radiography, special attention has been devoted to intensifying screens. Included are revised concepts of the relative importance of the effect of crystal size and active layer thickness on image sharpness; the intrinsic and extrinsic factors affecting screen speed; and comparative data on medium and high speed screens.

Because of the increasing interest in automatic processing of films, a section has been included to summarize present information in this important field.

The chapter on radiographic quality has been carefully reworked. The more accurate term *definition* has been substituted for *detail* to indicate image sharpness. The factors influencing definition have been reclassified and clarified. In the chapter on devices for improving radioactive quality, emphasis has been placed on modern collimators in preference to conventional cones, especially with regard to patient protection. The newer types of Bucky mechanisms have also been described.

In view of the recent downward revision of the maximum permissible dose, the chapter on radiation protection has been reoriented accordingly. Emphasis has also been placed on radiation monitoring methods for radiologic personnel. Furthermore, the current agitation regarding the exposure of the population to ionizing radiation has led to a more detailed treatment of the various methods that can be utilized to reduce patient dosage in radiography and fluoroscopy.

Finally, answers to the sample problems at the end of certain chapters have been included in the Appendix as an aid to the student in checking the correctness of his solutions.

As before, the author expresses his sincere appreciation to Mr. Charles C Thomas, Mr. Payne Thomas, and their competent staff for their interest in the preparation of the Third Edition.

J.S.

PREFACE TO SECOND EDITION

ALTHOUGH great advances are continuously being made in Physics, the basic concepts required for the instruction of student x-ray technicians and Radiology residents have changed very little since the publication of the First Edition. Nevertheless, new data which are considered to be of sufficient interest and importance have been incorporated in the Second Edition.

The original format has been preserved almost intact because it has proved successful in actual classroom instruction in numerous schools of x-ray technology. Simplicity is retained throughout, and abundant line diagrams are employed again to clarify the explanation of basic principles and the description of equipment.

The introductory chapter on Mathematics now includes the notation of large and small numbers as powers of 10. Terminology applied to the factors in an electric current and the heating effects of currents has been revised and simplified.

Brems radiation has received more emphasis in the discussion of x-ray production. The descriptive material relating to the interaction of radiation and matter has been enlarged to include pair production.

Fluoroscopic image intensification is introduced and described in detail, since this device and its future modifications promise to revolutionize fluoroscopy in the next few years.

More space has been allotted to the inverse square law, a simplified formula being presented for use in protection and therapy problems. Considerable revision of the chapter on radiation protection was necessitated by recent changes in the recommendations of official bodies. Emphasis is placed also on the roentgen dosage received by patients during various diagnostic procedures. Obsolete data have been eliminated.

Finally, the Bibliography has been expanded to include additional choice references for the more venturesome student.

In addition to the acknowledgments already made in the First Edition, the author wishes to thank the Westinghouse Electric Corporation and the North American Philips Company for valuable data on image intensification.

Again, the author appreciates the interest shown by the publisher, Mr. Charles C Thomas, in making possible the Second Edition.

J.S.

PREFACE TO FIRST EDITION

I T IS OBVIOUS to anyone who has had experience in teaching radiologic physics to student x-ray technicians that the majority of students have had poor preparation for this course of study. Those students who may have been exposed to physics and mathematics in high school often retain so little knowledge of these subjects that they must learn anew even the simplest principles. The student x-ray technician with a background of college training in the sciences is indeed a rarity.

Many teachers devoted to the training of student x-ray technicians have long recognized the dearth of textbooks in physics designed for technicians. A desirable textbook of this type must lead the student, as painlessly as possible, from the most elementary considerations all the way to radiologic physics, a task which is by no means simple. The subject matter must be presented in great detail in order that the student may derive a more complete understanding of it. At the same time, the text must be as nonmathematical as possible and couched in language that is readily comprehensible.

On the basis of lecture notes and other data used in the instruction of student technicians over a period of years, the author has written the present book with the primary purpose of simplifying for the student x-ray technician the subject of radiologic physics in all its theoretical and practical aspects as it confronts the technician. With this aim in view, basic principles of physics and chemistry are emphasized and presented in greatest possible detail. At the same time, the simplest available terminology is employed in order to avoid a language barrier to the comprehension of these important principles. In accordance with the familiar pedagogic rule of repetition, the more significant physical principles are repeated, presented from various standpoints, and correlated wherever possible throughout the text.

Recognizing the value of visual aids to education, the author has made free use of numerous line drawings to facilitate the study of the text. Tables have been included only to emphasize certain points rather than as a source of reference for specific data. Throughout the book, fundamental principles are stressed, and if these are grasped by the student, he is then in a better position to understand the specific data furnished by the manufacturer for the equipment or supplies in use in his radiology department.

Mathematics of the simplest type is employed only where deemed essential to the understanding of fundamental principles. A summary of elementary mathematics introduces the book so that the student's memory can be more easily refreshed. It embodies all of the mathematical principles that are to appear in later chapters, so that if the first chapter is mastered the student should encounter no difficulty with the algebra and geometry employed in subsequent chapters.

There has been included a somewhat detailed consideration of the intimate structure of matter, and some space has been devoted to the quantum theory. This may be criticized by those teachers who feel that too much emphasis is already being placed on physics in the students' overburdened curriculum. However, it is felt, in view of the great strides that have been made in atomic physics in the last few years and the growing importance of radioactive isotopes, that the student should have at least a minimum concept of atomic structure and atomic energy.

The material has been so organized that certain sections may be omitted at the instructor's discretion without seriously interfering with the continuity of the text. On the other hand, these more advanced considerations will appeal to the student technician fortunate enough to have a better-than-average scientific background.

Although it has been pointed out repeatedly that this book has been conceived primarily for the student x-ray technician, it is felt that it will also be of distinct advantage to the resident in radiology who is just entering upon his period of training and needs an introductory textbook to prepare him for more advanced reading as his knowledge of the subject develops.

With some exceptions, the author makes no claim to originality, but it is impossible to mention by name the thousands of radiologists, physicists, and technicians who have developed the science of radiology to its present high position. Grateful acknowledgment is hereby accorded to the following who so kindly took time from their busy curriculum to review certain sections of the text and offered invaluable suggestions and criticisms: T. W. Bonner, Ph.D., Professor of Physics at the Rice Institute; Otto Glasser, Ph.D., Professor of Biophysics at the Cleveland Clinic Foundation; and Mr. W. S. Cornwell and his associates at the Eastman Kodak Company. The illustrations were prepared from the author's sketches by Mr. Howard Marlin, Tyler, Texas. The manuscript and typing was ably executed by Miss Betty Presley of Tyler, Texas.

The author appreciates the kindness of the Machlett Laboratories, Inc., and of the General Electric X-ray Corporation for furnishing the basic drawings of their x-ray and valve tubes; and of the Eastman Kodak Company, E. I. duPont de Nemours, Inc., and Ansco for the data on x-ray films, film processing, and screens. Finally, the author is grateful to the publisher, Mr. Charles C Thomas, for his encouragement, patience, cooperation, and sound advice.

JOSEPH SELMAN, M.D.

Tyler, Texas

CONTENTS

Contents

THE FUNDAMENTALS OF
X-RAY AND RADIUM PHYSICS

CHAPTER 1   SIMPLIFIED MATHEMATICS

A LL OF THE PHYSICAL SCIENCES have in common a firm basis in mathematics. This is no less true of radiologic physics, an important branch of the physical sciences. Clearly, then, in approaching a course in radiologic physics you, as a student technologist, should find your path smoothed by an adequate background in the appropriate areas of mathematics.

We shall assume here that you have had at least the required high school exposure to mathematics, although this may vary widely from place to place. However, realizing that much of this material may have become hazy with time, we shall review the simple but necessary aspects of arithmetic, algebra, and plane geometry. Such a review should be beneficial in at least two ways. First, it should make it easier to understand the basic principles and concepts of radiologic physics. Second, it should aid in the solution of such everyday problems as conversion of radiographic technics, interpretation of tube rating charts, determination of radiographic magnification, and many others that may arise from time to time.

The discussion will be subdivided as follows: (1) arithmetic, (2) algebra, (3) ratio and proportion, (4) geometry, (5) graphs and charts, and (6) large and small numbers. Only fundamental principles will be included.

ARITHMETIC

Arithmetic is calculation or problem solving by means of definite numbers. We shall assume that you are familiar with addition, subtraction, multiplication, and division and shall therefore omit these operations.

3

Fractions

In arithmetic, *a fraction may be defined as one or more equal parts of a unit.* For example, $1/2$, $1/3$, and $2/5$ are fractions. The quantity below the line is called the *denominator;* it indicates the number of equal parts into which the unit is divided. The quantity above the line is the *numerator;* it indicates the number of equal parts taken. Thus, if a pie were divided into three equal parts, the denominator would be 3; and if two of these parts were taken, the numerator would be 2. Hence, the two segments would represent $2/3$ of the pie.

In a more general sense, fractions represent *the division of one quantity by another.* This extends the concept of fractions to expressions in which the numerator is larger than the denominator, as in the fraction $5/2$.

If the numerator is smaller than the denominator, as $3/5$, we have a *proper fraction.* If the numerator is larger than the denominator, as $5/3$, we have an *improper fraction,* because $5 \div 3 = 1\frac{2}{3}$, which is really an integer plus a fraction.

In *adding* fractions, all of which have the *same* denominator, we add all the numerators first and then place the sum over the denominator:

$$\frac{2}{7} + \frac{3}{7} + \frac{6}{7} + \frac{5}{7} = \frac{2 + 3 + 6 + 5}{7} = \frac{16}{7}$$

$$\frac{16}{7} = 2\frac{2}{7}$$

Subtraction of fractions having identical denominators follows the same rule:

$$\frac{6}{7} - \frac{4}{7} = \frac{6 - 4}{7} = \frac{2}{7}$$

If a series of fractions is to be added or subtracted, and the denominators are *different,* then the *least common denominator* must be found. This is the smallest number which is exactly divisible by all the denominators. Thus,

$$\frac{1}{2} + \frac{2}{3} - \frac{3}{4} = ?$$

The smallest number which is divided exactly by each denominator is 12. Place 12 in the denominator of a new fraction:

$$\frac{}{12}$$

Divide the denominator of each of the fractions in the old equation into 12, and then multiply the answer by the numerator of that fraction; each result is then placed in the numerator of the new fraction:

$$\frac{6+8-9}{12}=\frac{5}{12}$$

When numbers are *multiplied, we take their product.* In multiplying fractions, we take the product of the numerators and place it over the product of the denominators,

$$\frac{4}{5}\times\frac{3}{10}=\frac{4\times3}{5\times10}=\frac{12}{50}$$

The resulting fraction can be reduced by dividing the numerator and the denominator by the *same* number, in this case, 2:

$$\frac{12}{50}\div\frac{2}{2}=\frac{6}{25}$$

which cannot be further simplified.

Note that when the numerator and the denominator are both multiplied or divided by the same number, the value of the fraction does not change. For instance,

$$\frac{3}{5}\times\frac{2}{2}=\frac{6}{10}$$

$$\textit{is the same as }\frac{3}{5}\times1=\frac{3}{5}$$

When two fractions are to be divided, as 4/5 ÷ 3/7, the fraction that is to be divided is the *dividend,* and the fraction that does the dividing is called the *divisor.* In this case, 4/5 is the dividend and 3/7 the divisor. The rule is to invert the divisor (called "taking the reciprocal") and multiply the dividend by it:

$$\frac{4}{5}\div\frac{3}{7}$$

$$\frac{4}{5} \times \frac{7}{3} = \frac{28}{15} = 1\frac{13}{15}$$

Percent

A special type of fraction, **percent,** is represented by the sign %
to indicate that the number standing with it is to be divided by
100. Thus, 95% = $95/100$. We do not use percentages directly in
mathematical computations, but first convert them to fractions or
decimals. For instance,

$$150 \times 40\% \text{ is changed to}$$
$$150 \times {}^{40}\!/100 \text{ or } 150 \times {}^{2}\!/5$$
$$\text{or } 150 \times 0.40.$$

All these expressions equal 60.

Decimal Fractions

Our common method of representing numbers as multiples of
ten is embodied in the ***decimal system.*** A ***decimal fraction*** has as its
denominator 10, or 10 raised to some power such as 100, 1000,
10,000, etc. The denominator is symbolized by a dot in a certain
position. For example, the decimal $0.2 = {}^{2}\!/10$; $0.02 = {}^{20}\!/100$;
$0.002 = {}^{20}\!/1000$, etc. Decimals can be multiplied or divided, but
care must be taken to place the decimal point in the proper
position:

$$
\begin{array}{r}
2.24 \\
\times\ 1.25 \\
\hline
1120 \\
448 \\
224 \\
\hline
2.8000 \\
\end{array}
$$

Note that we add the total number of digits to the right of the
decimal points in the numbers being multiplied, which in this case
turns out to be four. We then point off four places from the right in

Figure 1.1. With this calibrated scale we can estimate to the nearest tenth. Thus, the position of the pointer indicates 8.4 units, the 0.4 being the last significant figure.

the answer to determine the correct position of the decimal point. The decimal system is used everywhere in science and in the vast majority of countries in daily life.

Significant Figures

The precision (reproducibility of results) of any type of measurement is limited by the design of the measuring instrument. For example, a scale calibrated in grams as shown in Figure 1.1 allows an estimate to the nearest tenth of a gram. Thus, the scale in Figure 1.1 reads 8.4 grams. The last figure, 0.4, is estimated and is the *last significant figure*—that is, it is the last meaningful digit. Obviously, no greater precision is possible with this particular instrument. To improve precision, the scale would have to show a greater number of subdivisions.

Now let us see how significant figures are used in various operations. For example, in addition:

item 1	98.26 grams
item 2	1.350 g
item 3	260.1 g
	359.710 g

Notice that three digits appear after the decimal point in the answer. But in item (3) there is only one digit 1, after the decimal point; beyond this, the digits are unknown. Therefore, the digits after the 7 in the answer imply more than is known, since the answer can be no more precise than the least precise item being added. In this case, the answer should be properly stated as 359.7. Thus, in addition and subtraction the answer can have no more significant figures after the decimal point than the item with the *least number of significant figures after its decimal point.*

A different situation exists in multiplication and division. Here, the total number of significant figures in the answer equals that in the items having the **least total number of significant figures.** For example, in

$$25.23 \text{ cm}$$
$$\times \ 1.21 \text{ cm}$$

$$2523$$
$$5046$$
$$2523$$

$$30.5283 \text{ cm}^2$$

1.21 has fewer significant figures—three in all. Therefore the answer should have three significant figures and be read as 30.5 (dropping the 0.0283).

In general, to **round off** significant figures, we observe the following rule: if the digit following the last significant figure is equal to or greater than 5, the last significant figure is increased by 1; if less than 5, it is unchanged. The rule is applied in the following examples:

45.157 is rounded to 45.16
45.155 is rounded to 45.16
45.153 is rounded to 45.15

where the answer is to be expressed in four significant figures.

ALGEBRA

The word **algebra,** derived from the Arabic language, connotes that branch of mathematics which deals with the relationship of quantities usually represented by letters of the alphabet—Roman, Greek, or Hebrew.

Operations. Mathematical operations with **letter symbols** are the same as with **numerals,** since both are symbolic representations of numbers which, in themselves, are abstract concepts. For example, the concept "four" may be represented by 4, 2^2, 2×2, $2 + 2$, or $3 + 1$; or by the letter x if the value of x is specifically designated to represent "four." In algebra, just as in arithmetic, the fundamental operations include addition, subtraction, multiplication, and division; and there are fractions, proportions, and equations. Algebra provides a method of finding an unknown quantity when the relationship of certain known quantities is specified.

Algebraic operations are indicated by the same symbols as arithmetic:

$+$ (plus) add
$-$ (minus) subtract
$\times$ (times) multiply
$\div$ (divided by) divide
$=$ equals

To indicate ***addition*** in algebra, we may use the general expression

$$x + y \qquad (1)$$

The symbols x and y, called ***variables***, may represent any number or quantity we choose. Thus, if $x = 4$ and $y = 7$, then, substituting these values in equation (1),

$$4 + 7 = 11$$

Similarly, to indicate ***subtraction*** in algebra, we may use the general expression

$$x - y$$

If $x = 9$ and $y = 5$, then

$$9 - 5 = 4$$

Notice that algebraic symbols may represent whole numbers, fractions, zero, and negative numbers, among others. Negative numbers are those whose value is less than zero and are designated as ^-x. In algebraic terms, we may add a positive and a negative number as follows:

$$x + {}^-y$$

If $x = 8$ and $^-y = {}^-3$, then

$$8 + {}^-3$$

is the same as

$$8 - 3 = 5$$

The + sign is omitted in the designation of positive numbers, being reserved to indicate the operation of addition.

On the other hand, we may subtract a negative quantity from a positive one:

$$x - {}^-y$$

If $x = 4$ and $-y = -6$, then

$$4 - {}^-6$$

is the same as

$$4 + 6 = 10$$

Multiplication in algebra follows the same rules as in arithmetic. However, in the multiplication of letter symbols the $\times$ sign is omitted, $x \times y$ being written as xy. If $x = 3$ and $y = 5$, then substituting in the expression xy,

$$3 \times 5 = 15$$

Division in algebra is customarily expressed as a fraction. Thus, $x \div y$ is written as x/y. If $x = 3$ and $y = 5$, then

$$3 \div 5 = 3/5$$

When two negative quantities are multiplied or divided, the answer is positive. Thus, $-x \times -y = xy$; and $-x/-y = x/y$. When a positive and a negative quantity are multiplied or divided, the answer is negative; thus, $x \times -y = -xy$, and $x \div -y = -x/y$.

In solving an algebraic expression consisting of a collection of **terms** we must perform the indicated **multiplication and division first,** and then carry out the indicated addition and subtraction. An example will clarify this:

$$ab + c/d - f = ?$$

Suppose $a = 2, b = 3, c = 4, d = 8$, and $f = 5$. Substituting in the preceding expression,

$$2 \times 3 + \frac{4}{8} - 5 = ?$$

Performing **multiplication and division first,**

$$6 + \frac{4}{8} - 5 = ?$$

Then, performing addition and subtraction,

$$6\frac{4}{8} - 5 = 1\frac{4}{8} = 1\frac{1}{2}$$

A parenthesis inclosing a group of terms indicates that all of the terms inside the parenthesis are to be multiplied by the term outside the parenthesis. This is simplified by performing all the indicated operations in correct sequence—inside the parenthesis first—and then multiplying the result by the quantity outside the parenthesis. For example,

$$6\,(8 - 4 + 3 \times 2) =$$
$$6\,(8 - 4 + 6) =$$
$$6 \times 10 = 60$$

Equations. The simpler algebraic equations can be solved without difficulty if fundamental rules are applied. You can easily verify these rules by substituting numerals. In the equation

$$a + b = c + d \tag{2}$$

$a + b$ is called the **left side,** and $c + d$ the **right side.** Each letter is called a **term.** If any quantity is added to one side of the equation, the same quantity must be added to the other side in order for this to remain an equation. Similarly, if any quantity is subtracted from one side, the same quantity must be subtracted from the other side. To simplify the concept of the equation we may picture it as a see-saw as in Figure 1.2. If persons of equal weight are placed at each end, the board will remain horizontal— the equation is balanced. If a second person is now added to one end of the see-saw, a person of similar weight must be added to the other end in order to keep the board level.

Return again to the simple equation:

$$a + b = c + d$$

in which each term is a variable. If any three of the variables are known, the fourth can be found. Suppose, a is 3, b is 4, c is 1, and d is unknown. Substituting these values in the equation,

$$3 + 4 = 1 + d$$

How can d be found? Simply rearrange the equation so that d is

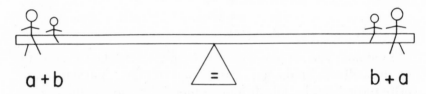

Figure 1.2. Analogy of algebraic equation to a see-saw.

alone, that is, *the only term in its side.* In this case, subtract 1 from both sides of the equation. However, a mathematical short cut can be used: *a term may be transposed from one side of an equation to the other side, provided it is given the opposite sign.* Following this rule, 1 becomes a minus 1 when moved to the left side. Thus,

$$3 + 4 - 1 = d$$
$$6 = d$$
$$\text{or,} \quad d = 6$$

Usually, in solving algebraic equations, we rearrange the terms before substituting their numerical values. In the equation

$$a + b = c + d$$

to find d, transpose c to the left side and change its sign.

$$a + b - c = d$$
$$\text{or,} \quad d = a + b - c$$

(Reversing both sides of an equation does not alter its equality.)

In algebraic equations in which terms are multiplied or divided, analogous rules apply. For example, equation

$$x = y/z$$

may be solved for y by multiplying both sides by z,

$$xz = yz/z$$
$$xz = y$$
$$\text{or,} \quad y = xz$$

The same result may be obtained by moving z from the denominator of the right side to the numerator of the left side. Thus, we have the short-cut rule for cross-multiplication: *if the denominator of one side of an equation is moved, it multiplies the numerator of the other side and, conversely, if the numerator of one side is moved, it multiplies the denominator of the other side.*

Suppose that in the equation $x = y/z$, x and y are known; then z is solved as follows: move z into the numerator of the opposite side as a multiplier,

$$xz = y$$

and move x into the denominator of the right side as a multiplier, and

$$z = y/x \tag{3}$$

The above rule can be readily tested. Suppose that y is 12, and x is 3. Substituting in equation (3),

$$z = 12/3$$
$$z = 4$$
$$4 = 12/3 \tag{4}$$

If we wish to move 3, we must place it in the numerator of the left side of equations (4),

$$4 \times 3 = 12 \tag{4a}$$

Note that numerical equations (4) and (4a) balance.

Now, referring again to equation (4), suppose we wish to move 12. We must place it in the denominator of the left side

$$4/12 = 1/3$$

Again, it is evident that the equation balances.

RATIO AND PROPORTION

A *ratio* is a fixed relationship between two quantities, simply indicating how many times larger or smaller one quantity is relative to another. It has essentially the same meaning as a fraction.

One symbol that expresses a ratio is the colon (:). Thus, $a{:}b$ is read "a is to b." Or, 1:2 is read "1 is to 2." In modern mathematics ratios are usually represented as fractions:

$a{:}b$ is the same as a/b
1:2 is the same as $1/2$

As noted above, the fraction $1/2$ indicates that the numerator is $1/2$ as large as the denominator. Similarly, $2/3$ indicates that the numerator is $2/3$ as large as the denominator.

The meaning of ratio is important to the technologist, because it underlies the concept of ***proportion,*** defined as ***an expression showing that two given ratios are equal.*** Thus, we may have an algebraic proportion,

$$a/b = c/d \qquad (5)$$

which is read "a is to b as c is to d." The same idea can also be presented numerically. For example,

$$3/6 = 4/8$$

If any three terms of a proportion are known, the fourth may easily be determined. Suppose in proportion (5) a is 2, b is 4, d is 8, and c is to be found. Then,

$$2/4 = c/8$$

Moving 8 to the numerator of the left side (crossmultiplying),

$$\frac{2 \times 8}{4} = c$$

$$c = 16/4 = 4$$

There are three general types of proportions that are of interest in radiography.

1. ***Direct proportion.*** Here, one quantity maintains the same ratio to another quantity as the latter changes. For example, the statement "a is proportional to b" means that if b is doubled, a is automatically doubled; if b is tripled, a is tripled, etc. In order to represent this mathematically, let us assume that the quantity a_1 exists when b_1 exists; and that if b_1 is changed to b_2, then a_1 becomes a_2. Thus,

$$a_1/b_1 = a_2/b_2$$

The numbers below the letters are called "subscripts" and have no significance except to label a_2 as being different from a_1. Such a direct proportion is solved by the method described above.

2. *Inverse proportion.* Here, one quantity varies in the opposite direction from another quantity as the latter changes. Thus, the statement "a is inversely proportional to b" means that if b is doubled a is halved, if b is tripled, a is divided by 3, etc. Such a proportion is set up as follows:

$$\frac{a_1}{1/b_1} = \frac{a_2}{1/b_2}$$

Crossmultiplying,

$$a_1/b_2 = a_2/b_1 \tag{6}$$

A numerical example should help clarify this. Suppose that when a_1 is 2, b_1 is 4; if a is inversely proportional to b, what will a_1 become if b_1 is changed to 8? In this case, a_2 is the unknown, and b_2 is 8. Substituting in equation (6),

$$2/8 = a_2/4$$
$$a_2 = 8/8 = 1$$

Thus, a is halved when b is doubled.

3. *Inverse Square Proportion.* See pages 354–355.

PLANE GEOMETRY

Plane geometry is that branch of mathematics which deals with figures lying entirely in one plane; that is, on a flat surface. Some of the elementary rules of plane geometry will now be listed.

1. A *straight line* (in classical geometry) is the shortest distance between two points. It has only one dimension—length.

2. A *rectangle* is a plane figure composed of four straight lines meeting at right angles. Its opposite sides are equal. The sum of the lengths of the four sides is called the *perimeter*. The area of a rectangle is the product of two adjacent sides. Thus, in Figure 1.3 the perimeter is the sum $a + b + a + b = 2a + 2b$. The area is $a \times b$ or ab.

3. A *square* is a special rectangle in which all four sides are equal.

Figure 1.3. Rectangle.
Perimeter $= a + b + a + b$
$= 2a + 2b$

Figure 1.4. Square.
Perimeter $= 4a$
Area $= a \times a = a^2$

4. A ***triangle*** is a figure made up of three straight lines connecting three points that are not in the same line and lie in the same plane. The perimeter of a triangle is the sum of the three sides. The area of a triangle is one half the base times the altitude (the altitude is the perpendicular distance from the apex to the base). This is shown in Figure 1.5.

5. A ***circle*** is a closed curved line which is everywhere at an equal distance from one point called the center, lying in the same plane as the center. A straight line from the center to any point on the circle is the ***radius.*** A straight line passing through the center

and meeting the circle at two points is the ***diameter***, which is obviously equal to twice the radius. The length of the circle is its ***circumference***, obtained by multiplying the diameter by a constant, π (pi). Pi always equals about 3.14. The area enclosed by a circle equals π times the square of the radius. Figure 1.6 shows these relationships.

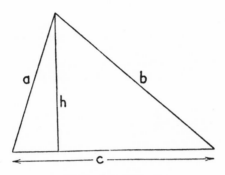

Figure 1.5. Triangle.
Perimeter $= a + b + c$
Area $= \frac{1}{2}ch$

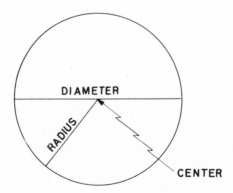

Figure 1.6. Circle.
Circumference $= \pi \times$ diameter $= \pi d$
Area $= \pi \times$ radius$^2 = \pi r^2$

Similar Triangles

Of great importance in radiology, and closely related to ratio and proportion, is the proportionality of **similar triangles.** Such triangles have identical shape, although they differ in size. *In similar triangles the corresponding sides are directly proportional and the corresponding angles are equal.* Thus, similar triangles represent the geometric equivalent of direct proportion.

Figure 1.7 shows two similar triangles. The corresponding sides (those opposite the equal corresponding angles) are proportional, so that

$$a/A = b/B, \text{ or}$$
$$a/A = c/C, \text{ or}$$
$$b/B = c/C$$

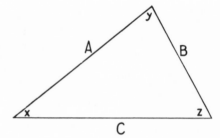

Figure 1.7. Similar triangles. The corresponding angles are *equal;* that is, $x = x$, $y = y$, $z = z$. The corresponding sides are proportional; thus, $a/A = b/B = c/C$.

A line drawn across any triangle parallel to its base produces two similar triangles, one partly superimposed on the other, as shown in Figure 1.8. Line *BE* has been drawn parallel to the base *CD*. Then triangle *ABE* is similar to triangle *ACD* and their corresponding sides are proportional. This may be simplified by separating the two triangles as in Figure 1.7.

A thorough comprehension of similar triangles is essential to the understanding of photographic and radiographic projection. Suppose an object is placed in a beam of light originating at a point source and allowed to cast a shadow or image on a surface (see Figure 1.9). The image has to be larger than the object. Knowing

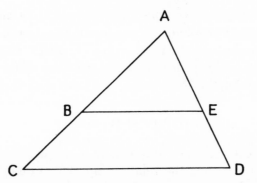

Figure 1.8. Similar triangles. *BE* is parallel to *CD*. Triangle *ABE* is similar to triangle *ACD*. Therefore,

$$AB/AC = AE/AD = BE/CD.$$

the distances of the object and image, respectively, from the light source, as well as the object size, we can determine the image size from the similarity of triangles ABC and ADE. We do this by setting up the following proportion:

Figure 1.9. Projection of the shadow image of an object by a point source of light. *DE/BC = AG/AF*

$$\frac{\text{image size}}{\text{object size}} = \frac{\text{image distance}}{\text{object distance}}$$

Substituting the known values in the equation, we can predict the size of the image by solving the equation. Note that if any three of the values are known, the fourth can be readily obtained from the same equation. This principle also applies in radiography, as will be shown in Chapter 18.

GRAPHS AND CHARTS

For practical purposes, graphs and charts may be regarded as diagrams representing the relationship of two quantities, one of which depends on the other. The dependent factor is called the *dependent variable.* The factor which changes independently is called the *independent variable.*

When data are accumulated, showing how a dependent variable changes with a change in the independent variable, they can either be compiled in a table, or represented by a graph. However, tables do not give intermediate values as do graphs.

The construction and interpretation of a graph may be exemplified as follows: the optimum developing time for x-ray film increases as the temperature of the developing solution decreases (not inversely proportional, however). Table 1.1 reproduces the data actually obtained with a particular developer. To chart this information on graph paper, first plot the temperature (independent variable) along the horizontal axis of the graph. Then plot the developing time (dependent variable) on the vertical axis, as shown in Figure 1.10. In mathematics, the dependent variable is said to be a *function* of the independent variable. To graph the tabulated data, take the first temperature listed in the table and locate it on the horizontal axis. Trace vertically upward from this point to the horizontal line corresponding to the correct developing time, and mark the intersection with a dot. Repeat this for all the values in the table, and then draw a line that best fits the dots. This constitutes a *line graph* or *curve.*

Having constructed a graph, how do we read it? Suppose that we wish to determine the correct developing time for a temperature of 18.5 C (65 F). Locate 18.5 C (65 F) on the horizontal axis and trace vertically upward to the intersection with the curve; from this point of intersection trace horizontally to the vertical axis

TABLE 1.1
TIME–TEMPERATURE DEVELOPMENT DATA

Temperature		Developing Time in Minutes
C	F	
17	62	4½
18.5	65	3½
20	68	3
21	70	2¾
22	72	2½
24	75	2

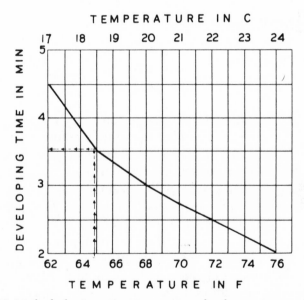

Figure 1.10. Method of using a time-temperature development curve. Select the correct temperature on the horizontal axis, in this case 18.5 C (65 F). Follow vertically, as shown by the arrows, to the curve. Then follow horizontally to the time axis where the correct developing time in this case is seen to be 3½ min.

on the left, where the correct developing time can be read. This is shown in Figure 1.10, where the tracing lines are formed by broken lines with arrows. The horizontal tracing line meets the vertical axis at approximately 3½ minutes, which is the correct developing time at this temperature. Thus, a properly constructed graph gives the developing times for temperature readings that did not appear in the original table, a process called *interpolation.*

LARGE AND SMALL NUMBERS

Because ordinary notation is too cumbersome to express the extremely large numbers often encountered in physics, we resort to the *exponential system* in powers of 10. For example, the number 10^3 means that 10 is multiplied by itself three times: $10 \times 10 \times 10$. In the quantity 10^3, 10 is the *base* and 3 the *exponent,* and is read as "ten to the third power." In general,

$$10^1 = 10$$
$$10^2 = 100$$
$$10^3 = 1000, \text{ etc}$$

Note that the exponent of 10 indicates the number of zeroes required to express the number in ordinary notation.

Let us now apply this principle. The velocity of light in air is 30,000,000,000 cm per sec. Place a decimal point after 3; there are ten zeroes to the right of the decimal point. Therefore, this number may be simply expressed as 3.0×10^{10} cm per sec, read as "three point oh times ten to the tenth." A more complicated number such as 4,310,000,000,000,000 may be simplified in the same way by placing a decimal point after the first digit, 4, and counting the number of *places* to the right, in this case fifteen. The corresponding number in the powers-of-ten system is 4.31×10^{15}.

Suppose, instead, we are to convert 6.3×10^6 to *ordinary notation.* Count six places to the right of the decimal point, filling out the places with zeroes. Since the first place is already occupied by a digit, 3, five zeroes must follow. Therefore, the number is 6,300,000. In general, *any number followed by 10^6 is expressed in millions.*

The same system can be applied to *extremely small* numbers, by the use of negative exponents. This is based on

$$10^{-1} = 1/10 \quad = 0.1$$
$$10^{-2} = 1/100 \quad = 0.01$$
$$10^{-3} = 1/1000 = 0.001, \text{etc.}$$

From this you can see that a negative exponent indicates the number of decimal places to the **left** of a digit, **including the digit.** Thus, 0.004 would be expressed as 4×10^{-3}. To obtain this result, count the number of places to the right of the decimal point, including the first digit,

$$0.\overset{\cdot\,\cdot\,\cdot}{004}$$

The counted number of places (three in this instance) then becomes the negative exponent of 10; thus, 4×10^{-3}. A more complicated number such as 0.00000000000372 would be simply expressed as 3.72×10^{-12}, read as "three point seven two times ten to the minus twelfth."

The simplified system of notation facilitates the multiplication and division of large and small numbers. To multiply such numbers, we multiply the digits and make the exponent of 10 in the answer equal to the algebraic sum of the exponents of 10 in the multipliers. Thus,

$$4 \times 10^3 \times 2 \times 10^2 \quad = 4 \times 2 \times 10^{(3+2)} = 8 \times 10^5$$
$$3 \times 10^6 \times 2 \times 10^{-4} = 3 \times 2 \times 10^{(6-4)} = 6 \times 10^2$$

To divide numbers in this system, we divide the digits and derive the exponent of 10 in the answer by subtracting algebraically the exponent in the divisor from the exponent in the dividend:

$$\frac{6 \times 10^5}{2 \times 10^3} = \frac{6 \times 10^{(5-3)}}{2} = 3 \times 10^2$$

$$\frac{9 \times 10^7}{3 \times 10^{-2}} = \frac{9 \times 10^{(7+2)}}{3} = 3 \times 10^9$$

Note in the above examples that when a power number is moved from the denominator of a fraction to the numerator, or *vice versa,* we simply change the sign of the exponent. Thus,

$$\frac{8}{3 \times 10^{-5}} = \frac{8 \times 10^5}{3}$$

QUESTIONS AND PROBLEMS

1. Reduce the following fractions:
   (a) 4/8   (b) 9/12   (c) 10/150   (d) 4/5

2. Solve the following problems:
   (a) $3/5 + 2/5 + 4/5 =$
   (b) $2/3 + 3/4 + 3/7 =$
   (c) $1/2 + 2/3 + 4/5 =$

3. Mr. Jones has 100 bushels of potatoes and sells 75 percent of this crop. How many bushels does he have left?

4. Divide as indicated:
   (a) $4/5 \div 3/5$ (b) $4/9 \div 7/16$ (c) $8/9 \div 3/5$

5. If $a = b/c$, what is b in terms of a and c? What is c in terms of a and b?

6. Solve the following equations for the unknown term:
   (a) $x + 4 = 7 - 3 + 8$
   (b) $6 + 3 - 1 = 4 + 1 - a$
   (c) $x/3 = 7/9$
   (d) $4/y = \dfrac{6 + 3}{10}$
   (e) $\dfrac{x + 4}{8} = 7 + 2 - 3$

7. Solve the following proportions for the unknown quantity:
   (a) $a/7 = 2/21$ (c) $4/6 = 7/y$
   (b) $3/9 = x/15$ (d) $3/5 = 9/x$

8. The diameter of an x-ray beam is directly proportional to the distance from the tube target. If the diameter of the beam at a 20-in. distance is 10 cm, what will the diameter be at a 40-in. distance?

9. The exposure of a radiograph is directly proportional to the time of exposure. What will happen to the exposure if the time is tripled?

10. What is the area of a circle having a diameter of 4 cm?

11. What is the area of a rectangular plot of ground measuring 20 ft on one side and 30 ft on the adjacent side?
12. Using the time-temperature curve in Figure 1.10, determine the proper developing time when the temperature is 64 F.
13. Convert 3.6×10^6 to the ordinary number system.
14. Change 424,000 to the exponential system.
15. Solve $320,000 \times 1,200,000 \div 240,000$ using the exponential system.

CHAPTER *2* PHYSICS AND THE UNITS OF MEASUREMENT

Physics, as an exact science, requires a precise vocabulary in which each term has a clear and definite meaning. Not only does this simplify the learning process, but it also facilitates the organization of concepts and their accurate communication to others.

In order to appreciate the position of physics within the framework of science, we may use the term **natural science** to include the systematic study of the universe and its contents. Figure 2.1 shows the subdivision of natural science into its major categories. Here you can readily see that while physics is listed as one of the physical sciences, it actually underlies all of them. In fact, it is ultimately an important contributor even to the biologic sciences.

Figure 2.1. Subdivisions of natural science. Notice that physics directly or indirectly plays a part in all branches of science (dashed lines).

What, then, is physics? It may be defined as that branch of science which deals with matter and energy, and their relation to each other. It includes mechanics, heat, light, sound, electricity, and magnetism, and the fundamental structure and properties of matter. For our purpose, we shall be interested in those aspects of physics pertaining to the origin, nature, and behavior of x rays and related types of radiation; that is, *radiologic physics.*

Thus far, we have used the word science rather freely without definition. *Science is organized and classified knowledge.* Natural processes go on continually in the universe, with or without our knowledge. But these do not constitute a science until we have applied the scientific method to them. The *scientific method* comprises the systematic collection of facts, the study of their interrelationship, and the drawing of valid conclusions from the resulting data. Inherent in the scientific method is the assumption that nature is orderly and that sooner or later we can discover the rules by which she behaves.

Not only do we use the scientific method to describe and classify natural occurrences, but we also seek to correlate them by deriving certain principles known as *laws.* Scientific laws are based on human experience, being derived by observation of natural phenomena, by laboratory experiments, or by the application of mathematics. Such laws state as clearly and simply as possible, according to our present state of knowledge, that certain events will always follow in the same order, or that certain facts will always be related in the same way. For example, we know by experience that all objects fall to the ground; this observation has been expanded into the law of gravitation, which applies to the attraction between all bodies of matter.

Scientists are not satisfied with merely discovering the laws of nature. They also attempt to correlate various laws in order to determine their conformity to a *general pattern.* Thus, wherever possible, natural laws are so tied together that their operation can be expressed as a general concept, often on a mathematical basis. Such a broad, unified concept of the laws underlying certain natural phenomena is called a *theory.* Not only do theories provide a better insight into nature but they also suggest new lines of scientific research, since it is common experience that the solution of one problem in science ultimately gives rise to a host of new problems.

Standard Units

An exact science must include not only the observation and classification of natural occurrences, but also their **measurement.** In other words, physics as an exact science deals with both the "how" and the "how much" of physical phenomena. In order for these measurements to have the same meaning everywhere, they must be expressed in certain standard units. A **unit** is a quantity adopted as a standard of measurement by which other quantities of the **same** kind can be measured, such as the meter as an interval of distance, or the second as an interval of time. **Standard units** are the basic units in any particular system of measurement; they are used mathematically to describe natural phenomena, derive laws, and predict future events within the realm of nature. For example, by the application of science and mathematics, astronomers can foretell precisely the time of an eclipse of the sun or moon.

Units should have a size compatible with that which is being measured. Thus, we measure the length of a baby in centimeters, but we use a larger unit, the meter, to measure the height of a building; and a still larger unit, the kilometer, to measure the distance between cities.

The standard units employed in physics consist of two general types, the simpler **fundamental units** dealing with **length, mass** and time, and the more complicated **derived units,** obtained by various combinations of the fundamental units.

Fundamental Units

The fundamental units, arbitrarily selected and named, have been so standardized that a given unit has the same meaning everywhere. We now have two widely used systems of measurement, the **English** and the **metric.**

Since the metric system is used internationally in the exact sciences, it will be emphasized here, but the equivalents in the English system will also be indicated because we still use this in everyday life. The metric system is also known as the MKS (meter-kilogram-second) or CGS (centimeter-gram-second) system. These will gradually be replaced in science by the International System of Units, known as the *SI system,* which provides for the intercon-version of units among all branches of science. The SI system is based on the metric system, and insofar as the fundamental units are concerned, the two systems are identical.

1. **Length.** The unit of length in the metric system is the *meter,* originally defined as the distance between two scratches on a bar of platinum, kept at Sèvres, France, at the International Bureau of Weights and Measures. (It was redefined in 1960 as 1.65×10^6 times the wavelength of the orange-red radiation of krypton 56.) Roughly equal to a yard, the meter (m) can be conveniently subdivided into smaller units such as a centimeter (0.01 or 10^{-2} m) and millimeter (0.001 or 10^{-3} m); or it can be treated as a multiple such as a kilometer (1,000 or 10^3 m). In x-ray physics, we even have occasion to use very small fractions of these units; thus, the angstrom is $1/10,000,000,000$ or 10^{-10} m (or 10^{-8} cm). The following common equivalents should prove useful:

1 meter $= 100$ cm (centimeters) $= 1000$ mm (millimeters)
1 Å (angstrom) $= 1/100,000,000$ cm $= 10^{-8}$ cm
km (kilometer) $= 1,000$ m (meters) $=$ about $3/5$ mile
1 in. $= 2.54$ cm

2. **Mass.** Representing the quantity of matter in a body (or inertia) its *mass* is determined by weighing, a procedure which measures the force with which the earth attracts the body at some particular geographic location. Thus, the more massive the body, the greater the gravitational force and, therefore, the greater its weight. As implied in the above definition, the weight of a body may vary from place to place, but equal masses will have the same weight under identical conditions. The unit of mass is the *kilogram,* which is the weight of a standard piece of platinum-iridium (International Kilogram Prototype) kept at the International Bureau of Standards. All other kilograms are more or less exact copies of this standard unit. A more convenient unit is the gram, which is $1/1,000$ of a kilogram.

1 kg (kilogram) $= 1000$ or 10^3 g (grams)
1 kg $= 2.2$ lb
28 g $= 1$ oz

3. **Time.** This is a measure of the duration of events. We are all aware of the occurrence of events and the motion of objects, but to measure duration with relation to our senses alone is inaccurate. The standard unit of time is the *second,* defined as $1/86,400$ of a mean solar day. In other words, the second is a definite fraction of the average time it takes for the earth to make one rotation on its axis.

Derived Units

There are numerous derived units, but only those having a practical bearing on x-ray physics will be mentioned.

1. **Area** is the measure of a given surface, and depends on length. Thus, a square or rectangle has an area equal to the product of two sides. The area of a circle equals the radius squared times π. Figures 1.3, 1.4, 1.5, and 1.6 in Chapter 1 explain area in detail. In the metric system, area is represented by square meters for larger surfaces and square centimeters for smaller ones. Square centimeters are abbreviated either as sq cm or cm^2.

2. **Volume** is a measure of the capacity of a container, and is also derived from length. The volume of a cube equals the product of three sides. In metric units, volume may be expressed in cubic centimeters (cc) or milliliters (ml). One liter exactly equals 1,000 ml, and is very slightly larger than 1,000 cc—approximately one quart.

3. **Density** is the mass per unit volume of a substance, and may be expressed in kg per cubic meter (kg/m^3).

4. **Specific gravity** has *no units.* It is the ratio of the density of any material to the density of water. The density of water is 1.

5. **Velocity** is speed in a given direction, and can be expressed in cm per sec, or km per sec, or some other convenient units. Speed is commonly expressed in miles per hr (English system).

6. **Temperature** is a measure of the average energy of motion of the molecules of matter. Two systems are commonly employed today. In the metric system temperature is expressed in degrees Celsius (centigrade), but still the Fahrenheit system is the one generally used in the United States. The following data exemplify the differences between these systems:

CELSIUS   0 C = freezing point of water
                100 C = boiling point of water

FAHRENHEIT   32 F = freezing point of water
                212 F = boiling point of water

Conversion from one system to the other can be achieved by reference to tables, or by use of the following equations:

$$C = \frac{5}{9}(F - 32)$$
$$F = \frac{9}{5}C + 32$$

QUESTIONS AND PROBLEMS

1. Discuss the terms science; law; theory.
2. Why are standard units necessary?
3. Define natural science; physics; radiologic physics.
4. Which branch of natural science underlies all the others?
5. How were standard units in the metric system established?
6. With what do the fundamental units deal?
7. Discuss the metric system?
8. Explain the relation between mass and weight. Define the unit of mass.
9. What is the unit of time?
10. State the approximate equivalent of 1 meter in the English system? One gram? One liter?
11. The temperature of a solution is 68 F. Find the equivalent temperature in centigrade units.
12. A patient is found to have a temperature of 40 C. What is his temperature in Fahrenheit units?
13. Find the temperature value which is the same in both the C and F systems. (There are two methods, graphic and algebraic.)

CHAPTER *3*   *THE PHYSICAL CONCEPT OF ENERGY*

Force

ALL MATTER is endowed with a property called *inertia.* This may be defined as the tendency of a resting body (of matter) to remain at rest, and the tendency of a body moving at constant speed in a straight line to continue its state of motion. To set a resting object in motion, we must push or pull it; that is, we must apply a *force.* Conversely, to stop a moving object or change its direction, we must apply an opposing force. It should be pointed out that the **mass of a body is a measure of its inertia:** the greater the mass, the greater the external force needed to change its motion.

Work and Energy

Whenever a force acts upon a body over a distance, **work** is done. For example, to lift an object, we must apply a force to overcome the force of gravity. This applied force multiplied by the distance through which the object is lifted equals the work done. If the object is lifted twice the distance, then twice as much work will be done. Thus,

$$\text{work} = \text{force} \times \text{distance}$$

In a physical sense, work results from the expenditure of *energy.* What, then, is energy? **Energy may be defined as the actual or potential ability to do work.** It is obvious that work and energy must be measured in the same units, since the work done must be equal to the available energy.

There are two main types of **mechanical** energy, that is, the energy involved in the operation of various types of machines:

1. **Kinetic Energy.** Every moving body can do work because of its motion. The energy of such a moving body is called *kinetic energy.* The kinetic energy (K.E.) of a body is expressed by

$$K.E. = \frac{1}{2}mv^2$$

where m is the mass of the body in kg, and v is the velocity in m per sec. The unit of work is the joule (jool).

2. **Potential Energy.** A body may have energy because of its position or its temporarily deformed state. For example, a car parked on a hill will start to roll down once its brakes have been released. It is logical to assume that at the instant before the brakes were released the car possessed stored energy, which becomes energy of motion, or K.E., as the car rolls downhill. A wound-up clock spring and a stretched rubber band (temporarily deformed) are further examples of stored or potential energy (P.E.).

Thus, there are two types of mechanical energy—kinetic energy (energy of movement) and potential energy (stored energy).

Law of Conservation of Energy

What is the relationship between potential energy and kinetic energy? This is readily demonstrated by a simple example. Consider a rock poised on top of a cliff (see Figure 3.1). The rock has a certain amount of stored or potential energy. Where did this energy originate? A definite amount of work would have to be done to lift the rock to its position on top of the cliff against the force of gravity, such work being "stored" in the rock as *potential energy.* Now suppose the rock is shoved over the edge of the cliff; as it falls, its potential energy is gradually converted to kinetic energy. As the potential energy decreases, the kinetic energy increases correspondingly, so that at the instant the rock reaches the ground its initial potential energy has been completely changed to kinetic energy.

initial energy stored in rock (P.E.)	=	final energy of rock in motion (K.E.)

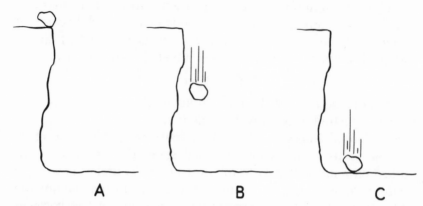

Figure 3.1. The relationship of potential energy to kinetic energy. In *A* the rock is at the top of the cliff, *external work* being required to lift it there against the force of gravity. This work is stored in the rock as *potential energy.* In *B* and *C* the rock is falling and the potential energy is thereby converted to *kinetic energy.* The external work = the potential energy = the kinetic energy.

Notice that the rock has different values of potential energy along its course; in other words, its potential energy gradually decreases as it falls toward the foot of the cliff. If the potential energy at any point above the ground is called an **energy level**, then it follows that the energy levels decrease at successively lower points. This important concept will be applied again later in the discussion of the energy levels of the electron shells in the atom. As exemplified in Figure 3.2, the **difference between any two energy levels equals the amount of potential energy that has been changed to kinetic energy. The rock will not of its own accord move from a lower to a higher energy level; external work is required.** This is another way of saying that **matter will move only from a higher to a lower energy level in the absence of outside work.**

It should be emphasized that the work required to lift the rock to the top of the cliff equals the potential energy of the rock at the summit of the cliff; and this, in turn, equals the kinetic energy attained by the rock at the instant it reaches the ground. At the instant the rock strikes the ground its kinetic energy is converted to heat.

The foregoing discussion exemplifies the **Law of Conservation of**

Figure 3.2. Potential energy at A — potential energy at B = kinetic energy at B; or, energy level at A — energy level at B = kinetic energy at B. If potential energy at $A = y$, and potential energy at $B = z$, then the difference in energy levels is $y - z$ = x. Thus, x represents the amount of potential energy converted to kinetic energy when the rock drops from A to B.

Energy, which states that energy can be neither created nor destroyed, the total amount of energy in the universe being constant. However, energy in one form can be changed into an equivalent amount of energy in other forms.

What are the so-called *"forms of energy?"* They may be listed simply as mechanical, thermal (heat), light, electrical, chemical, atomic, molecular, and nuclear. These can be changed from one form to another. For example, an electric motor converts electrical energy to mechanical energy which is almost equal to the initial electrical energy, any difference being due to the waste of some of the energy due to the production of heat.

$$\frac{\textbf{electrical}}{\textbf{energy}} = \frac{\textbf{mechanical}}{\textbf{energy}} + \frac{\textbf{heat}}{\textbf{energy}}$$

Other examples of the transformation of energy include: the conversion of chemical to electrical energy in a battery; the conversion of heat to mechanical energy in a steam engine; and the conversion of chemical to mechanical energy in a gasoline engine. Each of these transformations obeys the Law of Conservation of Energy; any energy disappearing in one form appears in some other form, and is never destroyed.

The most remarkable transformation of all, that of matter and energy, was formulated by Einstein in his famous equation

$$E = mc^2$$

in which E is energy, m is mass, and c is the speed of light in a vacuum. According to this equation, mass and energy are mutually convertible, one to the other. Thus, **matter cannot be destroyed, but can be changed to an equivalent amount of energy, and vice versa.** In fact, an extremely small amount of matter can give rise to a tremendous amount of energy. On this basis, we may expand the conservation law as follows: the sum total of mass and energy in the universe (or in a closed system) remains constant.

QUESTIONS

1. What is the physical concept of work?
2. Define energy; force.
3. Discuss kinetic energy and potential energy. State the equation for kinetic energy and identify the terms and their units.
4. Name the various forms of energy.
5. Define the law of conservation of energy and explain with the aid of an example.
6. What is the source of electrical energy in a battery?
7. Suppose that 1000 energy units of heat are applied to a steam turbine. What is the maximum number of energy units of electricity that can be obtained, neglecting the loss of energy due to friction?
8. Discuss the concept of energy levels.
9. Explain the significance of $E = mc^2$.

CHAPTER *4*   THE STRUCTURE OF MATTER

S PECULATION ON THE BASIC STRUCTURE OF MATTER has occu-pied the mind of man since ancient times. In fact, a Greek philosopher, Democritus, in about 400 B.C., actually suspected that matter is composed of invisible and indivisible particles which he called *atoms* (from Greek *atomos* = uncut).

One of the methods of studying something is to break it down, a process called *analysis*. For instance, the most satisfactory way to ascertain the mechanism of a clock is to take it apart, study its individual components, and find their relationship to one another. If this has been done properly it should then be possible to reassemble the component parts into a perfectly operating clock. Such a recombination of parts is called *synthesis*.

Subdivisions of Matter

Let us now apply the process of analysis, based on logic and experiment, to the structure of matter. By definition, *matter is anything which occupies space and has inertia.*

Matter is usually found in nature in impure form, as a *mixture* of indefinite composition. An example is *rock salt,* a mixture of certain minerals (sodium chloride, calcium carbonate, magnesium chloride, calcium sulfate, etc) that can be separated in pure form. One of these constituents is ordinary salt—sodium chloride. If a piece of pure salt is now broken into smaller and smaller fragments, there will eventually remain the tiniest particle that is still recognizable as salt; that is, it will have the same properties of color, odor, taste, hardness, melting point, etc, as the original piece of pure salt. This particle, much too small to be visible, is called a *molecule* of salt. *A molecule is the smallest subdivision of a substance having the characteristic properties of that substance.*

The degree of attraction among the molecules of a given body of matter determines whether it will be a *solid,* a *liquid,* or a *gas.* Molecular attraction is strongest in solids, relatively weak in liquids, and weakest in gases.

How can a *molecule* be further subdivided? This cannot be done by ordinary physical means, such as crushing, because the salt molecule is made up of two *atoms*—one of the element sodium and one of the element chlorine—held together by a strong electro-chemical force called a *bond* (see Figure 4.1). *The atom is the smallest particle of an element that has the characteristic properties of that element.* In general, an element can combine chemically with one or more atoms of another element (or elements) to form compounds.

Figure 4.1. Atoms of certain elements are held together by strong electrochemical forces called *bonds,* to form compounds. Elements and compounds are both *substances* because they have a definite, constant structure.

Two new terms have been introduced in the above discussion— *substance* and *element.* These will now be defined. *A substance is any material that has a definite, constant composition,* such as pure salt. (Wood and air are not substances because their composition varies; they are examples of mixtures.) Substances may be *simple* or *complex.* The simple ones, called *elements, cannot be decomposed to simpler substances by ordinary means.* Examples of elements are sodium, iron, lead, oxygen, hydrogen, and chlorine. There are in all ninety-two such naturally occurring elements. (See Table 4.1 on pages 46 and 47.)

The complex substances are *compounds,* formed by the *chemical union of two or more elements in definite proportions.* Thus, as we have just seen, salt is a *compound* of equal numbers of atoms of the elements sodium and chlorine in chemical combination (see Figure 4.1); every molecule of salt contains one atom of sodium (Na) and one atom of chlorine (Cl). Thus, the compound is called sodium chloride, symbolized by NaCl. Note that *all elements and compounds are also substances* since they have a definite composition. Compounds may consist of combinations of many atoms, ranging into the thousands.

The commonly occurring gases such as oxygen (O_2), nitrogen (N_2), and hydrogen (H_2) occur in nature in the form of molecules consisting of two atoms. Hence they are known as *diatomic* (two-atom) gases.

Figure 4.2 illustrates the structure of matter down to the atomic level.

Figure 4.2. Schematic analysis of matter.

In summary then, rock salt is an indefinite *mixture* of *substances* each of which has a definite composition. Pure salt is both a *compound* and a *substance* because it has a definite composition, chemically combined atoms of sodium and chlorine in equal numbers. The smallest particle of salt (as well as other compounds) is a *molecule*, which can be separated chemically into simpler substances—*elements*. Thus, each molecule of salt consists of an atom of sodium and an atom of chlorine (see Figure 4.1). The *atom* is the smallest fragment of a particular element that is still recognizable as such. Atoms cannot be further subdivided by ordinary chemical or electrical methods, but can be broken down into smaller particles by special high energy, atom-smashing machines such as the nuclear reactor and the cyclotron.

Atomic Structure—the Electrical Nature of Matter

Let us now examine the makeup of the atom itself. An atom is not a homogeneous particle, but consists of even smaller particles that are present in the atoms of all elements. Although scientists have given us a highly satisfactory concept of atomic structure, it is inconceivable that anyone will ever actually be able to peer inside an atom.

Modern theory has it that the atom is fundamentally *electrical* in nature. Note that the structure of the atom may be represented by a diagram (not an actual picture) to help correlate certain experimental observations that have been treated mathematically.

In 1913 Niels Bohr, a Danish physicist, first proposed the most widely held theory of atomic structure. Although it has been radically revised since his time, his early model of the atom adequately serves to explain the phenomena that we shall encounter in radiologic physics in this course. We shall therefore represent the atom as a submicroscopic system analogous to our solar system in which planets revolve around a central sun (see Figure 4.3). In the center of the atom lies the positively charged core known as the *nucleus*, containing almost the entire mass of the atom. Revolving around the nucleus are the much lighter *orbital electrons*, each carrying a single *negative charge*. Each electron moves continuously in its own *orbit* or path around the nucleus. However, the electrons whose orbits are at a particular distance from the nucleus are grouped together and designated as belonging to a particular *shell* or *energy level*. These shells are identified by letters of the alphabet, the innermost being called the *K* shell, the next the *L* shell, and so on to *Q* (see Figure 4.3). The atoms of various elements differ in

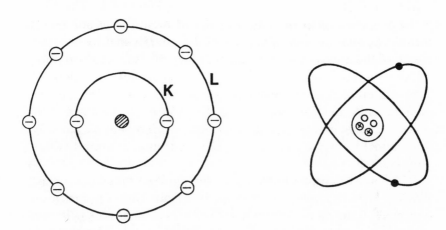

Figure 4.3. A shows a greatly simplified atomic model, according to the Bohr Theory, with the nucleus at the center surrounded by some of the *shells* of the electrons. The K shell can hold no more than two electrons, L no more than eight. The number of electrons that additional shells (up to Q) can hold has been determined. The electrons revolve very rapidly in their orbits and, at the same time, spin on their axes. Actually, each electron moves in its own path or *orbital* as in B, where the nucleus is shown to contain, in this case, two protons ($\oplus$) and two neutrons ($\bigcirc$).

the number of electrons that are normally present in the shells.

There is a specific maximum number of electrons that can occupy a particular shell, listed as follows:

K shell	2 electrons
L shell	8 electrons
M shell	18 electrons
N shell	32 electrons

A shell may contain fewer than the maximum allowable number of electrons; thus, starting with the M shell, the outermost shell does not have to contain its maximum complement of electrons before electrons begin appearing in the next higher shell. In fact, an atom tends to be chemically stable when there are eight electrons or **octet** in the outer shell. For example, the element potassium has two *K* electrons, eight *L* electrons, eight *M* electrons, and one *N* electron, despite the fact that the *M* shell can hold a maximum of eighteen electrons.

In a neutral atom the total number of orbital electrons exactly equals the total number of positive charges in the nucleus.

All of the atoms of a given element have the same total number of positive nuclear charges, but the atoms of different elements have different total nuclear charges. *An atom of a given element maintains its identity only if its nuclear charge is unaltered.* If the nuclear charge is altered, as by irradiation with subatomic particles, the element may be transmuted (changed) into an entirely different element.

Nuclear Structure. Of what does the *nucleus* of an atom consist? We know that the nucleus contains two main kinds of particles or *nucleons*—protons and neutrons. The proton carries a single positive charge (equal and opposite to the negative charge of an electron) and has an extremely small mass, about 1.6×10^{-24} gram, but this is still about 1,828 times the mass of an electron. Ordinarily, protons exist only in the nucleus and can be liberated from the nucleus only under special conditions. Protons of all elements are identical, but *each element has its own characteristic number of nuclear protons.* It must be emphasized that the protons alone give the nucleus its positive charge.

The other important constituent of the nucleus, the *neutron,* is a particle having about the same mass as a proton but carrying no charge; that is, the neutron is electrically *neutral.* (It is incorrect to speak of the neutron as having a neutral charge; rather, it is characterized by absence of charge.) Thus, protons and neutrons comprise virtually the entire mass of the nucleus but *only the protons contribute positive charges to the nucleus.* Other nuclear particles have been discovered but will not be considered here.

In summary, we can state that the atoms of various elements consist of the same *building blocks:* protons, neutrons, and electrons. Atoms of various elements differ from one another by virtue of different combinations of these same building blocks. The structure of an atom may be outlined as follows:

1. *Nucleus*—contains one or more:

a. **Protons**—elementary positive particles, and
b. **Neutrons**—elementary neutral particles having virtually the same mass as the proton.
2. *Shells*—represent energy levels of one or more:
   a. **Electrons**—elementary negative particles in orbits.

The number of electrons in the shells must equal the number of protons in the nucleus of a *neutral* atom.

Atomic Number

What determines the identity of an element and makes it distinctly different from any other element? The answer lies in the number of nuclear *protons.* In a neutral atom the number of orbital electrons exactly equals the number of nuclear protons (see Figure 4.4). This number is characteristically the same for all atoms of a given element and is different for the atoms of different elements. *The number of protons or positive charges in the nucleus of an atom denotes its atomic number.* Thus, each element has a particular atomic number and, because of the corresponding specific number and arrangement of orbital electrons, its own distinctive chemical properties.

NUCLEUS

6 protons

7 neutrons

Atomic Number = 6
Mass Number = 13

Figure 4.4. Nuclear composition (simplified).

Mass Number

What determines the mass of an atom? We have already indicated that nearly the entire mass resides in the nucleus and, more specifically, in the nuclear protons and neutrons. These particles comprise the units of atomic mass. Therefore, the **total number of protons and neutrons in the nucleus of an atom denotes its mass number** (see Figure 4.4). Protons and neutrons are often called **nucleons.**

Isotopes

If we were to examine a sample of a particular element, we would find that it consists of two or more kinds of atoms that differ in mass number, even though they must all have the same atomic number. For example, the familiar element oxygen is a mixture of atoms of mass number 16, 17, and 18, although all these oxygen atoms have the same atomic number — 8. Such atoms of the same element having different mass numbers are called **isotopes.** Any particular kind of atom, having a specific number of protons and neutrons, is called a **nuclide.**

Hydrogen, the simplest element, has three isotopes, as shown in Figure 4.5. All three hydrogen nuclides have atomic number 1, but they have different mass numbers — 1, 2, and 3. The reason for the difference is immediately evident from the figure; **they differ only in the number of nuclear neutrons.**

The preceding discussion may be generalized as follows: **isotopes may be defined as atoms that have the same number of nuclear protons (equal to the atomic number of the element) but different numbers of nuclear neutrons.** This definition explains the difference in the mass numbers of isotopes.

Note that the atomic number and the mass number **together** specify the nuclear composition of any given atom, thereby designating a particular **nuclide;** the atomic number alone specifies the number of nuclear protons, and hence identifies the element.

Atomic weight refers to the mass of any atom relative to the mass of an atom of carbon 12 isotope taken as 12. The **atomic mass unit** (**amu**) is therefore defined as one-twelfth the mass of the carbon

HYDROGEN   DEUTERIUM   TRITIUM
MASS NO. I   MASS NO. 2   MASS NO. 3
(I PROTON)   (I PROTON + I NEUTRON)   (I PROTON + 2 NEUTRONS)

Figure 4.5. Isotopes of hydrogen. These particular isotopes have the same atomic number, 1, but have different mass numbers. They are called *isotopes* of the same element, hydrogen. Their different mass numbers depend on the different numbers of neutrons in the nucleus. Ordinary hydrogen (mass no. 1) is sometimes called *protium*. Tritium (pronounced trit'-ē-um) is an artificial isotope and is radioactive.

12 nucleus. Because elements consist of mixtures of isotopes, the atomic weight is an average and is therefore almost never a whole number. However, since atomic weight, and mass number, are so nearly equal, these terms are often used interchangeably.

The Periodic Table

The preceding discussion will be made clearer by actual examples. All of the elements can be arranged in an orderly series, called the *periodic table*, from the lightest to the heaviest (on the basis of atomic weight), or from the lowest atomic number to the highest (see Table 4.1). For instance, ordinary *hydrogen* is the simplest element, since it has only one proton and one orbital electron. The atomic number of ordinary hydrogen is therefore 1, and so is its mass number (see Figure 4.6.).

The second element in the periodic series is *helium*, with two protons and two neutrons in the nucleus and two electrons in the *K shell* (see Figure 4.7). The atomic number of this element is 2 and the mass number is 4.

Lithium is the third element. Its atomic number is 3, and one of its isotopes has a mass number of 7 (see Figure 4.8). Note that the

TABLE 4.1

ATOMIC PERIODIC TABLE

The numbers above each element represent atomic weight.
The numbers below each element represent atomic number.
Elements of particular interest to radiologic technologists are in dark type.
Transuranic elements (that is, beyond uranium) are man made.

Period	Group I	Group II	Group III	Group IV	Group V	Group VI	Group VII	Group VIII
0	1.008 Hydrogen (H) 1							4.003 Helium (He) 2
1	6.940 Lithium (Li) 3	9.02 Beryllium (Be) 4	10.82 Boron (B) 5	12.01 Carbon (C) 6	14.008 Nitrogen (N) 7	16.000 Oxygen (O) 8	19.00 Fluorine (F) 9	20.183 Neon (Ne) 10
2	22.997 Sodium (Na) 11	24.32 Magnesium (Mg) 12	26.97 Aluminum (Al) 13	28.06 Silicon (Si) 14	30.98 Phosphorus (P) 15	32.06 Sulfur (S) 16	35.457 Chlorine (Cl) 17	39.994 Argon (A) 18
3	39.096 Potassium (K) 19	40.08 Calcium (Ca) 20	45.10 Scandium (Sc) 21	47.90 Titanium (Ti) 22	50.95 Vanadium (V) 23	52.01 Chromium (Cr) 24	54.93 Manganese (Mn) 25	55.85 Iron (Fe) 26 / 58.94 Cobalt (Co) 27 / 58.69 Nickel (Ni) 28
3	63.57 Copper (Cu) 29	65.38 Zinc (Zn) 30	69.72 Gallium (Ga) 31	72.60 Germanium (Ge) 32	74.91 Arsenic (As) 33	79.00 Selenium (Se) 34	79.92 Bromine (Br) 35	83.7 Krypton (Kr) 36
4	85.48 Rubidium (Rb) 37	87.63 Strontium (Sr) 38	88.92 Yttrium (Y) 39	91.22 Zirconium (Zr) 40	92.91 Columbium (Cb) 41	96.0 Molybdenum (Mo) 42	99 Technetium (Tc) 43	101.7 Ruthenium (Ru) 44 / 102.9 Rhodium (Rh) 45 / 106.7 Palladium (Pd) 46
4	107.88 Silver (Ag) 47	112.41 Cadmium (Cd) 48	118.70 Indium (In) 49	121.77 Tin (Sn) 50	127.6 Antimony (Sb) 51	126.93 Tellurium (Te) 52	126.92 Iodine (I) 53	131.3 Xenon (Xe) 54
	132.9 Cesium (Cs) 55	137.4 Barium (Ba) 56	Rare Earths 57-71	178.6 Hafnium (Hf) 72	180.9 Tantalum (Ta) 73	183.9 Tungsten (W) 74	186.3 Rhenium (Re) 75	190.2 Osmium (Os) 76 / 193.1 Iridium (Ir) 77 / 195.2 Platinum (Pt) 78

The Structure of Matter

5	197.2 *Gold* *(Au)* 79	200.6 Mercury (Hg) 80	204.4 Thallium (Tl) 81	207.2 *Lead* *(Pb)* 82	209.0 *Bismuth* *(Bi)* 83	210 Polonium (Po) 84	211 Astatine (At) 85	222 *Radon* *(Rn)* 86
6	224 Virginium (Vi) 87	226.05 *Radium* *(Ra)* 88	Actinide* Series 89–103					

Actinide Series

227 Actinium (Ac) 89	232 Thorium (Th) 90	231 Protoactinium (Pa) 91	238.1 Uranium (U) 92
(237) Neptunium (Np) 93	(242) Plutonium (Pu) 94	(243) Americium (Am) 95	(247) Curium (Cm) 96
(249) Berkelium (Bk) 97	(251) Californium (Cf) 98	(254) Einsteinium (Es) 99	(257) Fermium (Fm) 100
(256) Mendelevium (Md) 101	(254) Nobelium (No) 102	(257) Lawrencium (Lw) 103	

(Number in parenthesis is mass number of most stable nuclide.)

Figure 4.6. Atomic model of ordinary hydrogen.

first shell has the maximum number of electrons, two, and the third electron is in the next shell. Thus, the *K* shell of lithium has two electrons, and the *L* shell, one.

Chemical Behavior

In tabulating the elements in order of increasing atomic number (periodic table), we find that they fall into *eight vertical groups* and *seven horizontal periods* (see Table 4.1). It turns out that the *vertical groups* represent families of elements with surprisingly similar chemical properties. In other words, they participate in chemical reactions in a similar fashion. This relationship of the various elements was first discovered in 1870 by Mendeleev, the eminent Russian chemist. The *periods* (horizontal rows), on the other hand, consist of elements with the same number of electron shells, but with different chemical properties.

Figure 4.7. Atomic model of helium.

Figure 4.8. Atomic model of lithium.

Why do the elements in any vertical group have similar chemical properties? These depend on the number of electrons in their *outermost shells.* For instance, lithium (Li), sodium (Na), and potassium (K), shown in Table 4.1, belong to the same family—Group I. Their atomic structure is shown in Figure 4.9. The neutrons are omitted here because they do not influence chemical behavior. The diagram shows that although these elements have different numbers of shells, they have one thing in common: *the outermost shell of each has one electron* which it can readily give up, leaving the atom with eight electrons in its outermost shell—the stable *octet* (eight) configuration. This determines the similarity of their chemical behavior.

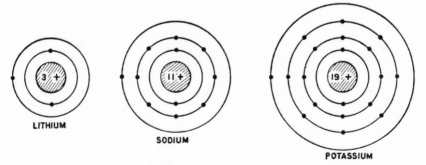

Figure 4.9. Elements with valence of +1.

Consider now vertical group VII: fluorine (F), chlorine (Cl), and bromine (Br). As shown in Figure 4.10, these elements have different numbers of shells, but are similar in that they all have one less electron in the outermost shell than the number of electrons needed to saturate it to a chemically stable octet configuration. Therefore, these elements resemble each other in their chemical properties.

The number of electrons in the outermost shell determines their combining ability or *valence.* The family of elements represented by lithium, sodium, and potassium has one electron in the outermost shell, and the valence is $+1$, because these elements can *give* that electron to an element which needs an electron to saturate its outermost shell and form an octet. On the other hand, the elements in the fluorine, chlorine, bromine family, as described above, have one less electron in the outermost shell than the number needed to form an octet. Their valence is -1. These elements can *accept* an electron from the lithium family. The atom that gives up the electron now has one excess positive charge, whereas the atom that accepts the electron has one excess negative charge. Such charged atoms are called *ions* which, because of their opposite charges, firmly attract each other to form a *compound.* The attraction between the two ions is a *chemical bond,* this type being called an *ionic bond* (see Figure 4.11).

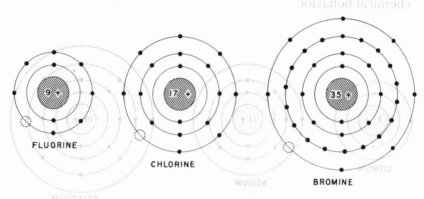

Figure 4.10. Elements with valence of -1.

Another type of bond is the *covalent bond* which involves the

SODIUM + CHLORINE ⟶ SODIUM CHLORIDE

Figure 4.11. Combination of sodium and chlorine chemically to form sodium chloride. The chemical bond is *ionic,* common to the formation of almost all inorganic compounds.

sharing of outer orbital electrons. This is exemplified by the water molecule which consists of two atoms of hydrogen bonded to one atom of oxygen by a sharing of the hydrogen valence electron as shown in Figure 4.12. With this type of bond a shared electron divides its time orbiting around the hydrogen nucleus and the oxygen nucleus, slightly more around the latter. Therefore, the oxygen side of the water molecule is slightly negative with respect to the oxygen side, so we call this *polar covalent bonding.*

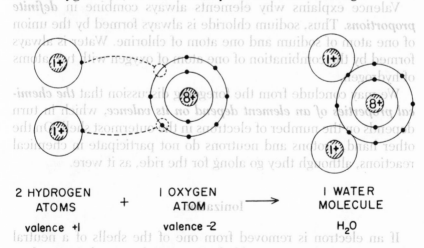

| 2 HYDROGEN ATOMS | + | I OXYGEN ATOM | ⟶ | I WATER MOLECULE |
| valence +l | | valence -2 | | H_2O |

Figure 4.12. Chemical combination of hydrogen and oxygen to form water, by sharing of two electrons—that is, a *covalent bond.*

Suppose a particular element normally were to have its outer shell saturated with electrons, or in octet configuration. It could not enter into a chemical reaction, since it would be unable to give up, accept, or share an electron. Referring again to Table 4.1, notice that there is such a family of elements—Group O—known as the *inert elements.* They include helium, neon, argon, etc, as shown in Figure 4.13. (It has been possible, recently, to bring about chemical union of inert elements in very small quantities.)

HELIUM   NEON   ARGON

Figure 4.13. Three members of the family of inert elements, with valence of 0. The outer shell in each case is completely filled with electrons. Therefore, these elements do not ordinarily enter into chemical reactions.

Valence explains why elements always combine in *definite proportions.* Thus, sodium chloride is always formed by the union of one atom of sodium and one atom of chlorine. Water is always formed by the combination of one atom of oxygen with two atoms of hydrogen.

We may conclude from the foregoing discussion that *the chemical properties of an element depend on its valence,* which in turn depends on the number of electrons in the outermost shell. On the other hand, protons and neutrons do not participate in chemical reactions, although they go along for the ride, as it were.

Ionization

If an electron is removed from one of the shells of a neutral atom, or if an electron is added to a neutral atom, the atom does not lose its identity because it retains the same charge on its nucleus so that its atomic number is unaltered. However, the atom is now electrically charged. Thus, if an electron is *removed,* the atom becomes *positively charged* because one of its nuclear charges is now unbalanced and the atom has an excess of positive electricity. If an electron is *added* to a neutral atom, the atom now has an excess of negative electricity and is *negatively charged.* Such charged atoms will drift when placed in an electric field, as will be discussed later, and are called *ions* (from Greek *ienai* = to go). The process of converting atoms to ions is termed *ionization.*

Note that *ionization is produced exclusively through the addition or removal of orbital electrons;* the protons do not participate in this process, their role being entirely passive.

1. **Exposure of Matter to X Rays or Gamma Rays.** These may remove electrons from the atoms of matter lying in their path. Such atoms become positively charged, that is, positive ions. The removed electrons may ionize other atoms, combine with neutral atoms to produce negative ions, or recombine with positive ions to form neutral atoms.

2. **Exposure of Matter to a Stream of Electrons.** The fast-moving electrons in an electron beam or the electrons released from atoms by x rays as in (1) may interact with and remove orbital electrons from other atoms. An atom, on losing an electron, now has an excess positive charge, but it is soon neutralized by picking up a free electron. Ionization by x rays or fast electrons is of extremely short duration—the ion become neutralized almost instantaneously.

3. **Spontaneous Breakdown of Radioactive Nuclides.** The radiation emitted by the radium series, including charged particles and gamma rays, can produce ionization. The same applies to other radioactive nuclides.

4. **Exposure of Certain Elements to Light.** When light strikes the surface of certain metals such as cesium or potassium, electrons are liberated from the atoms and emitted from the surface of the metal. This principle is utilized in the photoelectric cell, which is the main component of the x-ray phototimer.

5. **Chemical Ionization.** If two neutral atoms such as sodium and chlorine are brought together, the sodium atom with valence +1 gives up its outermost or valence electron to the chlorine atom to fill its outermost shell. The sodium atom becomes a positive sodium ion (deficiency of one electron), while the chlorine becomes a negative chlorine ion (excess of one electron). When the com-

pound sodium chloride is dissolved in water its ions separate so that the water now contains sodium ions (Na+) and chlorine ions (Cl-). If the poles of a battery are connected to electrodes and these are immersed in the solution, the Na+ ions move toward the negative electrode (cathode) as *cations,* while the Cl- ions move toward the positive electrode (anode) as *anions,* as shown in Figure 4.14. On arriving at the *cathode,* each Na+ ion picks up an electron and becomes a neutral sodium atom. Each Cl- ion gives up its extra electron to the *anode* and becomes a neutral chlorine atom. These effects of an electric current are called *electrolysis.*

6. **Thermionic Emission.** Heating a metal to incandescence (glowing hot) entails the release of electrons from its surface. These electrons are the loosely bound, outermost orbital electrons of the atoms of the metal; heating the metal imparts sufficient kinetic energy to the electrons to facilitate their escape from the surface, analogous to the evaporation of water molecules from a body of water. The ejection of electrons in this manner is called *thermionic emission,* or *thermionic effect;* it is essential to the operation of an x-ray tube.

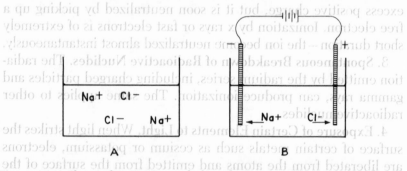

Figure 4.14. Chemical ionization and electrolysis. In *A* is shown a solution of ordinary salt (sodium chloride = NaCl) whose ions have separated to form equal numbers of Na+ an Cl- ions. In *B* a pair of electrodes has been immersed in the solution; the Na+ ions move toward the negative electrode (cathode) and the Cl- ions drift toward the positive electrode (anode), a process called *electrolysis.*

Ionization is an extremely important process. Many chemical reactions take place between ions in solution. Ionization of air by x rays underlies the modern measurement of the exposure rate of an x-ray beam. Ionization of body tissues indirectly through preliminary release of electrons underlies the fundamental mode of action of x and gamma rays in therapy.

QUESTIONS AND PROBLEMS

1. Define element; compound; substance.
2. State briefly the Bohr concept of atomic structure.
3. Draw a model of the hydrogen atom and label the parts.
4. What constitutes the nucleus of an atom?
5. Define orbit; shell; octet.
6. How does the mass of a proton compare with that of an electron?
7. A neutral atom has twelve electrons revolving in the orbits around the nucleus. What is its atomic number?
8. An atom has a nucleus containing six protons and two neutrons. What is its atomic number (Z)? Mass number (A)?
9. Define isotope, and give an example. Define nuclide.
10. How do elements combine chemically in fixed or definite proportions?
11. What is an ion? By what methods can ionization be produced?
12. Explain the similarity of chemical behavior of certain elements.
13. Discuss two types of chemical bonds. Give an example of a compound formed by each type.
14. Where are the following located in the atom: proton, neutron, electron? Why are they called the building blocks of matter?

CHAPTER *5*   *ELECTROSTATICS*

Definition

THE TERM *electrostatics* is defined as *the branch of physics that deals with stationary or resting electric charges.* Another name for resting charges is *static electricity.*

Electrification

We have previously pointed out that all atoms contain electrons in motion about a nucleus. If one or more of these electrons are removed, the atom is left with an excess positive charge. Should the removed electron become attached to a neutral atom, then the latter will become negatively charged. Thus, *there are only two kinds of electric charges, positive and negative.*

The same principle holds for a body of matter (made up of atoms) from which electrons may be removed or to which electrons may be added, a process called *electrification.* So an electrified or charged body has either an excess or a deficiency of electrons, being negatively charged in the first instance and positively charged in the second.

Methods of Electrification

How can we electrify a body? We can do so in three ways:

1. **Electrification by Friction.** You have probably observed after walking over a woolen carpet that touching a metal door knob will cause a spark to jump between your hand and the metal. Again, you may have noted that in combing your hair a crackling sound is heard as the comb seems to draw the hair to it. These are examples of *electrification by friction,* that is, the removal of electrons

from one object by rubbing it with another of a different kind. This phenomenon was known to the ancient Greeks who observed that amber, when rubbed with fur, attracts small bits of straw or dried leaves. Since the Greek word for amber is *elektron,* the origin of the root word for *electricity* is obvious.

On the basis of the two kinds of charges developed by friction, we conventionally designate one *negative* and the other *positive.* When a glass rod is rubbed with silk, some electrons are removed from the rod, leaving it positively charged; this is *positive electrification.* At the same time, the silk acquires an excess of electrons and is negatively charged, a process called *negative electrification.*

If amber is rubbed with fur, the amber picks up electrons and becomes negatively charged, thereby undergoing negative electrification, while the fur undergoes positive electrification. It should be emphasized that friction is the simplest and most fundamental method of electrification.

2. **Electrification by Contact.** When a body charged by friction touches an uncharged object, the latter acquires the same charge. This is called *electrification by contact.* If the first object is negatively charged, it will give up some of its electrons to the second object, imparting to it a negative charge. If, on the other hand, the first object has a positive charge, it will remove electrons from the second object, leaving it positively charged. *We can conclude that a charged object confers the same kind of charge on any uncharged body with which it comes in contact.*

3. **Electrification by Induction.** Matter can be classified on the basis of its electrical conductivity, that is, how readily it allows the flow of electrons. The materials in the first group are called *nonconductors* or *insulators* because electrons do not flow freely in them; examples are plastics, hard rubber, and glass. The materials in the second class are called *conductors* because they allow a free flow of electrons; they are exemplified by *metals,* such as silver, copper, and aluminum. Electrification by induction utilizes metallic conductors. Another class, intermediate in conducting ability, comprises the *semiconductors* (see pages 241 to 249).

Surrounding every charged body there is a region in which a force is exerted on another charged body. This region or zone is called an *electric field.* An uncharged metallic object experiences a shift of electrons when brought into the electric field of a charged object, a process called *electrification by induction.* Note that *only the electrons move.* In Figure 5.1, if the negatively charged rod, *B,* is brought *near* the originally uncharged metal body, *A,* but not touching it, the negative field near *B* will repel electrons on *A* distally, leaving the end of *A* nearest *B* positively charged. The reverse is also true; if *B* were a positively charged rod, the end of *A* nearest *B* would become negatively charged. As *B,* in either case, is withdrawn from the electric field of *A,* the electrons on *A* are redistributed to their original position and *A* is no longer charged.

It is possible to charge a piece of metal by induction so that it

Figure 5.1. Temporary electrification by induction. *A* is a metallic rod. *B* is a charged body. In I electrons on *A* have been repelled to the left by the negative charge on *B*. In II the electrons on *A* have been attracted to the right by the positive charge on *B* (see Figure 5.3).

will *retain its charge* even after the charging body has been removed. In Figure 5.2, A is shown first as it is affected by the electric field of B. Connecting the negative end of A temporarily to a water pipe (ground) causes the excess electrons to pass down to ground. If the ground connection is broken and B is *then* removed, A remains positively charged. It must be emphasized that *in electrification by induction, the charged body confers the opposite kind of charge on the metallic body which is placed in its field.*

Figure 5.2. Semipermanent electrification by induction. A is a metallic rod. B is a charged body.

What is meant by ground? Since the earth is essentially an infinite reservoir of electrons, any charged body can be neutralized (same number of positive and negative charges) if it is grounded, that is, connected to wet earth by a conductor. Thus, grounding a positively charged body causes electrons to move up from the ground to neutralize the body. On the other hand, grounding a negatively charged body drives its excess electrons to ground, again neutralizing the body. In both instances, the charged body is neutralized by being brought to the same electrical potential energy level as ground. *Ground potential equals zero.* The symbol for ground is ⏚ .

Laws of Electrostatics

There are five fundamental laws of electrostatics:

1. **Like Charges Repel Each Other; Unlike Charges Attract Each Other.** As noted previously, every charge has around it an electric field of force. This field consists of lines of force which start at a positive charge, pass through space, and end on a negative charge (see Figure 5.3). There is a resulting force of attraction between such oppositely charged bodies due to the electric field of force. If, on the other hand, we have two similarly charged bodies, their electric lines of force repel each other as in Figure 5.4 and so there is a repelling or separating force between them. Figure 5.5 shows this law demonstrated experimentally.

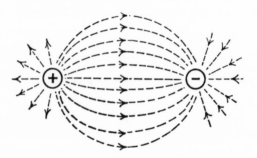

Figure 5.3. Electric fields. The electric lines of force are assumed to start on a positive charge, pass through space, and converge on a negative charge. A negative charge, such as an electron, placed in the field would drift toward the positive charge.

A   B

Figure 5.4. When like charges are brought near each other, their electric fields exert a force of repulsion or separation between the like charges.

Figure 5.5. Like charges repel. Unlike charges attract.

2. **The Electrostatic Force Between Two Charges is Directly Proportional to the Product of Their Quantities, and Inversely Proportional to the Square of the Distance Between Them.** The force may be one of attraction or repulsion, depending on whether the charges are different or alike. For example, if we have two unlike charges and the strength of one is doubled, the force of attraction between them is doubled. If both are doubled, the force of attraction between them is $2 \times 2 = 4$ times as great. If the distance between the original charges is doubled, the force between them is $1/2 \times 1/2 = 1/4$ as great. If the distance is halved, the force is $2 \times 2 = 4$ times as great.

3. **Electric Charges Reside Only on External Surfaces of Conductors.** When a hollow metal ball is charged, all of the charges are on the outside surface, while the inside remains uncharged, as is evident from Figure 5.6. This is explained by the mutual repulsion of like charges which tend to move as far away from each other as possible. The greatest distance obviously exists between them if they move to the outer surface of the object.

4. **The Concentration of Charges on a Curved Surface of a Conductor Is Greatest Where the Curvature Is Greatest.** This is shown in Figure 5.7. The greatest possible concentration of charges occurs on a point which represents an extremely high degree of curvature; in fact, charges become so crowded on a point that they easily leak away.

5. **Only Negative Charges (Electrons) Can Move in Solid Conductors.** The positive charges are actually charged atoms which do not drift in solid conductors.

Figure 5.6. Electric charges tend to distribute themselves on the outer surface of a hollow metallic sphere.

Figure 5.7. Electric charges tend to concentrate in region of sharpest curvature.

Electroscope

An electroscope detects the presence and sign of an electric charge. Under suitable conditions, it can be calibrated to determine the size of a charge. A simple electroscope is shown as a diagram in Figure 5.8.

We can charge an electroscope either by contact or by induction.

1. **Charging an Electroscope by Contact.** Figure 5.9 shows how this is done. If a *negatively* charged rod is allowed to touch the metal knob, as in A, electrons will move from the rod to the knob, stem, and gold leaves of the electroscope. Since the leaves now have the same negative charge, they repel each other and spread apart. The electroscope is now charged *negatively*. On the other hand, if a *positively* charged rod is brought into contact with the

Figure 5.8. Gold leaf electroscope. When an electric charge is imparted to the electroscope, the leaves repel each other and spread apart.

metal knob of the electroscope, some electrons will move from the electroscope to the rod, leaving the electroscope with a *positive* charge; the leaves will diverge just as when they were negatively charged.

Figure 5.9. Charging an electroscope by contact.

2. **Charging an Electroscope by Induction.** In Figure 5.10, a negatively charged rod is brought *near*, but not touching, the metal knob of the electroscope. The rod's negative electrostatic field repels electrons from the knob down to the leaves, causing them to separate. If the knob is then grounded while the rod remains near

it, the leaves will collapse because they have lost their charge. If the ground connection is next broken and the rod is **then removed,** there will be a deficiency of electrons in the electroscope (the excess electrons having passed to ground), leaving the electroscope with a positive charge. This causes the leaves to spread. In general, the larger the charge, the greater will be the separation of the gold leaves.

Figure 5.10. Charging an electroscope by induction. The successive steps are indicated in the diagrams from left to right.

An electroscope can be used not only to detect electric charges, but also to determine their sign, that is, whether they are positive or negative. When a positively charged body is brought near the knob of a negatively charged electroscope, some of the electrons will be attracted from the leaves up to the knob, and the leaves will come together. But when a negatively charged body is brought near the knob of a negatively charged electroscope, some of the electrons from the knob will be repelled down to the already negative leaves and they will diverge even further. We can therefore deduce that a charged body brought near a similarly charged electroscope causes the leaves to diverge farther. But a charged body brought near an electroscope that has an opposite charge causes the leaves to come together.

A charged electroscope can be used to detect the presence of x rays because of the ionization they produce in air. The resulting ions neutralize the charge on the electroscope, causing the leaves to collapse.

Static Discharge

Suppose we have two oppositely charged bodies separated by an air space or insulator. The surplus electrons on the negatively charged body naturally tend to move over to the positively charged body, but this may be prevented by the air space or insulator between the bodies. However, if the electrons continue to be piled up on the negatively charged body, the electric field becomes correspondingly stronger. Eventually, continued buildup of electric charge causes breakdown of the insulator as the electrons jump from the more negative to the less negative body, producing a *spark*.

There is a difference of electrical potential energy between two oppositely charged bodies, or between two bodies having like charges of different sizes. The point where electrons are in excess is at a higher negative potential than the point at which they are deficient. Therefore, the electrons move downhill, so to speak, from the point of higher to the point of lower negative potential. This is analogous to the difference in mechanical potential energy in the example cited on pages 33 to 35.

The above discussion can best be brought home by considering the familiar *lightning discharge*. A thunder cloud may have a positive charge on its upper side and a negative charge on its lower side, or *vice versa,* built up by its motion through the air. The earth beneath develops an opposite charge by electrostatic induction. When the difference of electrical potential between a negatively charged cloud and the earth exceeds a certain critical value, electrons rush between the two in the form of a bolt of lightning. Since this usually involves a sudden transfer of excess electrons to the earth, they may rush back toward the cloud, then back to the earth, repeating the process of oscillation many times within a few millionths of a second.

QUESTIONS

1. Discuss electrification. By what three methods can it be accomplished?

2. What happens if two similarly charged bodies are brought close together? Oppositely charged bodies?
3. How many kinds of electricity are there? Which one is capable of drifting in a solid conductor?
4. If a negatively charged object is touched to a neutral object, what kind of charge does the latter acquire?
5. State the five laws of electrostatics.
6. Of what value is the electroscope in radiology? How does it work?
7. What is meant by an electric field?
8. Describe electrification by contact; by induction.
9. Explain static discharge and give an example.
10. Define conductor; insulator; semiconductor. Give examples.

CHAPTER 6 ELECTRODYNAMICS— ELECTRIC CURRENT

Definition

IN THE PRECEDING chapter we described the characteristics of stationary electric charges. Under certain conditions, electric charges can be made to drift through a suitable material known as a *conductor. The science of electric charges in motion is known as electrodynamics, or current electricity.*

The Nature of an Electric Current

Fundamentally, *an electric current consists of a flow of charged particles.* This may occur under the following conditions:

1. **In a Vacuum**—electrons may jump a gap between two oppositely charged electrodes in a vacuum tube. This will be discussed in detail later in connection with x-ray and valve tubes.

2. **In a Gas**—two oppositely charged electrodes placed in a gas will cause positive ions, usually present in the gas, to drift toward the negative electrode (cathode) and negative ions to drift toward the positive electrode (anode). This occurs in an ordinary neon tube.

3. **In an Ionic Solution**—as already described on page 53, upon being dissolved in water a salt separates into its component ions. If electrodes are then immersed in the solution and connected to a source of direct current, the positive ions move toward the cathode while the negative ions move toward the anode. Such migration of ions in opposite directions characterizes the flow of an electric current in an ionic solution (see Figure 4.14).

4. **In a Metallic Conductor**—this will be our main concern in the present chapter, and in later ones as well. *An electric current in a*

solid conductor consists of a flow of electrons only. In the atoms of metallic conductors, the valence (outermost) electrons are "free" and, under certain conditions, these free electrons can be made to drift through the conductor in the so-called conduction band (see pages 241–242). An electron does not move instantaneously from one end of a wire to the other, the individual electron drift being relatively slow—less than 1 mm per sec. However, the electrical impulse or ***current*** moves with tremendous speed, approaching that of light in a vacuum (3×10^8 meters per sec). To make electrons flow, the conductor must have an excess of electrons at one end, and a relative deficiency at the other. The net result is that electrons will then flow from the point of excess (higher negative potential) to the point of deficiency (lower negative potential), just as a body will fall from a point of higher potential energy to a point of lower potential energy (see pages 34–35 and Figure 6.1).

Figure 6.1. Diagrammatic representation of electron flow in a solid conductor. As an electron enters the conductor at A where there is an excess of electrons, another electron leaves at B where there is a deficiency of electrons.

An ***electric circuit is defined as the path over which the current flows.*** Electrons will not flow in a nonconductor such as glass or plastic because of the gap between the valence band and the conduction band (see pages 241–242), and, in semiconductors, they flow under certain conditions. Figure 6.2 shows diagrammatically the components of a simple electric circuit.

Sources of Electric Current

Various methods are available for piling up electrons at one point and simultaneously removing them at another point, thereby setting up a difference of electrical potential and causing an elec-

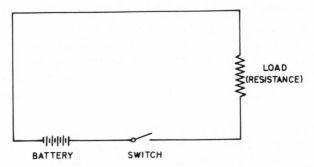

Figure 6.2. Simple resistance circuit. The load represents the total resistance of electrical devices in the circuit.

tric current to flow in a conductor. They all require the expenditure of energy as exemplified by the following two main types of devices:

1. *Cells* or *batteries* which convert *chemical energy* to electrical energy.

2. *Dynamo* or *generator* which converts *mechanical energy* to electrical energy.

Other sources include *solar energy* (sunlight) and *atomic energy.* However, these are still incompletely developed and are not widely used as sources of electrical energy.

Factors in an Electric Circuit

Three main factors characterize a simple electric circuit, which is carrying a *steady direct current,* that is, a current of constant strength flowing always in the same direction. They include *potential difference, current,* and *resistance.* These factors can best be understood by comparing them with those governing the flow of water through a pipe.

1. **Potential Difference.** We may define potential difference as a *difference in electrical potential energy between two points in an electric circuit,* due to an excess of electrons at one point relative to the other. A piling up of electrons at one point and simultaneous removal at another point are brought about through the use of a

battery or generator. The potential difference between two points actually represents the amount of ***work*** expended in moving a unit charge from one point to the other. This resembles the situation shown in Figure 6.3, in which there are two containers of water at different levels connected by a pipe closed by a valve. A difference of pressure exists between the water in both containers, proportional to the difference in height *d* of the water levels. As soon as the valve is opened, the difference in pressure causes the water to flow from container *A* to container *B* until their levels become equalized and the pressure difference disappears.

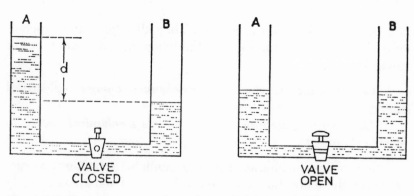

Figure 6.3. Water pressure analogy of electrical potential difference or voltage. With the valve closed, there is a difference of pressure between the water in arms *A* and *B*, proportional to the difference in water levels, *d*. (This is analogous to the potential difference between the poles of a battery on open circuit with no current flowing.) When the valve is opened, water flows from arm *A* into arm *B* until the difference in pressure disappears. (In a closed electric circuit, current continues to flow as long as potential difference is applied.)

Similarly, an excess of electrons at one end of a conductor causes a difference of electrical pressure or a ***potential difference*** to be set up, ***even if the conductor is interrupted by an open switch*** as in Figure 6.2. Closing the switch causes electrons to rush from the point of excess (higher negative potential) to the point of deficiency (lower negative potential). Thus, just as with the water analogy, it is ***the difference of potential that drives the electrons.*** If the difference of potential can be maintained by a battery or generator, electron current will persist as long as the switch is closed.

As the current flows, electrical potential gradually falls along the circuit. Similarly, with water flowing through a pipe, the water pressure decreases gradually along the pipe.

It would be well to review the section in Chapter 3 on the difference of potential energy between two points at different levels above ground, and the movement of a rock from a higher to a lower energy level. The analogy with the difference in water pressure and the difference of electrical potential is self-evident.

The term *electromotive force* (emf) applies to the maximum difference of potential between the terminals of a battery or generator. As noted above, this is not really a force but rather a quantity of work or energy needed to move a unit electric charge through the circuit.

The unit of potential difference (or emf) is the *volt, defined as that potential difference which will maintain a current of one ampere in a circuit whose resistance is one ohm.*

2. Current. The second factor in an electric circuit is *current, defined as the amount of electric charge flowing per second.* (In a water pipe, there is a definite amount of water flowing per second past a given point). Since an electric current consists of a flow of electrons, the more electrons flowing per second the "stronger" is the current. Similarly, the more water flowing per second in a pipe, the stronger is the current of water.

The unit of current is the *ampere, which may be defined as one coulomb quantity of electric charge flowing per second* (ie, 6.3×10^{10} free electrons per sec). A current of one ampere will deposit a standard weight of silver per second from a solution of silver nitrate by electrolysis (to be exact, 0.001118 g per sec).

3. Resistance. The third factor in an electric circuit is *resistance,* a property of the materials making up the circuit itself. *Electrical resistance is that property of the circuit which opposes or hinders the flow of an electric current.* As an analogy, there is resistance to the flow of water in a pipe because of the friction of the molecules of water against the molecules of the pipe material. Note that the very large resistance of a nonconductor prevents the flow of current.

The unit of electrical resistance is the *ohm* (symbol Ω), defined by the International Electrical Congress of 1893 as follows: *one ohm is the resistance of a standard volume of mercury under standard conditions* (to be exact, it is the resistance to a steady current by a column of mercury weighing 14.45 g, having a length of 106.3 cm and a uniform cross-sectional area, at 0 C).

On what does the resistance of a conductor depend? It depends on four things: material, length, cross-sectional area, and temperature.

a. *Material.* Certain materials, known as conductors, readily allow the flow of electrons. They are best exemplified by metals, such as copper and silver. Although copper is a poorer conductor than silver, it is much cheaper and therefore widely used in electric wires. Other materials, such as glass, wood, and plastic, being nonconductors, have virtually no free electrons and hence offer tremendous resistance to the flow of electricity. Such nonconducting materials are called *insulators* or *dielectrics.* Intermediate in resistance are the *semiconductors* (see pages 243–249).

b. *Length.* A long conductor, such as a long wire, has more resistance than a short one. In fact, the *resistance is directly proportional to the length of the conductor.* Similarly, the resistance of a pipe to the flow of water increases with its length.

c. *Cross-sectional Area.* A conductor with a large cross-sectional area has a lower resistance than one with a small cross-sectional area. More specifically, *the resistance of a conductor is inversely proportional to the cross-sectional area.* Similarly, a water pipe having a large cross-sectional area offers less resistance than a small pipe.

d. *Temperature.* With metallic conductors, the *resistance becomes greater as the temperature rises.*

The following equation summarizes the determining factors in resistance:

$$R = \rho \frac{L}{A} \qquad (1)$$

where R is the resistance in ohms; ρ is the resistivity, a proportionality factor depending on the material of the conductor and the temperature; L is the length in meters; and A is the cross-sectional area in m^2.

Ohm's Law

Georg Simon Ohm (1787–1854), a German physicist, discovered that when a steady direct current is flowing in a resistance circuit (ie, one in which resistance is the only obstacle to current flow), there is a definite relation between the potential difference (volts), current (amperes), and resistance (ohms). This is expressed in *Ohm's Law,* which states that *the value of the current in a metallic circuit equals the potential difference divided by the resistance:*

$$I = \frac{V}{R} \tag{2}$$

where $I =$ current in amperes
          $V =$ potential difference in volts
          $R =$ resistance in ohms

If any two of these values are known, the third may be found by substituting in the equation and solving for the unknown. The letter E is often used instead of V to denote potential difference.

Two rules must be observed in applying this law:

1. When Ohm's Law is applied to a *portion of a circuit,* the current in that portion of the circuit equals the voltage across that portion of the circuit divided by the resistance of that portion of the circuit.

2. When Ohm's Law is applied to the *whole circuit,* the current in the circuit equals the total voltage across the circuit divided by the total resistance of the circuit.

Batteries or Cells

Let us turn now to some of the *chemical devices* that act as sources of electric current. There are two main types, the *dry cell* and the *wet cell.*

1. **Dry Cell.** An ordinary dry cell, such as that used in a flashlight, consists of a carbon rod surrounded by manganese dioxide and immersed in a paste composed of ammonium chloride, zinc chloride, cellulose, and a small amount of water. These ingredients are placed in a zinc can, the top of which is closed by a layer of asphalt varnish (see Figure 6.4).

The **alkaline-type** dry cell consists of a manganese dioxide rod immersed in an alkaline potassium hydroxide paste contained in a zinc cylinder. The manganese dioxide rod forms the anode, and the zinc container the cathode. An alkaline cell has a useful life about ten times that of an ordinary dry cell.

Dry cells are actually moist. Note that the central rod nowhere comes in contact with the zinc can. A chemical reaction sets up a potential difference of 1.5 volts between the battery terminals or electrodes; that is, between the zinc and the central rod. The zinc becomes the negative electrode (cathode), while the central rod becomes the positive electrode (anode).

2. **Wet Cell.** An example of the wet cell is the lead storage cell used in automobiles. It consists of a hard rubber or plastic case containing sulfuric acid in which are immersed two electrodes, one lead and the other lead oxide. As the result of a chemical reaction with the sulfuric acid, the lead becomes negative while the lead oxide becomes positive. Each cell in a storage battery produces a potential difference of about 2 volts. Automobile batteries usually have three or six wet cells.

CARBON ROD (ANODE)

ZINC (CATHODE)

CHEMICAL PASTE

Figure 6.4. Diagram of an ordinary dry cell.

Of special interest is the sealed **rechargeable nickel-cadmium** or **nicad** cell. It has a nickel oxide anode and a cadmium cathode. The plates are each wrapped in a separator and immersed in potassium hydroxide.

Components of Elementary Electric Circuits

Certain fundamental principles having been presented, we can now examine the simplest type of electric circuit; that is, one supplied by a *battery* as the source of potential difference. The current is a *steady direct current* (DC) flowing in *one direction only.* Since the only hindrance to the flow of current in such a circuit is resistance, it is often termed a *resistance circuit.*

Essential Parts. The simplest electric circuit has three components: (1) battery, (2) conductor, and (3) load or resistance. The circuit may be represented by a diagram which shows, incidentally, some of the more common electrical symbols (see Figure 6.2).

Current flows only when the switch is *closed.* If the circuit is broken at any point, it is then called an *open circuit.* When completed it becomes a *closed circuit.* However, keep in mind that there is a potential difference even on open circuit.

Polarity of Circuits. The current in a circuit supplied by a battery has a definite direction, or *polarity.* Most physics books have again come to regard the direction of flow of the current to be from positive to negative. However, for the sake of simplicity, we shall assume the *direction of the current to be the same as that of the flow of electrons; that is, from the cathode (−), through the external circuit, to the anode (+)* (see Figure 6.5).

**DIRECTION OF FLOW
OF ELECTRONS**

Figure 6.5. The direction of *electron flow* determines the direction of an electric current. The *conventional direction* is opposite to this.

Connection of Meters. The polarity of DC circuits requires the proper connection of DC measuring devices or meters. Since these devices also have *polarity*, the two terminals on a meter are labeled (+) and (−) and, to avoid damage, must be so connected that the (+) terminal is on the (+) side of the circuit and the (−) terminal on the (−) side.

A *voltmeter* measures, in volts, the potential difference between any two points in a circuit. (Potential difference is often referred to as *voltage drop*.) Therefore, the voltmeter is always connected in *parallel;* that is, it is placed in a small circuit which is a branch of the main circuit, as in Figure 6.6. Obviously, a voltmeter connected successively between various pairs of points in a circuit where the resistances may differ, will give different voltage readings—they will be larger across the higher resistance and smaller across the lower resistance. Similarly, the drop in pressure between any pair of points in a water pipe will be different if the bore of the pipe is not uniform, there being a greater fall in pressure where the pipe is narrower, that is, where there is greater resistance to flow of water.

Figure 6.6. Correct connection of a voltmeter—in parallel.

An *ammeter* (ampere + meter) measures, in amperes, the quantity of electric charge flowing per second. It is connected directly into the circuit, that is, in *series* (see Figure 6.7). When so connected, *an ammeter will read the same no matter where it is placed in a series circuit.*

Figure 6.7. Correct connection of an ammeter—in series.

Ammeters and voltmeters look alike externally and consist of a box enclosing the mechanism, with a glass window in which a pointer moves over a calibrated scale, as shown in Figure 6.8. The instrument is always labeled "voltmeter" or "ammeter." The construction of these devices will be described later.

Series and Parallel Circuits

Electric appliances (toasters, flatirons, fans, etc) and electric sources (batteries, generators) may be connected in a circuit in two principal ways. One is called *a series circuit, which may be defined as an electric circuit whose component parts are arranged end-to-end so that the current passes consecutively through each part* (see Figure 6.9). The other arrangement is called a *parallel circuit, wherein the component parts are connected as branches of the main circuit so that the current is divided among them* (see Figure 6.10).

1. Series Circuit. When *current-consuming devices* such as electric appliances are connected in series as shown in Figure 6.9, the total resistance is equal to the sum of the separate resistances. Thus, if R = total resistance of the whole circuit, and r_1, r_2, and r_3 represent the resistances of various devices connected in series, and disregarding the small internal resistance of the battery, then,

$$R = r_1 + r_2 + r_3 \qquad (3)$$

Figure 6.8. Voltmeter or ammeter.

Figure 6.9. Resistors in series. Ohm's Law applies to the entire circuit, and to any portion of it. The total voltage drop, 90 V, is equal to the sum of the voltage drops across all the resistors, 15 V + 30 V + 45 V. The current, 15 amp, is the same everywhere in the circuit. The voltage drop across each resistor is proportional to the resistance, because $V = IR$ and I is constant in this circuit.

Suppose in this case, $r_1 = 1$ ohm, $r_2 = 2$ ohms, and $r_3 = 3$ ohms, and the ammeter reads 15 amp. (Remember that the current is the same everywhere in a series circuit.) What is the voltage across the **entire** circuit? First substitute the given values of resistance in equation (3),

$$R = 1 + 2 + 3 = 6 \text{ ohms}$$

Then apply Ohm's Law

$$I = V/R$$

or

$$V = IR \qquad (4)$$

and substitute the values of I and R (obtained above)

$$V = 15 \text{ amp} \times 6 \text{ ohms} = 90 \text{ volts}$$

There is another approach to this problem—the application of Ohm's Law to **each part** of the circuit. Again, recall that the current I remains constant throughout the circuit. Since $V = IR$ the voltage across each resistor in Figure 6.9 is equal to the current times the resistance of each resistor:

$$v_1 = Ir_1 = 15 \times 1 = 15 \text{ volts}$$
$$v_2 = Ir_2 = 15 \times 2 = 30$$
$$v_3 = Ir_3 = 15 \times 3 = 45$$

The total voltage is then

$$V = v_1 + v_2 + v_3$$
$$V = 15 + 30 + 45 = 90 \text{ volts}$$

which is the same result obtained above by applying Ohm's Law to the entire circuit.

What is the real significance of the equation $V = IR$? It actually states that the **voltage across a resistor equals the current times the resistance**. But, besides this, it indicates that there is a fall or drop in potential across a resistor, and as the resistance increases so does the potential drop. Sometimes this is called a voltage drop or, what is the same thing, an **IR drop.** Keep in mind that the terms potential difference (in volts), voltage, voltage drop, and *IR* drop are used interchangeably.

In summary, then, voltage is a measure of the potential difference across a resistor. The voltage drop across the resistor increases as the resistance increases. It is obvious from the above examples that the voltage drop across an entire series circuit must equal the sum of the voltage drops across the resistors.

If **current-producing devices** such as electric cells are connected in series, **the total voltage equals the sum of the individual voltages.** In such a circuit, the positive pole of one cell is connected to the negative pole of the next, as in Figure 6.10. If V is the total voltage, and v_1, v_2, v_3, and v_4 are the voltages of the individual cells, then

Figure 6.10. A circuit containing batteries in series.

$$V = v_1 + v_2 + v_3 + v_4 \qquad (5)$$

The total current in such a circuit can be computed from the total voltage and the total resistance simply by applying Ohm's Law.

2. **Parallel Circuit.** Figure 6.11 shows a parallel circuit; careful comparison of *A* and *B* reveals that the circuits are essentially identical, although they have been drawn somewhat differently. The conductors themselves have so little resistance that it may be disregarded. In a parallel circuit the **voltage drop is the same across all branches, regardless of their resistance.** Thus, the voltage drop across r_1 is the same as that across r_2 and that across r_3, and the voltage drop in each case is therefore equal to *V,* the voltage supplied by the battery. However, application of Ohm's Law to each portion of the circuit will show that the current in each branch is **inversely** proportional to the resistance of that branch. In other words, the largest current will flow in the branch having the least resistance.

What is the resistance of a circuit with several parallel branches? It is obvious that in such a circuit, the current divides among the several branches or paths, so that the total resistance must be less than that in an individual path. Another way of looking at this is as follows: as more resistors are added in **parallel,** there is an increase in their total cross-sectional area so that the total resistance decreases.

The total resistance of a **parallel circuit** is expressed by the following equation:

$$1/R = 1/r_1 + 1/r_2 + 1/r_3 + \ldots 1/r_n \qquad (6)$$

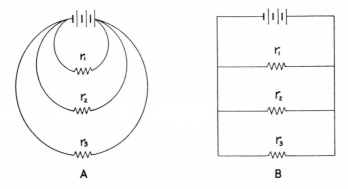

Figure 6.11. *A* and *B* are different methods of representing a parallel circuit. Note that they are fundamentally identical.

where R is the total resistance and r_1, r_2, etc are the resistances of the separate branches.

Thus, the total resistance of a parallel circuit can be found by the rule based on equation (6): *the reciprocal of the whole resistance equals the sum of the reciprocals of the separate resistances in a parallel circuit.*

A typical example is presented in Figure 6.12 to clarify this rule. If the resistances in the branches of a parallel circuit are 1, 2, and 3 ohms respectively, what is the total resistance of the circuit? Substituting the values of r in equation (6), we find that the total resistance is less than any of the resistances in the individual branches.

$$1/R = 1/1 + 1/2 + 1/3$$
$$1/R = \frac{6 + 3 + 2}{6}$$
$$1/R = 11/6$$

Inverting both sides of the equation,

$$R = 6/11 = 0.55 \text{ ohm}$$

Suppose, in the above example, that the potential difference across the circuit is 6 volts. How do we find the current in each branch and in the main lines? Since this is a parallel circuit, the

Figure 6.12. Resistors in parallel. The voltage drop, 6 V, is the same across the whole circuit and across each branch. The current differs in the branches, the smallest current flowing in the branch having the largest resistance. The total current, 11 amp, equals the sum of the branch currents: 6 amp + 3 amp + 2 amp. The total resistance is found by $1/R = 1/r_1 + 1/r_2 + 1/r_3$.

voltage drop across each branch must be the same—6 volts. Then, applying Ohm's Law to each branch,

$$i = v/r$$

$$i_1 = 6/1 = 6 \text{ amp}$$

$$i_2 = 6/2 = 3 \text{ amp}$$

$$i_3 = 6/3 = 2 \text{ amp}$$

The **current in the main lines of a parallel circuit equals the sum of the branch currents,**

$$I = i_1 + i_2 + i_3 \tag{7}$$

Substituting the values of the branch currents just obtained,

$$I = 6 + 3 + 2 = 11 \text{ amp}$$

To verify the answer, we apply Ohm's Law to the entire circuit. Since the total current is 11 amp and the total resistance is 0.55 ohm,

$$V = IR \qquad\qquad V = 11 \times 0.55 = 6 \text{ volts}$$

As expected, the current divides among the branches so that the **smallest current flows in the branch having the greatest resistance.** Since V is equal in all branches, if r in a given branch is greater, i must be smaller, and *vice versa,* in accordance with $V = IR$.

With **current-producing devices** connected in parallel, the total voltage is the same as that of a single source, if all the sources are alike. Figure 6.13 shows this type of connection. The total current, that is, in the main line, equals the sum of the currents provided by all the sources.

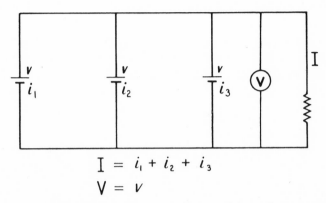

$$I = i_1 + i_2 + i_3$$
$$V = v$$

Figure 6.13. A circuit containing cells arranged in parallel. Total current, $I = i_1 + i_2 + i_3$. Voltage across entire circuit, $V = v$.

The parallel circuit is used in electrical wiring of homes, factories, and other buildings. With a series circuit, electrical failure of one appliance, such as a light bulb, causes all other lights in the circuit to go out. Besides, as more appliances are added in a series circuit, each appliance receives less voltage, since the total voltage drops must be divided among more appliances; thus, as more electric lights are added, all become dimmer.

The main advantage of the parallel circuit is that failure of one appliance does not prevent operation of the others, since they are on branches of the main circuit. As more branches are added, the total resistance decreases and the total amperage increases while the voltage remains unchanged. Thus, the more appliances added, the greater is the amperage in the **main circuit.** Adding too many appliances may cause the amperage in the main line to become excessive and **overload** the circuit. Under these conditions the wiring system could become hot enough to ruin one or more appliances, or start a fire. This danger can be avoided by connecting protective devices such as circuit breakers or fuses in the circuit. A *fuse* contains a wire which melts more easily than the wires of the circuit being protected (see Figure 14.3). When the amperage exceeds the safe maximum, the fuse melts, thereby opening the circuit and stopping the flow of current before the circuit can become overheated. Such a fuse, in which the protective wire has melted, is called a ***blown fuse.*** Contact between two non-insulated wires carrying a current results in a ***short circuit;*** there is a marked fall in resistance and a corresponding rise in amperage which is usually sufficient to blow a fuse. The ***circuit breaker,*** another type of protective device, will be discussed later.

Electric Capacitor (Condenser)

We have already noted that electrical energy can be obtained from a chemical reaction in a dry or wet cell; this may be regarded as ***stored electricity.*** There is another method of storing electrical energy that does not depend on chemical reaction. You should recall from the chapter on Electrostatics that a charge on a conducting body is distributed entirely on its surface. Such an electrically charged body ***stores*** electrical energy, provided it is insulated so that the charge does not "leak" away; it is an ***electric capacitor*** or ***condenser.***

One of the simplest types is the ***parallel-plate capacitor,*** consisting of a pair of flat metallic plates arranged parallel to each other and ***separated*** by a small space containing air or special insulating material. Capacitor operation is shown in Figure 6.14. When the capacitor is connected to a source of direct current, such as a battery, electrons move from the negative terminal of the battery to the plate to which it is connected. At the same time, an equal number of electrons pass from the opposite plate to the positive terminal of the battery. This is indicated in Figure 6.14A. ***No electrons pass from one plate to the other across the space between them,*** unless there is a breakdown of the insulator due to application of excessively high voltage. When the capacitor acquires a full charge, the difference of potential (voltage) across its plates reaches a maximum that is equal and opposite in direction to that of the charging current. The current now ceases to flow in the wires.

If the capacitor is then disconnected from the battery, it retains

CAPACITOR

A   **B**

Figure 6.14. Parallel plate capacitor. In *A* the capacitor is connected to a battery and is being charged. In *B* the capacitor has been disconnected and its plates connected by a wire, whereupon it loses its charge. The arrows indicate the direction of electron flow in the wire.

its electrical charge until the plates are connected by a conductor as in Figure 6.14B, whereupon the capacitor discharges and once more becomes neutral. The direction of the discharging current is *opposite* to that of the original charging current, and stops flowing as soon as the capacitor is completely discharged. (With an alternating current the capacitor plates repeatedly change polarity and the current continues to flow.)

How much electricity can a capacitor store? The quantity of electric charge in coulombs stored per volt applied to the capacitor is called its **capacitance,** the unit of capacitance being the *farad,* a very large unit; a more practical unit is the microfarad (millionth of a farad). The larger the area of the plates, and the smaller the space between them, the greater is the capacitance or electrical storing ability. The insulator or, as it is more often called, the **dielectric** between the plates also determines the capacitance for a given plate size and spacing; if the **dielectric constant** (insulating ability) of air is taken as 1, then wax paper has a dielectric constant of 2, and glass a constant of about 7. These materials will increase the capacitance of a given capacitor two times, and seven times, respectively, as compared with an air dielectric. In practice, a capacitor is usually made up of multiple parallel plates to increase the capacitance.

The Work and Power of an Electric Current

Electrical energy, just as any other form of energy, is capable of performing work. According to the Law of Conservation of Energy, a given amount of electrical energy is convertible to a definite amount of work and/or heat.

The *power* of a steady direct current, or the *electric energy expended per second,* is simply the product of the current and voltage:

$$P = IV \qquad (8)$$

power $=$ *amperage* $\times$ *voltage*
(in *watts*)

a relationship known as the *power rule.* The unit of power is the *watt,* 746 watts being equal to 1 horsepower.

It is well known that an electric current produces heat in a circuit. To find the power loss in terms of the heat produced per second, we must convert equation (8) to a form which contains the term resistance, since this remains constant regardless of the voltage or current. Applying Ohm's Law,

$$I = V/R$$
$$V = IR$$

Substituting *IR* for *V* in equation (8),

$$P = I \times IR$$

Power Loss $= I^2R$ *watts* $\qquad (9)$
(heat production/sec)

where I is the current in amperes and R the resistance in ohms.

Two conclusions may be drawn from equation (9). First, the power loss due to the heating effect of the current is proportional to the resistance; thus, that portion of the circuit having the greatest resistance will sustain the greatest amount of heat production.

Second, the power loss in the form of heat increases very rapidly with an increase in the current. Since *the power loss is proportional to the square of the current,* doubling the current increases the power loss by a factor of 2^2, or four times. Tripling the current increases the power loss by a factor of 3^2, or nine times. The importance of this principle will be discussed later.

QUESTIONS AND PROBLEMS

1. How does an electric current flow along a wire? In a salt solution? Under what other conditions do electrons flow?
2. Describe the two main sources of electric current.
3. Define potential difference. What is the unit of measurement? State the difference between potential difference, electromotive force, and voltage?
4. What is meant by electrical resistance, and on what does it depend?
5. Define electric current strength and state its unit.
6. In which direction does an electric current flow? What is meant by the "conventional" direction?
7. State and explain Ohm's Law.
8. An electric circuit has, in series, appliances with these resistances: 4 ohms, 10 ohms, 6 ohms, 40 ohms. Find the value of the current when the applied potential difference is 120 volts?
9. What voltage is required to produce a current of 30 amperes in a circuit having a resistance of 5 ohms?
10. What type of electric circuit is used in ordinary house wiring? Why?
11. A circuit has the following resistances connected in *parallel:* 3 ohms, 6 ohms, 18 ohms. What is the total resistance of the circuit? With 12 volts applied across the circuit, what is the amperage in each branch *and* in the main lines?
12. State the power formula? Name the unit of power?
13. A circuit has a current of ·2 amperes flowing under an impressed electromotive force of 12 volts. Find the power delivered to the circuit.
14. What is the function of an electric capacitor? Describe its construction and explain its operation with the aid of a diagram. Contrast its behavior in a direct current with that in an alternating current.

CHAPTER 7 MAGNETISM

Definition

Magnetism may be defined as the ability of certain materials to attract iron, cobalt, or nickel. In general, any material that attracts these materials is called a *magnet*. The various types of magnets will be described in the next section.

Classification of Magnets

There are three main types of magnets: *natural magnets, artificial permanent magnets,* and *electromagnets.*

1. **Natural magnets** include, first, the *earth* itself, a gigantic magnet which, in common with all others, can deflect the needle of a compass. Another example is the ore *lodestone*, consisting of iron oxide (magnetite) that has become magnetized by lying in the earth's magnetic field for an extraordinarily long period of time. In some parts of the world there are actually magnetic mountains consisting of such ores. The ancient Greeks recognized the magnetism of lodestone more than 2500 years ago.

2. **Artificial permanent magnets** usually consist of a piece of *hard steel* in the shape of a horseshoe or bar which has been *artificially* magnetized so that it is capable of attracting iron (see Figure 7.1). The *magnetic compass* is simply a small permanent magnetic needle swinging freely on a pivot at its center, used to detect the presence of magnetic materials and to locate the earth's magnetic poles. A widely used alloy of aluminum, nickel, and cobalt—*alnico*—can be made into an extremely powerful permanent magnet that has many times the lifting ability of a steel magnet. It is interesting to note, however, that aluminum itself cannot be magnetized.

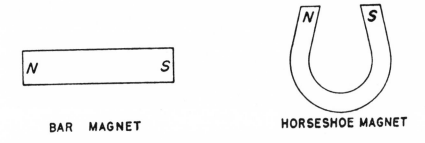

BAR MAGNET   HORSESHOE MAGNET

Figure 7.1. Permanent magnets.

3. **Electromagnets** are temporary magnets produced by means of an electric current, as will be described later.

Laws of Magnetism

The *three fundamental laws of magnetism* are as follows:

1. *Every magnet has two poles,* one at each end. This concept is based on the observation that when a magnet is inserted into a container of iron filings and then removed, iron particles will cling to its ends or *poles,* as illustrated in Figure 7.2. When allowed to swing freely (as in a magnetic compass), one pole of the magnet points north and the other end south. The poles are therefore called, respectively, *north* and *south* poles.

IRON
FILINGS   IRON
                             FILINGS

Figure 7.2. Polarity of a magnet. This is demonstrated by immersing first one end, then the other, of a magnet into a box of iron filings which cling mainly at the ends or *poles.*

2. *Like magnetic poles repel* each other; *unlike poles attract* each other. Thus, if two bar magnets are brought together with their south poles facing each other as in Figure 7.3A, there is a force which tends to push them apart. If, on the other hand, the magnets

are brought together with opposite poles facing each other, a force tends to pull them together, as in Figure 7.3B.

3. *The force of attraction (or repulsion) between two magnetic poles varies directly as the strength of the poles, and inversely as the square of the distance between them.* Thus, doubling the strength of one pole doubles the force between the poles. Tripling the strength triples the force. On the other hand, doubling the distance between two poles reduces the force between them to $(1/2)^2$ or one-quarter. Tripling the distance reduces the force to $(1/3)^2$ or one-ninth.

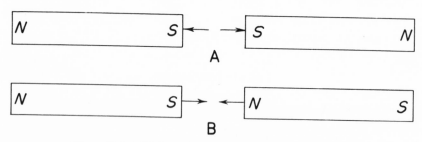

Figure 7.3. (A) Like poles repel. (B) Unlike poles attract.

Nature of Magnetism

Why are some materials magnetic (iron-attracting) whereas others are not? The most widely accepted explanation, an outgrowth of Weber's theory of magnetism first proposed in the early nineteenth century, is based on observations such as the following:

1. Breaking a magnet results in each fragment becoming a *whole magnet* with its own north and south poles, as in Figure 7.4.

2. Heating or hammering a piece of steel while it lies near a magnet causes the steel to become a magnet (i.e. magnetized).

3. Stroking an iron bar repeatedly with one end of a magnet causes the bar to become magnetized.

4. Gently jarring a test tube of iron filings near a magnet causes them to become magnetized. If the test tube is now shaken vigorously, it loses its magnetism.

These observations suggested that elements such as iron, nickel,

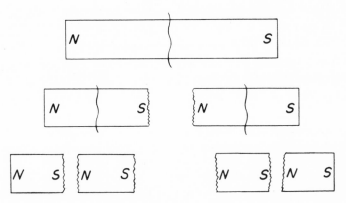

Figure 7.4. When a magnet is broken, each part becomes a whole magnet with a north and a south pole.

and cobalt consist of extremely small, discrete magnets. But only with the advent of modern atomic science has the true nature of such elements been fully explained. According to atomic theory, the orbital electrons in magnetic elements spin predominantly in one direction, resulting in the formation of *magnetic poles in the atom as a whole.* These atomic magnets are believed to form groups called *magnetic domains.*

A *magnetic element* can exist either in the magnetized or nonmagnetized state. In a *nonmagnetized* piece of iron, the domains are in a state of random disorder as in Figure 7.5A. Therefore, the iron does not have magnetic poles. On the other hand, in *magnetized* iron the domains are aligned in orderly fashion, all their north poles pointing in one direction, and their south poles in the opposite direction, as shown in Figure 7.5B.

In *nonmagnetic elements* such as copper, just as many electrons spin in one direction as in the other, so their opposing magnetic effects cancel out. Therefore, in such elements the atoms are not magnetic, no domains are formed, and they *cannot* be magnetized.

Magnetic Fields

What is there about a magnet that causes it to attract iron? Surrounding a magnet there is a zone of influence called a *magnetic*

A. NON-MAGNETIZED IRON

B. MAGNETIZED IRON
(MAGNET)

Figure 7.5. Magnetic domains in a magnetic substance. In *A*, when a ferromagnetic substance such as iron is not magnetized, the domains are arranged haphazardly and there is no net polarity. In *B* the iron has been magnetized and the domains are arranged in orderly fashion to produce opposite poles.

field, representing a summation of the fields of all the domains. The magnetic field can be demonstrated by placing a piece of cardboard over a magnet and sprinkling iron filings on the cardboard. If the latter is gently tapped, the filings arrange themselves into a pattern resembling the one in Figure 7.6. The lines along which the filings arrange themselves are called *lines of force* or *magnetic flux.* In other words, the magnetic field consists of lines of force, and the more closely spaced these lines, the stronger is the field. In fact, the *strength of a magnetic field is proportional to the number of lines per square centimeter.*

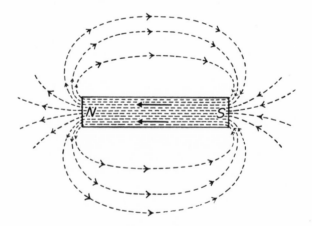

Figure 7.6. The magnetic lines of force about and in a magnet. The lines have been mapped by a small magnetic compass held successively in the indicated positions outside the magnet. They can also be shown by means of iron filings. (The direction of the lines within the magnet are not mapped, but are assumed.)

The lines of force can be mapped out by means of a small magnetic compass. Starting at the north pole of a bar magnet, one simply moves the compass around it toward its south pole and observes the behavior of the needle which acts as though it were following a line through space from the north to the south pole of the magnet, as shown in Figure 7.6.

Characteristics of Lines of Force

Magnetic lines of force may be pictured as follows:

1. They are directed from the north pole to the south pole of a magnet as curved lines in the surrounding space. Within the magnet they are directed from the south pole to the north pole (see Figure 7.6).

2. Lines of force seem to repel each other when they are in the same direction, and attract each other when they are in opposite directions (see Figure 7.7).

3. The field is distorted by magnetic materials, but is not affected by nonmagnetic materials (see Figure 7.8).

Magnetic Induction (Magnetization)

In an ordinary piece of iron the magnetic domains are jumbled helter-skelter by molecular motion and so the iron does not behave as a magnet (see Figure 7.9A). When such a piece of nonmagnetized iron is brought near one pole of a magnet, the end of the pole nearest the iron assumes the *opposite polarity* as a result of *magnetic induction;* the magnetic field of the pole exerts a force on the magnetic domains of the iron, making them line up in an orderly arrangement as in Figure 7.9B. The iron thus becomes temporarily magnetized and behaves as a magnet while lying in the field. When the iron is removed from the field, its magnetic domains return to their disorderly arrangement and the iron no longer is magnetized (ie, it no longer behaves as a magnet).

In summary, then, whenever a magnetic material (iron, cobalt, or nickel) is brought near a magnet, it first becomes magnetized (magnetic induction), its end nearer the magnetic pole acquiring

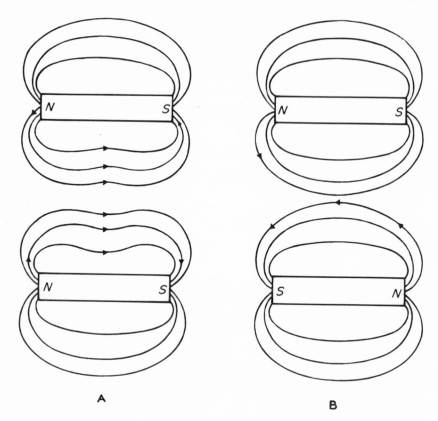

A   B

Figure 7.7. Magnetic lines of force act upon one another, depending on their relative directions. In A the lines ·of force are in the same direction and the resultant force tends to separate the magnets. In B the lines of force are in opposite directions and the magnets attract each other.

opposite polarity. These unlike poles then experience a force of attraction, resulting in attraction by the magnet.

Magnetic Permeability and Retentivity

Some materials are more susceptible than others to magnetic induction; that is, their magnetic domains can be readily lined up when placed in a magnetic field. The ease with which a given material can be magnetized in this way is designated as its *magnetic permeability.*

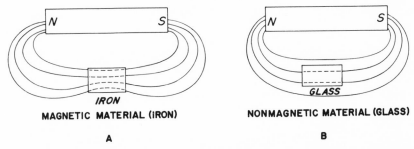

MAGNETIC MATERIAL (IRON)   **NONMAGNETIC MATERIAL (GLASS)**

A   B

Figure 7.8. The effect of magnetic and nonmagnetic materials on a magnetic field. In *A*, the iron "concentrates" the lines of force because of its magnetic permeability: this results from the summation of the lines of force associated with induced magnetism in the iron, and the lines of force of the magnetic field already present. In *B*, glass, a nonmagnetic material cannot become magnetized and so it has no effect on the magnetic field.

Some materials such as steel do not readily become demagnetized after they have been removed from the magnetizing field; that is, once the magnetic domains have been aligned they tend to remain so. The ability of a magnet to resist demagnetization is called *magnetic retentivity.*

Examples of the above include:

1. "Soft" iron—high permeability, low retentivity.
2. "Hard" steel—low permeability, high retentivity.

Thus, a metal which is easily magnetized is also easily demagnetized (ordinary iron). On the other hand, a metal which is difficult to magnetize is also difficult to demagnetize (hard steel).

Magnetic Classification of Matter

All matter can be classified on the basis of its behavior when brought into a magnetic field.

1. **Ferromagnetic materials** (ordinarily called magnetic materials) include *iron, cobalt,* and *nickel.* They are strongly attracted by a magnet because of their extremely high permeability, that is, their great susceptibility to magnetic induction. Ferromagnetic substances become *permanently* magnetized under certain conditions. For example, steel is a form of iron that has been hardened by special

A

**IRON
DEMAGNETIZED**

B

**PERMANENT   IRON
MAGNET   MAGNETIZED**

Figure 7.9. Magnetic induction. In *A*, the magnetic domains in the iron are normally jumbled, so the iron does not behave as a magnet. In *B*, the iron has been brought into the magnetic field of a magnet; the magnetic domains in the iron line up in an orderly arrangement and the iron is now magnetized. Note that the end of the iron near one pole of the magnet assumes the opposite polarity. When the iron is removed from the magnetic field of the permanent magnet, its magnetic domains return to their disorderly arrangement and the iron no longer behaves as a magnet.

treatment, as a result of which its magnetic permeability decreases while its retentivity increases; it is therefore susceptible to permanent magnetization. Another example is the alloy *alnico*, composed of aluminum, nickel, and cobalt, which, when magnetized, can lift many times its own weight. It has been used to remove magnetic foreign bodies such as nails and bobby pins from the stomach, under fluoroscopic control.

2. **Paramagnetic materials** are feebly attracted by a magnet. Platinum, an example of such a material, has extremely low magnetic permeability.

3. **Nonmagnetic materials** are not attracted by a magnet because they are not susceptible to magnetic induction. In such materials, just as many electrons spin in one direction as in the other so that the atoms are nonmagnetic and therefore do not form magnetic domains. Examples of nonmagnetic materials include wood, glass, and plastic.

4. **Diamagnetic materials** are actually repelled by a magnet, although this action is feeble. Only a few elements exhibit this property, among them beryllium and bismuth.

Detection of Magnetism

We can detect magnetism most easily by using a ***magnetic compass.*** This consists of a horizontal ***magnetized steel needle*** which swings freely about a vertical axis at its center. When brought near a magnet the needle, since it is a magnet, is deflected according to the laws of magnetism. Thus, the south pole of the compass needle turns toward a magnetic north pole, while the north pole of the compass needle turns toward a magnetic south pole. Notice that the north pole of a compass (or any other magnet) is really a geographic "north-seeking" pole, since it points north when allowed to swing freely. Hence the earth's geographic "north" pole is actually a south magnetic pole, whereas the earth's geographic "south" pole is a north magnetic pole.

QUESTIONS

1. Define magnetism in your own terms.
2. Name and discuss briefly the three main types of magnets.
3. What is the present concept of the intimate structure of a magnet? Show by diagram. State three facts which support this theory.
4. State the laws of magnetism.
5. Explain magnetic induction. How does a magnet attract a piece of iron?
6. Compare ordinary iron and hard steel with regard to their magnetization and demagnetization.
7. Define magnetic field; magnetic flux.

8. What happens to a magnetic field when a piece of ordinary iron is placed in it?
9. Indicate the direction of magnetic lines of force in space? Within the magnet?
10. How is magnetism detected?
11. State the magnetic classification of matter.
12. Define the following terms pertaining to magnetism:
    a. Domain
    b. Permeability
    c. Retentivity
    d. Flux
    e. Field
    f. Poles
    g. Compass

CHAPTER *8* ELECTROMAGNETISM

Definition

E VERY ELECTRIC CURRENT is accompanied by magnetic effects. *Electromagnetism is defined as the branch of physics that deals with the relationship between electricity and magnetism.*

Electromagnetic Phenomena

In 1820, Oersted, a Danish scientist, discovered that a magnetic compass needle turns when placed near copper wire carrying a direct current but returns to its normal position when the current stops flowing. Since this indicated the presence of a magnetic field, Oersted concluded that *a magnetic field always surrounds a conductor in which an electric current is flowing.* Actually, a magnetic field surrounds any stream of charged particles, whether in a metallic conductor or in space.

What is the direction of this magnetic field? It is specified by the *left thumb rule: if the wire is grasped in the left hand with the thumb pointing in the direction of the electron current [(−) to (+)], then the fingers encircling the wire will indicate the direction of the magnetic lines around the current* (see Figure 8.1).

These lines of force can be demonstrated by Davy's Experiment. A wire is pushed through a hole in a piece of cardboard and connected to a source of direct current. If iron filings are sprinkled on the cardboard, and the cardboard is then gently tapped, the iron particles arrange themselves in concentric circles around the wire. This is illustrated in Figure 8.2, in which the concentric circles represent the magnetic lines of force, or *magnetic flux,* surrounding the electric current in the wire.

Note carefully this very important fact: *a magnetic field exists*

99

around a wire only while an electric current is flowing. The magnetic field disappears on open circuit because no electric current is flowing.

Figure 8.1. Left hand thumb rule. The thumb points in the direction of the electron current. The fingers designate the direction of the magnetic field around the conductor.

Figure 8.2. The magnetic lines of force around a conductor carrying a direct current. The dotted lines represent the magnetic flux when the electron current is in the indicated direction.

A magnetic field is present also around an alternating current, but because of the rapid reversal of field direction, it cannot be demonstrated by a compass or by Davy's Experiment.

The Electromagnet

While a current flows in a wire *helix* (coil), one end of the helix behaves as though it were the north pole and the opposite end the south pole of a magnet. By applying the thumb rule to each turn of the wire in the coil, we can predict not only the direction of the magnetic flux inside the coil, but also which end of the coil will be the north pole. Such a helix carrying an electric current is known as a *solenoid.* In modern x-ray equipment, solenoids are used to lock various movable parts, such as tube stand or Bucky tray, in almost any desired position.

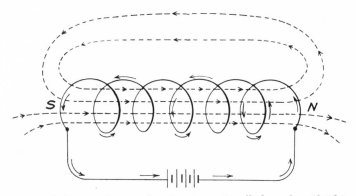

Figure 8.3. A helix carrying an electric current is called a *solenoid.* This shows the magnetic field associated with a solenoid.

As noted earlier (page 94), certain metals, such as iron, possess a high degree of magnetic permeability. Placing an iron rod inside a solenoid increases the strength of the associated magnetic flux because the iron becomes magnetized by the magnetic field of the solenoid. *Such a solenoid with an iron core is called an electromagnet.* Figure 8.4 shows the main features of a simple electromagnet.

The electromagnet has many practical applications, the best known being the electric bell and the telegraph. In x-ray equipment, electromagnets are used in remote control switches and relays of various kinds. These will be discussed later under the appropriate headings.

Electromagnetic Induction

You have just learned that electrons moving in a conductor are surrounded by a magnetic field. Under suitable conditions the reverse is also true; *moving magnetic fields can produce electric currents.* In 1831, Michael Faraday discovered how to convert mechanical energy to electrical energy. On rapidly passing a closed wire between the poles of a horseshoe magnet, he found that an electric current was generated in the wire. This is the principle of *electromagnetic induction,* stated more precisely as follows: *whenever a conductor cuts across magnetic flux, or is cut by magnetic flux, an electromotive force (emf) or potential difference is induced in the conductor.* The practical unit of emf is the volt, which is also the unit of potential difference. Interaction between a line of force and a single loop conductor is called a *flux linkage.*

IRON CORE

WIRE COIL
(WINDING)

Figure 8.4. Electromagnet. Note that it is a solenoid into which has been inserted an iron core to increase the strength of the magnetic field. If the current were reversed in the illustration, the magnetic poles would be reversed. If the current were interrupted, the electromagnet would lose its magnetism because of the low retentivity of the soft iron core.

The magnitude or size of the induced emf depends on the number of lines of force cut per second, or the number of flux linkages per second. This is determined by four factors:

1. The *speed* with which a conductor cuts the magnetic lines of force or magnetic flux; *the more flux lines cut per second, the higher the induced emf.*

2. The *strength* of the magnetic field, or the degree of crowding of the magnetic flux lines—*the stronger the magnetic field the higher the induced emf.* A moment's thought will reveal that this is essentially the same as statement (1); the closer the spacing of the magnetic lines, the more flux cut per second.

3. The *angle* between the conductor and the direction of the magnetic field. As this angle approaches 90° the spaces between the lines of force become smaller, progressively more flux lines are cut per second, and therefore a correspondingly larger emf is induced, as shown in Figure 8.5.

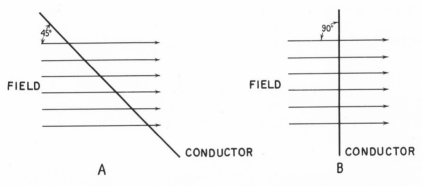

Figure 8.5. In *A*, where the conductor cuts the magnetic field at a 45° angle (down through this page), the induced emf is less than in *B*, where the wire cuts the field at 90°.

4. The number of *"turns"* in the conductor if it is wound into a coil, because the lines cut by each turn of the coil are additive; that is, there are more flux linkages per second. The induced emf is directly proportional to the number of turns in the coil.

Bear in mind that *an emf is induced only while the wire is moving across the field.* If the motion of the wire ceases, the induced emf drops to zero. But the motion of the wire need only be relative; thus, *if the wire is stationary and the magnetic flux passes across it, an emf will be induced in it* just as well, and the above four principles apply. Finally, *if the wire is stationary and the magnetic flux changes (varies in strength) an emf will be induced in the wire.*

An emf is induced in a conductor moving relative to a magnetic field *even if the circuit is open* because emf represents the potential difference between the ends of the conductor. However, no current flows unless the circuit is closed.

In summary, we may state that there are three ways to induce an emf or voltage in a wire by electromagnetic induction:

1. The wire may move across a stationary magnetic flux, or

2. The magnetic flux may move across a stationary wire, or

3. The magnetic flux may vary in strength while a stationary wire lies in it. This principle is extremely important in the electric transformer, to be described later.

We may conclude that *whenever a conductor and a magnetic flux move with relation to each other, an emf is induced in the conductor, the magnitude of the induced emf being directly proportional to the number of lines of force per second crossing the conductor.*

Direction of Induced Electric Current

An induced electric current resulting from an induced emf has a definite direction depending on the relationship between the motion of the conductor and the magnetic field. This is stated in the *left hand rule* or *dynamo rule: first, hold the thumb and first two fingers of the left hand so that each is at right angles to the others, as in Figure 8.6. Next, let the index finger point in the direction of the magnetic flux, and the thumb point in the direction the conductor is moving. The middle finger will then point in the direction of the induced electron current.*

The relationships among the direction of the magnetic flux, the motion of the conductor (wire or coil), and the induced electron current are summarized in Figure 8.7. This principle underlies the electric generator, which will be discussed in detail in the next chapter.

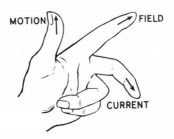

Figure 8.6. Left hand dynamo rule. This shows the direction of *electron* current flow.

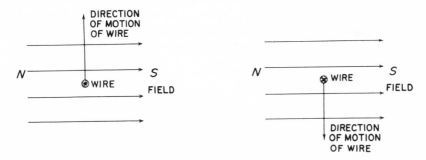

Figure 8.7. The direction of the electron current induced in a wire. The wire is shown in cross section. ⊗ indicates that the current is moving into this page. ☉ indicates that it is moving out of this page, toward the reader.

Self-induction

Suppose we have a coil in a direct current circuit whose switch is open. Now suppose we close the switch; at this instant a magnetic field is set up about the coil, building up rapidly to a maximum, where it remains **while the primary current continues to flow**. During this **brief interval** in which the magnetic field "grows up" around the coil, immediately after closure of the switch, the magnetic flux is really expanding, thereby **cutting the coil itself**. By the rules of electromagnetic induction, an emf is induced in the coil in a direction **opposite** to the **applied emf**, a phenomenon known as *self-induction.* Thus, at the instant of switch closure, the self-induced current tends to *oppose* the flow of primary current in the coil (see Figure 8.8).

While the switch is closed and the primary current is flowing steadily in one direction, the surrounding magnetic field is also constant and therefore does not move relative to the coil. Consequently, *the self-induced current falls to zero.*

If the switch is then opened, the magnetic field collapses, sweeping across the coil in a reverse direction from that occurring when the switch was closed. As a result, the self-induced emf reverses and tends to maintain the current in the coil momentarily after the switch has been opened.

PRIMARY EMF (BATTERY) ⟶
BACK EMF (COIL) ⟵

PRIMARY EMF (BATTERY) ⟶
FORWARD EMF (COIL) ⟶

Figure 8.8. Self-induction. On the "make" (instant of switch closure) there is a *momentary* self-induced emf bucking or opposing the primary battery emf. On the "break" (instant of switch opening), the self-induced emf is reversed momentarily while the battery emf is unchanged.

In summary, then, closing the switch results in momentary induction of an emf opposing the applied emf, while opening the switch causes momentary reversal of the self-induced emf which is now in the same direction as the applied emf. Figure 8.8 describes self-induction, and Figure 8.9 shows graphically the relation of self-induced emf to switch opening and closing.

An iron core inserted into the coil produces an increase in the self-induced emf which opposes or *bucks* the applied emf. The size of the bucking effect depends on the depth of insertion of the core.

Although we have explained the principle of self-inductance by means of a direct current, in actual practice self-induction devices such as the choke coil operate only with *alternating current* (AC) as

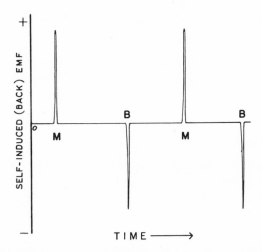

Figure 8.9. Self-induction of emf occurs only at the instant of "make" or "break" of a direct current. While a constant current flows in one direction, no emf is induced. M = make. B = break.

described on page 140. The rapid reversal in direction and magnitude of AC produces an effect similar to the manual opening and closing of a switch with DC.

QUESTIONS

1. Define electromagnetism in your own words. How can you easily determine its presence?
2. What is the left thumb rule? How is it applied?
3. Describe an electromagnet. In what two ways can you determine its polarity?
4. Define and discuss electromagnetic induction?
5. Discuss the four factors that determine the magnitude (size) of an induced emf? Name two terms used interchangeably with emf.
6. In Figure 8.10 (next page), what is the direction of the electromagnetically induced current?
7. Two coils of wire are lying parallel to each other. If one is connected to the terminals of a battery, what will happen in the second coil? What happens when the switch is opened? Closed?

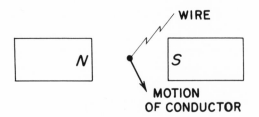

Figure 8.10.

8. Describe the difference between a helix, a solenoid, and an electromagnet.
9. Compare the self-inductance of AC and DC circuits.

CHAPTER *9*   *ELECTRIC GENERATORS AND MOTORS*

ELECTRIC GENERATOR

Definition

An electric generator or dynamo is a device that converts mechanical energy to electrical energy by electromagnetic induction.

Essential Features

As already described in the last chapter, electromagnetic induction is the setting up of an emf in a conductor as it cuts, or is cut by, magnetic flux. In actual practice, an electric generator has two components to bring about the continual cutting of magnetic flux by a conductor:

1. *A powerful electromagnet* to set up the necessary magnetic field. This is called the *field magnet.*

2. *An armature,* consisting of a coil of wire that is rotated mechanically in the magnetic field. The mechanical energy needed to turn the armature is usually supplied by a steam turbine which is heated by oil, gas, coal, or a nuclear reactor. Moreover, a water turbine energized by a waterfall as in Figure 9.1 can be used to turn the armature.

Simple Electric Generator

An *elementary form* of electric generator may be represented by a single loop of wire (armature) rotated mechanically between the poles of a magnet (see Figure 9.2). What are the size and direction of the current produced by such a generator? Examination of the

109

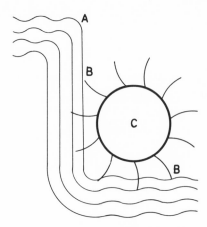

Figure 9.1. The waterfall at *A*, dropping on the blades *B* of a turbine, rotates it counterclockwise about the axis *C*. An armature connected to axis *C* will rotate with the turbine.

relationship between the armature and the magnetic field in which it is rotated should give the answer. In Figure 9.2 the armature is represented by the wire loop *AB* whose ends are **connected separately** to the metal **slip rings** *E* and *F* which rotate with the armature in the direction indicated by *C*. Carbon **"brushes"** rest firmly against each slip ring, at the same time letting the rings rotate. In this way the circuit is completed through the external circuit containing *R* (resistance, representing load or current-consuming devices). Magnetic flux passes from the *N* pole to the *S* pole.

When the armature is rotating clockwise, as in Figure 9.2A, with *A* passing up through the magnetic field, an emf is induced in it in the direction indicated by the straight arrow (according) to the left hand rule). At the same time, *B* is passing down through the field, so that its emf is in the direction of the straight arrow near *B*. The net effect is that the current leaves *A* through slip ring *E*, passes through the external circuit *R*, and enters slip ring *F*.

As the armature coil rotates, *A* and *B* exchange positions, as shown in Figure 9.2B. Now *A* is moving down through the field while *B* is moving up, and the current **leaves slip ring *F*** and **enters slip ring *E*.** Note that the current is now **reversed in both the coil and the external circuit.** This reversal takes place repeatedly as the

Figure 9.2. Simple alternating current generator. Armature *AB* rotates clockwise in the magnetic flux (which passes from *N* to *S*). In the upper diagram, side *A* moves up through the field while side *B* moves down. Arrows show the direction of the induced electron current which leaves the generator through slip ring *E*, passes through external circuit *R*, and completes the circuit through slip ring *F*. As the armature continues to rotate, sides *A* and *B* reverse positions as in the lower diagram, and the current is now reversed in the armature and in the external circuit *R*.

armature continues to rotate. A current which periodically reverses its direction is called an *alternating current,* usually abbreviated AC.

Let us now examine the magnitude of the induced voltage *from instant to instant* as the coil turns in the field. In Figure 9.3, the generator is simply shown end-on, *A* and *B* representing the cross section of the wire armature, rotating in the direction of the arrows around axis *C*. At the instant the armature is in position (1) it is moving parallel to the magnetic field and is therefore not cutting magnetic flux. Because no emf is induced at this instant, the graph shows armature voltage to be zero. As the armature continues to move toward position (2) it cuts progressively more magnetic flux lines per second until, at position (2), it is moving perpendicular (90°) to the flux lines. Now the induced emf in the armature is at maximum, as represented by the peak of the curve. At (3) the armature is again moving parallel to the flux and the induced emf is zero. At (4), with the armature again cutting the flux at an angle of 90° but in the opposite direction, the induced emf is reversed, and the peak of the curve is below the horizontal axis of the graph. Finally, the cycle is completed when the armature returns to its original position.

The alternating current curve embodies certain useful information. Such a curve is presented in Figure 9.3 to show the relationship of the AC to the successive positions of the generator armature as it rotates between the magnetic poles. This is a *sine curve* because it depends on the sine of the angle, from instant to instant, between the plane of the armature and the plane perpendicular to the magnetic field.

In Figure 9.4 the AC curve is shown again in its usual form. The *YY'* axis (vertical) may represent either the induced emf or the current while the *X* axis (horizontal) represents time. The distance between two successive *corresponding points* on the curve, for example *AB*, represents *one cycle* of the AC and indicates that the armature has made one complete revolution. In common use in the United States is 60-cycle (60-Hz) AC, consisting of sixty complete cycles such as *AB* in each second, and corresponding to sixty revolutions of the armature per second. *The number of cycles per second is called the frequency of an alternating current.* Note that

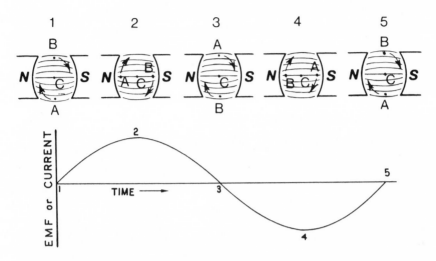

Figure 9.3. The relation of emf or current to the various positions of the rotating coil (armature) of an *AC* generator. *A* and *B* represent the single-loop coil in cross-section (see Figure 9.2). The induced emf depends on the angle at which the coil cuts the magnetic flux at any particular instant. *C* is the axis of rotation of the armature coil.

each cycle consists of two alternations; that is, the voltage starts at zero, rises gradually to a maximum in one direction (shown above the *X* axis), gradually returns to zero, increases to a maximum in the opposite direction (shown below the *X* axis), and finally returns to zero. Thus, there are 120 alternations per second with a 60-cycle current, which means that the *current flows back and forth in the conductor 120 times in each second.* The single sine curve represents a *single phase AC.*

Since the AC voltage and amperage vary from instant to instant, they cannot be expressed in the same way as in a direct current which flows steadily in one direction (see Figure 9.5). Instead, we must use the concept of *effective* or *root mean square (rms) value of an alternating current,* defined as *that direct current which has the same heating effect in a resistor as the alternating current in question.* For example, if a steady direct current of 1 ampere produces the same heating effect in a 1-ohm resistor as does a given AC, then the AC may be said to have an effective value of 1 amp. If we have

TIME

Figure 9.4. Sine curve representing a 60-cycle (60-Hz) alternating current (AC). The thick horizontal arrows show the direction of the *current* during different parts of the AC cycle. Note that the current reverses its direction every $1/120$ sec. The thin vertical arrows indicate the variation in voltage or amperage from instant to instant.

a pure sine wave as in Figure 9.4, then the relationship between the peak and the **effective** or **root mean square value** of the current is as follows:

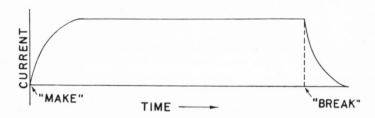

Figure 9.5. Curve representing a steady direct current with a coil in the circuit. The circuit is closed at "make." The current rises rapidly to a maximum and maintains that value at a constant level until the circuit is opened at "break," when it rapidly drops to zero.

effective or rms current = 0.707 × maximum current

or

maximum current = 1.41 × effective or rms current

The **effective** or **rms voltage** has the same relationship to the **maximum voltage:**

effective or rms voltage = 0.707 × maximum voltage

or

maximum voltage $= 1.41 \times$ effective or rms voltage

Properties of Alternating Current Circuits

In Chapter 6 we found that a circuit carrying a *steady direct current* has a property called resistance, which tends to hinder the flow of current. A coil of wire connected in series in such a circuit hinders the flow of current at the instant of switch closure, over and above its electrical resistance. This results from the *inductance* of the coil which sets up a back emf (see pages 105–107). Therefore, the direct current (DC) rapidly rises to a plateau and remains constant (see Figure 9.5), since the associated magnetic field becomes constant and there is no longer a back emf.

On the other hand, with an *alternating current* the rapid change in magnitude and direction of the current causes a corresponding fluctuation in the strength and direction of the magnetic field set up around a coil in the circuit. The coil is said to have *inductance,* defined as the opposition to a *change* in the amount of current flowing. The persistently changing magnetic field around the coil supplied by an AC sets up a *back emf* in a direction opposite the applied alternating voltage, first in one direction and then in the other. This "bucking" tendency of inductance is called *inductive reactance,* and is measured in ohms because it opposes the flow of current.

A *capacitor* in a DC circuit allows current to flow only until it has reached full charge, whereupon the current ceases to flow. However, if a capacitor is added to an AC circuit, it periodically reverses polarity as the current reverses. This offers a certain amount of hindrance to the flow of current, known as *capacitive reactance.*

The apparent total resistance of an AC circuit is called its *impedance,* and this depends on the inductive reactance, capacitive reactance, and true electrical resistance. The calculation of the impedance from these three factors is *not* that of simple addition, and is too complex for our discussion here.

It is interesting to note that Ohm's Law applies to AC if the above discussed properties are taken into consideration,

$$\text{effective current} = \frac{\text{effective voltage}}{\text{impedance}}$$

$$I = \frac{V}{Z} \tag{1}$$

where I is the effective current measured in amperes, V is the effective voltage measured in volts, and Z is the impedance measured in ohms.

Direct Current Generator

The principle of the AC generator also applies to the DC generator, but in the latter a *commutator* instead of slip rings feeds the generated current into the external circuit. Whenever the A and B segments of the armature exchange positions as shown in Figure 9.6, the corresponding half of the commutator always supplies current to the external circuit in the same direction even though there is an AC in the armature itself. The commutator actually consists of a metal ring split in two, with the halves separated by an insulator, each half being permanently fixed to its corresponding end of the wire.

Figure 9.6. Simple direct current (DC) generator. Note that a commutator ring is used, with the result that the current is always supplied to the external circuit in the same direction. (Compare with Figure 9.2, which illustrates the AC generator.)

The wave form of the current obtained from such a generator is represented in Figure 9.7. Note that the part of the sine wave which with AC would be below the horizontal line lies above the line. This is a ***pulsating direct current.*** In actual practice, a DC generator consists of numerous coils and a commutator which is divided into a corresponding number of segments. Since the coils are so arranged that some are always cutting magnetic flux during rotation of the armature, emf is always being induced. At no time does the voltage fall to zero, as in the simple one-coil DC generator illustrated above. Consequently, the voltage is steadier than that generated by a single-coil armature. Figure 9.8 shows the DC curve obtained with a multiple coil generator.

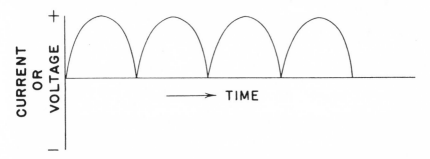

Figure 9.7. Wave form of a direct current curve obtained from a simple DC generator such as that shown in Figure 9.6. Note that the curve differs from a sine curve in that the portions of the curve that lie below the horizontal axis are turned up to lie above the axis. This is a *pulsating direct current,* in contrast to the steady DC supplied by a battery.

Advantages of Alternating Current

For at least two reasons, AC is employed much more frequently than DC.

1. AC is needed to operate transformers which are indispensable in radiographic equipment as well as in many areas of industry. A transformer will not operate adequately on voltage with the wave form shown in Figure 9.8.

2. The electric current generated at the power plant is often

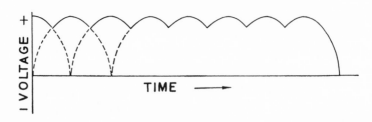

Figure 9.8. Direct current wave form produced by a multiple-coil generator. The solid line curve represents the voltage variation from instant to instant. This fluctuation is much less than that produced by any one of the coils alone (shown by the broken line).

transmitted over a great distance. It has been shown earlier that with **direct current** the power loss (in the form of heat) is related to the current and resistance as follows:

$$P = I^2R \qquad (2)$$

where P = loss of power in the form of heat,
                   measured in watts
              I = current in amperes
              R = resistance in ohms

According to this equation, the power loss is proportional to the **square of the amperage.** It is obvious, therefore, that if a current is transmitted at a very **low** amperage there will be a much smaller loss of electric power than if transmitted at high amperage. An example will illustrate this point.

Suppose we wish to transmit 50,000 watts of electric power over a distance of ten miles (a total of twenty miles of wire), the wire having a resistance of 0.15 ohm per mile. The total **R** is 0.15 × 20 = 3 ohms. If we use **DC** at 500 volts and 100 amps (500 V × 100 A = 50,000 watts), the power loss is obtained by the power equation:

$$Power\ loss = I^2R$$
$$= 100 \times 100 \times 3$$
$$= 30,000\ watts$$

Thus, three-fifths of the power is wasted as a result of the heating effect of the current in the transmission wires!

If, instead, we used **AC** at 5000 volts and 10 amperes (again

50,000 watts), the power loss would be much less. The above equation for power consumption cannot be applied accurately to AC without a correction known as the *power factor,* but it does give a rough approximation. Neglecting the power factor,

$$Power\ loss = I^2R$$
$$= 10 \times 10 \times 3$$
$$= 300\ watts$$

as contrasted with a power loss of 30,000 watts with DC transmitted at lower voltage and higher amperage.

Upon reaching its destination the high voltage (often called high tension) must be reduced to useful values, ordinarily 120 volts for lighting and 120 or 240 volts for most x-ray equipment. This is accomplished by means of a *transformer,* an electromagnetic device which will be described in detail in the next chapter.

ELECTRIC MOTOR

Definition

An electric motor is a device that converts electrical energy to mechanical energy. In other words, an electric current can be made to do useful work by means of a motor.

Principle

Whenever a conductor carrying an electric current is placed in a magnetic field, there is a force or side-thrust on the conductor. It should be emphasized that two conditions must prevail: *the conductor must carry a current, and it must be located in a magnetic field.* The conductor experiences a force that is directly proportional to its length or number of turns, the strength of the magnetic field, and the size of the current. The force is increased when the conductor is in the form of a coil.

The motor effect results from the interaction between the magnetic field around the electron current in the conductor, and the other magnetic field. Therefore, a magnetic field acts on a current-carrying wire as shown in Figure 9.9, where it is represented in cross section and the following conditions prevail:

1. The electric current in the wire is directed away from the reader in this particular case.

2. Magnetic flux surrounds the wire as shown by the small arrows (associated with the current in the wire).

3. Magnetic flux provided by the *field* magnets is directed to the right between the poles of the magnets.

Now look at the upper side of the wire; there the magnetic flux surrounding the wire is directed opposite to that of the flux between the field magnets. Such oppositely directed flux lines "attract" each other. At the same time, note that on the lower side of the wire the surrounding magnetic flux is in the same direction as the flux between the field magnets. Flux lines in the same direction "repel" each other. The net effect is for the wire to be thrust upward by the interaction of the two magnetic fields, as shown by the vertical arrow.

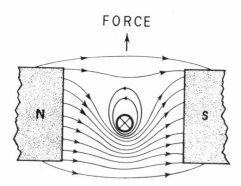

Figure 9.9. The dark circle represents a wire in cross section carrying a current "into the page." As explained in the text, the wire is forced upward by the weaker magnetic field above (flux lines in opposite directions) and by the stronger magnetic field below (flux lines in the same direction). Adapted from *The New Physics and Chemistry Dictionary and Handbook* by Robert W. Marks. Copyright © 1967 by Bantam Books, Inc.

This principle is embodied in the ***right hand or motor rule*** which mirrors the left hand rule. ***The right hand or motor rule states that*** *if the thumb and first two fingers of the right hand are held at right angles to each other; and if the index finger indicates the direction of the magnetic field, and the middle finger the direction of the electron current in the conductor, then the thumb will point in the direction that the conductor will move.* Applying this rule to Figure 9.9, we find that the same result is obtained as before: the wire is thrust upward. Note that according to this rule a conductor experiences a force that is perpendicular to both the magnetic field and the electron current.

Simple Electric Motor

The diagrams shown in the section on the electric generator apply also to the electric motor, except that current is supplied at the brushes instead of being withdrawn. An AC motor has *slip rings*, whereas a DC motor has a *commutator.*

In its elementary form, an electric motor may be represented, as in Figure 9.10, by a cross-sectional diagram of a single coil armature carrying an electric current and lying in a magnetic field. Applying the *right hand rule*, we find that as *A* is thrust upward *B* is thrust downward. The net result is that the armature turns in a clockwise direction about axis *C*.

Figure 9.10. Cross section of an elementary motor. *A* and *B* are the coil wire seen end-on. *C* is the axis of rotation. The curved arrows show the direction in which the coil armature rotates when the proper current is fed to the armature.

At this point we should mention the *back emf* of a motor. When the coil of a motor rotates in a magnetic field, an emf is induced in the coil by electromagnetic induction. This self-induced emf is in a direction *opposite* to the direction of the emf already applied to the coil and is therefore called *back emf.* Thus, an electric motor acts at the same time as a generator, sending some current back to the main lines. This is one of the reasons why a motor consumes less current than a heating device.

Types of Electric Motors

There are two main types of electric motors:

1. **Direct current motor.** This is the reverse of a direct current generator.

2. **Alternating current motors.** There are two kinds of alternating current motors, *synchronous* and *induction.*

The *synchronous motor,* supplied by AC, is built like a single-phase AC generator. However, current is fed to the armature, causing it to rotate in the magnetic field. Certain conditions are necessary for the operation of a synchronous motor. Its armature must rotate at the same speed (revolutions per minute) as the armature of the AC generator supplying the current, or at some fixed multiple of that speed. In other words, the speed of this type of motor *must be synchronous with the speed of the generator.* Special devices are required to bring the speed of the motor armature up to the required number of revolutions per minute. The synchronous motor is used in electric clocks and synchronous timers. The main *disadvantage* of the synchronous motor lies in the limited speeds with which it will operate, that is, it must be in step with the generator. At the same time, a fixed speed may be of *advantage* in certain types of equipment, such as electric clocks.

The *induction motor* has a *stator* which has an even number of stationary electromagnets distributed around the periphery. In the center is a rotating part or *rotor,* consisting of bars of copper arranged around a cylindrical iron core, and resembling a squirrel cage. There are no slip rings, commutators, or brushes because this type of motor works on a different principle from other types of motors and generators. The stator is supplied by a *multiphase* current, which means that the AC supplying one opposite pair of coils is out of phase (out of step) with that supplying the next pair of coils. Thus, successive pairs of coils set up magnetic fields which successively reach their peak strength, acting as though they were rotating, and dragging along the rotor. The drag on the rotor is

Figure 9.11. Principle of the induction motor. In phase *A* (left diagram) the magnetic flux is directed downward as shown. In the next ¼ cycle, phase *B* activates its stators and the magnetic flux is now directed from right to left (the flux in the preceding ¼ cycle having disappeared). In the next phase, the magnetic flux is directed upward, and finally from left to right. Eddy currents are set up in the rotor by electromagnetic induction. This process continues as long as current is supplied. In effect, then, we have a magnetic field that rotates clockwise, dragging the rotor with it and making it rotate. (The two-phase system is now obsolete but aids in understanding the principle of the rotating field.)

caused by eddy currents induced in its copper bars by the "moving" magnetic field. Each copper bar, now carrying an induced current while lying in a magnetic field, experiences a push or force according to the motor principle. This force causes rotation of the rotor.

Although an induction motor is usually designed for modified single-phase or three-phase operation, its principle can be more simply explained with a now obsolete two-phase system. Figure 9.11 describes such a motor. Its power source would have to be a two-phase generator with an armature consisting of two coils perpendicular to each other. The current produced by such a generator may be represented by two curves, one of which is one-fourth cycle ahead of the other, as shown in the upper part of Figure 9.11. This two-phase current is applied to the stator to induce a rotating magnetic field. The rotor is shown in cross section at the center.

A modified single-phase induction motor is used to rotate the anode in an x-ray tube.

Current-measuring Devices

An interesting and important application of the ***motor principle*** is in the construction of instruments for the measurement of current and voltage. The basic device employing this principle is the ***moving coil galvanometer,*** which consists essentially of a coil of fine copper wire suspended between the poles of a horseshoe field magnet. One end of the coil is fixed and the other is attached to a hairspring helix. When a ***direct current*** is passed through the coil as it lies in the magnetic field of the permanent magnet, the coil moves according to the motor principle. In this case, the construction of the instrument, as shown in Figure 9.12, is such that the coil must rotate through an arc that is usually less than one-half circle (180°). Rotation takes place against the spring, so that when the circuit is opened the coil returns to the zero position. Since the degree of rotation of the coil is proportional to the current, the attached pointer moving over a ***calibrated scale*** measures the current as shown in Figure 9.12.

A galvanometer with a low resistance in parallel is capable of measuring ***current*** when connected in ***series*** in a DC circuit; if it has been previously calibrated to read amperes, it is an ***ammeter*** (see Figure 6.8).

On the other hand, a galvanometer protected by a high resistance in series measures ***potential difference*** when connected in ***parallel*** with the circuit being measured; if it has been previously calibrated to indicate volts, it is a voltmeter (see Figure 6.8).

Thus, modifications of the same basic instrument—the galvanometer—allow measurement of amperage or voltage in a DC circuit, provided the instrument has been calibrated against known values of amperage or voltage, respectively.

A

SIDE VIEW OF
GALVANOMETER

B

GALVANOMETER ADAPTED
AS DIRECT READING AMMETER
OR VOLTMETER

Figure 9.12.

Further modification is necessary to measure the voltage and amperage of an ***alternating current,*** because the coil would "freeze" due to the rapid alternation of the current in the coil. (Recall that a 60-cycle AC sustains 120 reversals of direction per second.) Instead of using a horseshoe magnet, one must provide a magnetic field which reverses its direction in step with the current entering the coil. To do this, the AC being measured is, at the same time, used to supply the coils of a pair of field electromagnets. Since the current alternates simultaneously in the rotating coil and in the field coils, the rotation of the coil and hence the deflection of the pointer are unaffected by the alternations of the current, but are still affected by the size of the current. This device, called an ***electro-dynamometer,*** can be designed to read AC voltage or amperage. The same type of instrument can be modified to measure electric power in a circuit, reading the values directly in watts.

QUESTIONS

1. What is an electric generator? The generator rule?
2. List some of the commonly used sources of energy in a generator.
3. Describe, with the aid of a diagram, a simple electric generator.

Show how it produces an alternating current and relate it to the AC sine curve. Label the curve in detail.

4. How does an AC generator differ from a DC generator?
5. Compare the current curves of single phase AC, single phase DC, and an electric battery.
6. Why is AC generally preferred to DC? Prove by means of an example.
7. Define an electric motor. What is the motor principle?
8. Discuss the right hand or motor rule.
9. Under what conditions will a conductor, placed in a magnetic field, tend to move up through the field?
10. What are the two main types of motors?
11. Describe the principle and construction of an induction motor.
12. What is a synchronous motor? How does it differ from an induction motor?
13. Discuss the importance of the induction motor in radiographic equipment.
14. State the underlying principle of the galvanometer. Show with the aid of a simple diagram the construction of a DC voltmeter.

CHAPTER *10* *PRODUCTION AND CONTROL*
OF HIGH VOLTAGE—
REGULATION OF CURRENT

TRANSFORMER

F OR MOST ORDINARY PURPOSES, electric power to the consumer
is supplied at 120 or 240 volts. However, this will not operate
an x-ray tube. Much higher voltages are needed to give the electrons in the tube enough energy to generate x rays. Such high
voltages are made available by the *transformer*, also known as the
x-ray generator. It serves as a major component of an x-ray machine.

Principle

A transformer is an electromagnetic device which changes an
alternating current from low voltage to high voltage, or from high
voltage to low voltage, without loss of an appreciable amount of
electrical energy (usually less than 5 percent). The transformer
transfers electrical energy from one circuit to another *without the
use of moving parts or any electrical contact between the two
circuits*, employing the principle of *electromagnetic mutual induction.*
The simplest type of transformer—the *air core* transformer—
consists of two highly insulated coils of wire lying side by side. One
of these, the *primary coil*, is supplied with an alternating current
(AC). The other or *secondary coil* develops AC by mutual induction (see Figure 10.1). The primary coil is the *input side* of the
transformer, whereas the secondary coil is the *output side.*
How does a transformer function? An AC in the *primary* coil
sets up, in and around it, a magnetic field that varies rapidly in
direction and strength, just as does the AC itself. This changing
magnetic flux *cuts* or *links with* the secondary coil, inducing in it an

127

alternating emf by the process of electromagnetic induction. But the resulting AC in the secondary coil sets up an induced emf in the primary coil (opposite in direction to the primary current). Since emf is induced in each coil by the changing magnetic flux in the other, we call this process *mutual induction*, which is obviously a special case of electromagnetic induction.

Figure 10.1. Simplest type of transformer. An electromotive force is set up in the secondary coil by electromagnetic mutual induction.

Note here, again, the important principle of electromagnetic induction: the emf induced in any coil is directly proportional to the number of turns in the coil that cuts, is cut by, or links with, a given magnetic flux. This also applies to the transformer. Suppose the primary and secondary coils each have one turn. The AC in the primary coil sets up a magnetic field that cuts the one turn in the secondary coil; therefore, the emf is the same in both coils (neglecting any loss of energy during the process). But suppose the primary coil has one turn and the secondary has two turns. Now the *same* magnetic flux set up by the AC in the single-turn primary coil cuts the double-turn secondary coil, *doubling the emf in the latter.* Similarly, if the primary coil has two turns and the secondary one turn, the secondary emf will be half the primary emf.

Because the *induced* emf depends directly on the total number of turns (for a particular changing magnetic flux), we may assume that each turn makes the same contribution toward the total induced emf; that is, their individual induced emfs are additive. Therefore the relationship may be simplified in terms of *emf per turn,* or V/N, where V is the emf in volts, and N is the number of turns in the coil. For example, if the primary emf is 100 V and there are ten turns, then

$$100V/10 = 10 \text{ volts per turn in the primary coil}$$

Now, if the secondary coil has ten turns (note that they must link with the changing magnetic flux associated with the current in the primary coil), the induced emf in the secondary coil will be

$$10 \text{ turns} \times 10 \text{ volts/turn} = 100 \text{ V}$$

or the same as the primary voltage. But if the secondary coil has twenty turns, the induced emf in it will be

$$20 \text{ turns} \times 10V/\text{turn} = 200 \text{ V}$$

or twice the primary voltage.

The preceding discussion is embodied in the *transformer law: the emf induced in the secondary coil is to the emf in the primary coil, as the number of turns in the secondary coil is to the number of turns in the primary coil*, expressed simply in practical units in the following equation:

$$\frac{V_S}{V_P} = \frac{N_S}{N_P} \tag{1}$$

where V_S = voltage in secondary coil
V_P = voltage in primary coil
N_S = no. of turns in the secondary coil
N_P = no. of turns in the primary coil

Stated in words, this means that if the number of turns in the secondary coil is twice the number in the primary coil, then the voltage in the secondary will be twice the voltage in the primary. If the number of turns in the secondary coil is three times that in the primary coil, then the voltage induced in the secondary will be three times as great as in the primary, etc. Such a transformer, having more turns in the secondary coil than in the primary, puts out a *higher* voltage than is supplied to it and is therefore a *step-up transformer*.

If the secondary coil has fewer turns than the primary coil, the output voltage will be *less* than the input voltage, and the transformer is a *step-down transformer*.

What happens to the value of the *current* in a transformer? According to the Law of Conservation of Energy, there can be no more energy coming out of the transformer than is put in, and similarly, the power output (energy per unit time) can be no greater than the power input. Since the power in an electric circuit equals voltage multiplied by amperage, then (neglecting the power factor),

$$I_S V_S = I_P V_P \tag{2}$$

where I_S = current in amperes in the secondary coil
I_P = current in the primary coil
V_S = voltage in the secondary coil
V_P = voltage in the primary coil

Rearranging this equation, we get the proportion:

$$\frac{I_S}{I_P} = \frac{V_P}{V_S} \tag{3}$$

In other words, if the voltage is increased, as in a step-up transformer, the amperage is decreased; and if the voltage is decreased, as in a step-down transformer, the amperage is increased. Thus, a *step-up transformer increases the voltage, but decreases the amperage in an inverse ratio.* The power output of an x-ray transformer is rated in kVA (kilovolt-amperes or kilowatts). Thus, an x-ray generator that can deliver a tube current of 200 mA at 140 kVp is rated at 28 kVA (obtained from 140 kVp × 0.2 A).

In roentgen *diagnostic* equipment the step-up transformer takes 120 or 240 volts and multiplies this voltage to 30,000 to 150,000 volts (30 to 150 kilovolts), thereby providing the high voltage necessary to drive the electrons through an x-ray tube with sufficient speed. At the same time it decreases the current to thousandths of an ampere (milliamperes).

Construction of Transformers

Four main types of transformers will now be described.

1. **Air Core Transformer.** This consists simply of two insulated coils lying side by side as shown in Figure 10.1.

2. **Open Core Transformer.** An iron core inserted into a coil of wire carrying an electric current causes a marked intensification of the magnetic flux within the coil because of the magnetization of

the core. Therefore, a transformer becomes more efficient if each *insulated* coil has an iron core, as shown in Figure 10.2. This is known as an *open core transformer*. Although more efficient than an air core transformer, the open core type is still subject to an appreciable waste of power due to loss of magnetic flux at the ends of the cores, a condition termed *leakage flux.*

Figure 10.2. Open core transformer. There is some waste of power due to leakage of magnetic flux in the air at the ends of the iron cores.

3. **Closed Core Transformer.** Here the heavily insulated coils, often called *windings*, are wound around a square or circular iron ring or core as in Figure 10.3. With this type of transformer, the closed core provides a continuous path for the magnetic flux, so that only a small fraction of the magnetic energy is lost by leakage. An AC in the primary winding sets up an alternating magnetic flux in the iron core. Because this same flux links with (or cuts) both the primary and the secondary windings, it induces the same *voltage per turn in both windings* (coils). Therefore, the induced emf in *each* winding is proportional to the number of turns in that winding. Thus, the transformer law applies, namely, $V_s/V_p = N_s/N_p$ (see also pages 124–126).

The core is *laminated*, that is, it is made of layers of metal plates. Eddy currents (see page 133) are set up in the core by electromagnetic induction during transformer operation. Such eddy currents take energy from the current in the transformer coils, causing a waste of power known as *transformer loss.* Lamination of the core

Figure 10.3. Closed core transformer. This type of iron core provides a continuous path for the magnetic flux, thereby minimizing flux leakage.

hinders the formation of these eddy currents and thereby increases the efficiency of the transformer; in other words, there is less power wasted. Silicon steel is often used in laminated cores because its high electrical resistance further reduces eddy current power loss. Since the closed core transformer is much more efficient than the open core, it is the *one most commonly used in x-ray-generating equipment.* The highly insulated coils are submerged in a metal box containing a special type of oil for additional insulation. Furthermore, the oil helps to keep the transformer cool by improving the dissipation of heat produced during operation.

4. **Shell-type Transformer.** This, the most advanced type, is used as a commercial or power transformer. Here, too, a laminated core is used, consisting of a pile of sheets of silicon steel, each having two rectangular holes, as illustrated in Figure 10.4. The primary and secondary coils are both wound around the central section of the core for maximum efficiency, as shown in Figure 10.4. These windings must be highly insulated from each other by a special coating. In addition, the entire transformer is submerged in a tank filled with a special type of oil for maximum insulation and cooling.

Transformer Efficiency and Power Losses

The efficiency of a transformer is the ratio of the power output to the power input;

Figure 10.4. *A*, core of shell-type transformer. *B*, shell-type transformer, top view. Note the windings of the primary and secondary coils around the *same* central section of the core to provide high efficiency. Very heavy insulation is required.

$$\% \text{ efficiency} = \frac{\text{power output}}{\text{power input}} \times 100$$

Ideally, the power input and power output would be equal, with an efficiency of 100 percent. However, in practice the efficiency is more likely to be about 95 percent or more; that is, there is up to about 5 percent less power output than power input, the lost energy appearing as heat. In contrast to other types of electrical and mechanical equipment, this represents a small waste of energy, and the transformer is therefore a highly efficient device.

We shall now summarize the various kinds of *losses of electrical power* in a transformer and the methods of minimizing them to improve efficiency.

1. **Copper Losses.** These include mainly the loss of electrical power due to the *resistance* of the coils. Such loss of power can be reduced by using copper wire of adequate diameter. In a step-up transformer the primary winding carries a large current, so its wire must be thicker than the wire of the secondary coil which carries a small current (milliamperes). Recall that a thick wire, having less resistance than a thin one, can carry more current with less waste of energy in the form of heat (*Power Loss* $= I^2R$).

2. **Eddy Current Losses.** The alternating magnetic flux set up in the transformer *core* by the AC in the windings induces electrical *eddy currents* (swirling currents) in the core itself by electromag-

netic induction. Eddy currents, in turn, produce heat in the core because electrical power loss due to heat $= I^2R$. The wasted electric power must come from that supplied to the transformer, thereby contributing to the loss of efficiency. Eddy currents can be minimized by the use of *laminated (layered) silicon steel plates*, highly insulated from each other by a special coating. Lamination and high-resistance silicon steel increase the electrical resistance of the core, thereby decreasing the size of the eddy currents according to Ohm's Law (see Figure 10.5).

A   **B**

Figure 10.5. A. Dashed lines suggest the paths taken by eddy currents in a solid iron core. B. With the same volume of iron having three laminations (layers), the total paths for the eddy currents have been significantly increased; this means increased resistance and therefore smaller eddy current effect.

3. **Hysteresis Losses.** Since the transformer operates on and puts out AC, the tiny magnetic domains in the *core* are repeatedly rearranging themselves as the core is magnetized first in one direction and then the other by the AC in the windings. This rearrangement of the domains produces heat in the core, thereby wasting electrical power. Such a loss of power, called *hysteresis loss,* is reduced by the laminated silicon steel core.

REGULATION OF HIGH VOLTAGE

Properly designed x-ray equipment must provide some means of regulating the input voltage to permit the choice of a variety of kilovoltages to be applied to the x-ray tube. This allows the technologist to obtain x rays of appropriate penetrating power for a particular technic. Without flexible voltage regulation, modern radiographic procedures would be seriously hampered. The main device for changing *high voltage* is the *autotransformer.* Another type of voltage control device, the variable resistor or *rheostat,* is widely used to regulate filament voltage and current and, ultimately, tube current (mA). The rheostat also helps control high voltage in orthovoltage therapy equipment. A third device, the *choke coil,* was formerly used to control filament current and voltage.

Autotransformer

According to the description of the step-up transformer, you should realize that there is a *fixed ratio* of voltage output to voltage input. Furthermore, the voltage input is fixed at 120 or 240 volts, depending on the power supply and type of equipment. Without any further modification, we would have available only a single kilovoltage, a situation that would seriously limit the range of radiography, since various kilovoltages must be applied to the x-ray tube to obtain x-ray beams with a variety of penetrating abilities.

How can we modify the basic equipment so as to obtain the required range of kilovoltages? This is accomplished simply by *varying the voltage input to the transformer primary.* Thus, if the ratio of the step-up transformer is 500 to 1 and the input to the primary coil is 100 volts, then the transformer will put out 500 × 100 = 50,000 volts (50 kV). If the input is 180 volts, the output will be 500 × 180 = 90,000 volts (90 kV). To obtain the required variety of input voltages we connect a device known as an *autotransformer* between the source of AC and the primary side of the transformer. As you will see, the autotransformer is a *variable transformer* or *Variac.**

Construction. The autotransformer is made up of a single coil of insulated wire wound around a *large iron core.* At regular intervals along the core, insulation has been omitted and the bare points connected or tapped off to metal buttons, as shown in Figure 10.6. A movable contactor, *C*, varies the number of turns included in the secondary circuit of the autotransformer, thereby varying its out-

---

*General Radio Corporation

Figure 10.6. Diagram of an autotransformer (kV selector), which has only one winding or coil. The *autotransformer* secondary voltage stands in the same ratio to the primary voltage, as the ratio of the number of tapped turns (in this case, 2) is to the number of primary turns (7); that is, $2/7$, so the voltage is stepped down. If *C* is turned above 7, the ratio exceeds 1 and the voltage is stepped up.

put voltage. Thus, the autotransformer serves as a *kV selector.*

Principle. The autotransformer is an electromagnetic device which operates on the principle of *self-induction. A single coil or winding serves as both the primary and secondary, the number of turns being adjustable.* (This is in sharp contrast to the transformer, wherein the number of turns cannot be changed.) By turning the contactor to include more or fewer turns on the secondary side of the autotransformer, we can vary the ratio of the number of secondary turns to the number of primary turns, thereby varying the ratio of voltage output to voltage input. This relationship, similar to that in the transformer, is embodied in the *autotransformer law:*

$$\frac{\textbf{autotransformer secondary voltage}}{\textbf{autotransformer primary voltage}} = \frac{\textbf{number of tapped turns}}{\textbf{number of primary turns}}$$

Thus, in Figure 10.6, if the primary voltage is 240,

$$\frac{\text{autotransformer secondary voltage}}{240} = \frac{2}{7}$$

autotransformer secondary voltage = 68.6 volts

The secondary voltage of the autotransformer is applied to the primary side of the main step-up transformer (see Figures 10.6 and 14.12).

For those desiring a more detailed description of the operation of an autotransformer, a wiring diagram is shown in Figure 10.7. We may regard the voltage drop across the coil as being related to the number of turns, that is, *volts per turn.* Suppose that the applied potential is 240 volts and there are seven primary turns. We would then have 240/7 = 34 volts per turn. Now, looking at the secondary side of the autotransformer, we see that there are two tapped turns; therefore, the voltage drop across this side is 2 turns × 34 volts per turn = 68 volts. Accordingly, the ratio of the voltage output to input of the autotransformer is 68/240 = 2/7, the same result as that obtained by means of the autotransformer law.

AUTOTRANSFORMER

Figure 10.7. Further simplification of wiring diagram of autotransformer. If there are 7 primary turns N_P, and the applied potential is 240 volts, then there would be 240/7 = 34 volts per turn. On the secondary side there are 2 tapped turns N_S; therefore the voltage across the secondary side V_S = 2 turns × 34 volts per turn = 68 volts. So the voltage output to input = 68/240 = 2/7, the same result as that obtained with the autotransformer law.

Note that an autotransformer can be used only where there is a relatively small difference between its input and output voltage. Furthermore, *the position of the contactor should not be changed while the exposure switch is closed because sparking may occur between the metal buttons, thereby damaging them.*

Rheostat

Another device used for voltage control is the *rheostat,* a variable resistor which allows us to vary the resistance of a circuit. It can operate on either alternating or direct current.

Principle. In the discussion of Ohm's Law, we found that there is a fall of potential, or voltage drop, across a resistor in a circuit, as shown in the following equation:

$$V = I \times R$$

voltage drop   current in amps   resistance in ohms

The rheostat consists of a series of resistor coils and a sliding tap which can be moved to increase or decrease the resistance in the circuit. When placed in series in the ***primary circuit***, the rheostat can be used to vary the voltage applied to the primary of the transformer. This relationship is shown in Figure 10.8. If the primary current is I_P, then the voltage drop V_R across the rheostat $= I_PR$. Let V_P be the voltage across the primary circuit, and V_T the voltage across the transformer primary. The total voltage drop across the entire primary circuit V_P equals the sum of the voltage drops (in series) in the primary circuit,

$$V_P = I_PR + V_T$$

Therefore,

$$V_T = V_P - I_PR$$

Thus, it can be seen that as the rheostat resistance R is increased, I_PR increases and V_T decreases; and as R is decreased, V_T increases.

Note that a rheostat controls voltage by converting more or less electrical energy into heat. This is a very inefficient process.

Another important disadvantage is that the voltage drop in a circuit controlled by variable resistance depends also on the amperage, according to the equation, $V = IR$. When the exposure switch is closed and current flows through the x-ray tube, there is a momentary surge of current in the primary circuit of the transformer. Consequently, the IR or voltage drop across the rheostat increases, leaving less voltage across the primary of the transformer. This results in a smaller kV across the secondary of the transformer and the x-ray tube. Hence, voltage regulation is less stable with a rheostat than with an autotransformer which allows more current to flow in the primary circuit as more current is needed in the

Figure 10.8. Principle of the rheostat or variable resistor. In *A* most of the resistor is in the circuit, producing a large voltage drop; hence, only a small voltage V_T is available to the primary of the *transformer*. In *B* only a small segment of the resistor is in the circuit, producing a small voltage drop; now a large voltage is available to the primary of the transformer. Furthermore, according to Ohm's Law, the current in *A* is smaller than in *B*.

secondary circuit, without excessive decrease in kV across the tube. For this reason, the rheostat is no longer used for high voltage regulation in radiographic equipment, and has been superseded by the autotransformer.

In most orthovoltage x-ray machines (200–250 kV), the tube must be warmed before application of the full voltage in order to avoid damage. A rheostat answers this purpose, since it can be varied while the tube is in operation; whereas an autotransformer cannot because sparking may occur, charring the contacts. Thus, when the main switch is first closed, all the resistance is *in* the circuit, *in series with the primary coil* of the x-ray transformer; the resulting large voltage drop across the rheostat leaves a small voltage across the primary coil, inducing a low kV in the secondary coil. As the rheostat resistance is now reduced stepwise, manually or automatically, the voltage drop across it decreases, thereby gradually increasing the voltage available to the primary. This, in turn, induces a higher and higher kV in the secondary until the maximum desired kV is applied to the x-ray tube. An autotransformer, included with the rheostat, further regulates kV in ortho-voltage therapy units.

CONTROL OF FILAMENT CURRENT AND TUBE CURRENT

We have just learned that control of high voltage by means of an autotransformer allows convenient kV selection. Of equal importance is the capability of x-ray equipment to vary tube current or milliamperage (mA).

The construction and operation of an x-ray tube will be explained in detail later. At present it is enough to say that an x-ray tube has two circuits: (1) a filament circuit carrying the current needed to heat the filament and (2) the tube circuit itself carrying the tube current which passes between the electrodes of the x-ray tube and produces x rays. Of utmost significance is the fact that *a small change in filament current produces a large change in tube current*. Therefore, by regulating the filament current we can control the x-ray output in terms of exposure per unit of time, or exposure rate.

Three devices are available for controlling filament current: choke coil, rheostat, and saturable reactor.

Choke Coil

Principle. The choke coil, an electromagnetic device operating on the principle of *self-inductance*, requires *alternating current*.

In Chapter 8 we learned that an electric current in a coil sets up a magnetic field so that one end of the coil becomes a north pole and the opposite end a south pole. If the magnetic field varies in direction and strength, as when it is generated by an *alternating current*, the magnetic flux links with or cuts the coil itself and induces a voltage which *opposes* the voltage already applied across the coil. This is the *back emf of self-induction.*

The introduction of an *iron core* into the coil intensifies the magnetic field and increases the inductive reactance of the coil (analogous to, but not identical with, resistance) producing the following effects:

1. A larger voltage drop across the choke coil.

2. A smaller remaining voltage for the rest of the circuit.

3. A *decrease in current* due to the larger inductance of the circuit.

These effects become more pronounced with deeper insertion of the core into the coil. The principle of the choke coil is explained further in Figure 10.9.

Figure 10.9. Operation of a choke coil. Note that AC is required. Arrow length indicates the emf in that direction. In *A*, with the core completely out, back emf is minimal and voltage drop across the coil is small, so the resultant emf is only slightly less than the applied emf. In *B*, partial insertion of the core increases back emf and voltage drop across the coil. In *C*, with the core completely inserted, back emf of self-induction is maximal, producing a large voltage drop across the coil with a small resultant emf available for the rest of the circuit; *at the same time, the current is decreased.* The adjustable position of the core permits selection of the desired emf and current.

The choke coil was previously used to regulate filament current in the x-ray tube, to permit control of tube current (mA). However, it has been largely replaced by the rheostat and, more recently, by the saturable reactor.

Rheostat

We shall not repeat the entire discussion of the rheostat (variable resistor), which has already been presented in this chapter. However, as already mentioned, the choke coil has been replaced by the rheostat (and later by the saturable reactor) to regulate *filament current* in radiographic equipment, as shown in Figure 10.10. A variable resistor controls not only the voltage but also the current, according to Ohm's Law, $I = V/R$. If the rheostat resistance is increased, the current in the filament circuit decreases, so there will be less heating of the filament, a smaller electron emission, and a much smaller tube current. But at the same time, the increased rheostat resistance causes an increased voltage drop across the rheostat, thereby leaving a smaller voltage for the filament, provided the total voltage drop across the entire filament circuit is kept constant.

Figure 10.10. Diagram of a filament circuit where R_r is the resistance setting of the rheostat, and R_f is the resistance of the tube filament. In *A*, with a smaller value of rheostat resistance, a large current flows in the circuit including the filament, ie, filament circuit. In *B*, with a larger value of rheostat resistance, there is a small current in the circuit. In each instance there is a corresponding change in the filament voltage.

Saturable Reactor

In more advanced types of modern radiographic equipment, a new device, the *saturable reactor*, is coming into use for regulation of filament current. It depends on the electromagnetic principle, not discussed heretofore, that if an iron core within or near a coil is saturated with magnetic flux by an independent source of direct current, the inductance of the coil increases as the degree of saturation of the core increases. This variable degree of core saturation is accomplished by varying the size of the applied DC. As usual, an increase in the inductance of a circuit causes a decrease in the current, *I*. Figure 10.11 shows a simplified version of a saturable reactor.

Figure 10.11. Current control by a saturable reactor. The DC voltage in the left coil saturates the iron core with a steady magnetic flux whose strength can be changed by changing the voltage by means of a rheostat. The higher the saturation of the core, the greater will be the inductance of the right coil and the lower will be the current in the filament circuit.

QUESTIONS AND PROBLEMS

1. Why is a high voltage needed in x-ray equipment?
2. What device is used to change low voltage to high voltage?
3. Discuss the transformer law. A transformer is so constructed that there are 100 turns in the primary coil and 100,000 turns in the secondary. If the input is 110 volts, what is the output voltage?
4. Show by diagram a closed core transformer, first as a step-up transformer, second as a step-down transformer.

5. How are eddy currents reduced in a transformer? Why should they be kept to a minimum?
6. Why is a core used in a transformer?
7. What two types of insulation are used in a transformer and why?
8. Discuss the purpose and principle of an autotransformer. How does it operate? What is the autotransformer law?
9. Why is the autotransformer preferred in the control of high voltage in an x-ray machine?
10. The main electrical supply to an x-ray machine is 240 volts. If the x-ray transformer has a step-up ratio of 1000 and we wish to obtain 100 kV, what will be the step-down ratio of the autotransformer?
11. Describe a rheostat. In what type of x-ray equipment is it most widely used today? How does it operate?
12. Explain the principle of the choke coil. By what devices has it been replaced in radiographic equipment?
13. Which type of current (AC or DC) is needed for the operation of choke coil; autotransformer; rheostat?
14. Why is it necessary to regulate the filament current of an x-ray tube?
15. What purpose is served by the saturable reactor? How does it operate?

CHAPTER *11* RECTIFICATION

~~Definition~~

A S WE HAVE pointed out before, an alternating current (AC)
periodically reverses direction and varies in strength. While
an x-ray tube can operate on *any* high voltage AC, it *operates most
efficiently when supplied by high voltage direct current* (DC)—a
current that is *unidirectional,* flowing always in the same direction.
*Rectification may be defined as the process of changing alternating
current to direct current.*
There are two possible ways of rectifying the high voltage AC
supplied by the secondary side of the step-up transformer: (1) by
suppressing that half of the AC cycle represented by the portion of
the curve that lies below the line (ie, the negative half cycle) or (2)
by changing the negative half cycle to a positive one. The resulting
curves are shown in Figure 11.1.
As an aid to understanding the purpose and process of rectification, we shall summarize the structure and operation of x-ray
tubes, although Chapter 13 contains a detailed account of this
important subject.
An *x-ray tube* consists of a glass bulb from which the air has
been evacuated as completely as possible. Sealed into the ends of
the bulb—or *tube,* as it is better known—are two terminals or
electrodes: the *cathode* and the *anode.* The cathode consists of a
thin tungsten wire (filament) which, when heated to incandescence (white hot) by a *low voltage current,* gives off electrons.
These form a cloud or *space charge* near the filament. If, now, a
high voltage from the secondary of the transformer is applied
between the cathode and anode so as to produce a large negative
charge on the cathode and a large positive charge on the anode,
the resulting strong electric field drives the space charge electrons

145

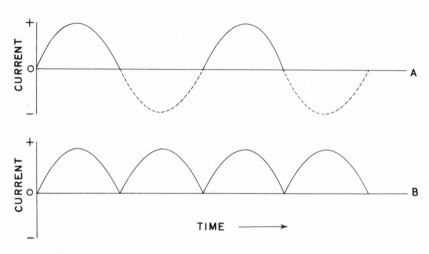

Figure 11.1. Two fundamental types of rectified circuits. In *A*, with half-wave rectification, the negative half lying below the line is *suppressed*. In *B* the negative half of the alternating current now lies above the line and becomes positive. In either case, a *pulsating* direct current is produced.

toward the anode at tremendous speeds. When the electrons strike the anode, their **kinetic energy** is changed to heat and x rays. During ordinary operation, this electron current can pass in **only one direction, from cathode to anode.** If the applied AC has first been rectified so that the resulting current is always directed from cathode to anode, the tube can withstand greater energy loading (ie, exposure factors) than if the current has not been rectified.

Methods of Rectifying an Alternating Current

There are two main systems of rectification: (1) self-rectification and (2) vacuum tube or solid state diode rectification. Vacuum tube diodes, also called **valve tubes** (see pages 233–236), have been used for many years in radiographic equipment. However, solid state diodes (see pages 236–244) have supplanted valve tubes in modern diagnostic units, both single-phase and three-phase. *All rectifying systems are located between the secondary side of the x-ray transformer and the x-ray tube.*

1. **Self-rectification.** In this, the simplest type, the high voltage is

applied *directly* to the terminals of the x-ray tube. Under ordinary conditions, an x-ray tube allows passage of electrons only from the cathode to the anode during the positive half cycle of the AC curve, when the anode is positively charged. This half of the voltage cycle is the *useful voltage* or *forward bias.*

During the negative half cycle the "anode" is negative and the "cathode" is positive, but despite the presence of a high voltage across the tube (however, in the "wrong" direction) no current will *normally* flow because there is no space charge near the anode. At the same time, the reverse voltage—also known as the *inverse voltage* or *reverse bias*—is actually higher than the useful voltage. This is caused by *transformer regulation,* a condition associated with power loss in the transformer core and characterized by a slight fall in kV accompanying the flow of tube current (mA) during positive or forward bias. Such a fall in kV does not occur during negative or reverse bias because there is no current in the tube.

The principal disadvantage of self-rectification is the low heat-loading capacity (ie, limitation to low exposure factors) of an x-ray tube in such a circuit. In a self-rectified circuit the anode must never be heated to the point of electron emission because then, during the negative half cycle, the inverse voltage would drive the electrons in the wrong direction—toward the filament—causing the filament to melt and ruining the tube. Therefore, with self-rectification, exposure factors (kV and mAs) must be limited to lower values (lower tube rating) than with full-wave rectification.

An important point to remember is that the milliammeter indicates average mA. In a self-rectified circuit, because only one-half the cycle is used, the *peak* mA and consequent anode heat must be greater, for the same milliammeter reading than in a full-wave rectified circuit in which both halves of the cycle are used.

Figure 11.2 describes the current through the tube in a self-rectified circuit. This type of rectification is known as *self-half-wave* or single-pulse rectification (one voltage peak per cycle).

Self-rectification was formerly used in mobile x-ray units, but it has been replaced by more sophisticated methods of rectification, to be described next.

2. **Diode Rectification.** A diode normally passes current in one

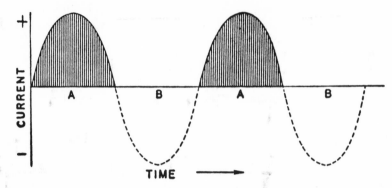

Figure 11.2. Curve of tube current in a self-rectified circuit (single-pulse rectification). During the first half cycle, *A,* the current passes through the tube; the applied voltage is the *effectual* or *useful voltage.* During the second half, *B,* no current flows from anode to cathode and now the applied voltage is *ineffectual* or *inverse voltage.* Note that the useful voltage is less than the inverse voltage.

direction only, that is, *electrons flow from cathode to anode.* Although it is customary in solid state circuitry to show the current passing from anode to cathode (flow of "holes," see Figure 13.26), we shall consistently trace the *flow of electrons* in x-ray circuits in this course since it is conceptually easier.

Either one or two diodes can provide half-wave rectification, also known as *one-pulse* rectification (one voltage peak per cycle). Figure 11.3 shows a circuit containing *one rectifier diode.* During the *positive half* of the AC cycle, the polarity of the secondary coil of the transformer is that shown in the figure, the direction of the electron current being from cathode to anode. The current flows through the rectifier and the x-ray tube as indicated by the arrows. During the negative half cycle, when the polarity of the transformer secondary is reversed, the rectifier diode is nonconductive; in fact, it behaves as an open switch, thereby preventing application of high voltage to the x-ray tube. Thus, the rectifier *suppresses the inverse voltage,* diminishing the possibility of reverse flow of electrons in the x-ray tube, should the anode become hot enough during operation to be a source of electron emission. Such a reverse flow of electrons could easily destroy the filament. Therefore, the diode allows greater loading of the x-ray tube than is possible with self-rectification, although we obtain half-

Figure 11.3. Half-wave rectification with a single rectifier diode. In *A*, electrons flow readily in both the x-ray tube and rectifier diode; this is *forward bias*. In *B*, during the next half cycle, the polarity of the transformer has reversed and electrons cannot flow from anode to cathode in the rectifier diode, thereby protecting the x-ray tube from the inverse voltage, also called *reverse bias*.

Figure 11.4. Half-wave rectification with two rectifier diodes. When the polarity of the transformer reverses, no current flows in the circuit.

wave or one-pulse rectification in either case (see Figure 11.2).

With *two rectifier diodes,* as shown in Figure 11.4, the high voltage during the negative half cycle is divided among the diodes and the x-ray tube, thereby increasing the efficiency of the system and improving the heat-loading capacity of the x-ray tube. The wave form of two-diode rectified current resembles that of self-rectified current (see Figure 11.2); in other words, it, too, is single- or one-pulse rectification.

Four rectifier diodes can be arranged to provide *full-wave rectification* as shown in Figure 11.5; this is *two-pulse rectification*

Figure 11.5. Full-wave rectification with four rectifier diodes. By following the numbered segments of the circuits in *A* and *B*, you can see that regardless of the polarity of the transformer engendered by the AC, the electron current always reaches the x-ray tube in the same direction; that is, both half cycles are used. This is called two-pulse rectification because of the two voltage peaks per cycle.

since there are two voltage peaks per cycle. In *A*, the current flows from the negative pole of the transformer through the successively numbered portions of the circuit to the cathode of the x-ray tube, eventually returning to the positive end of the transformer. (Remember that each rectifier diode permits the current to flow only in one direction, from cathode to anode.) In *B*, the polarity of the transformer reverses due to alternation of the current. The current again follows the successively numbered portions of the circuit to the cathode of the x-ray tube, finally reaching the positive end of the transformer. Note that at some time during its course through the circuit, the current arrives at the junction of two rectifier cathodes, as at point *S* in *A*; the current passes through one of the diodes because passage through the other diode would lead it back to a point of higher potential and this is physically impossible (analogy: a ball will not, of itself, roll uphill to a point of higher potential energy).

You should encounter no difficulty in learning the proper connection of the rectifier diodes once you have mastered the following simple rules:

(1) First arrange a circuit without indicating the diodes, as shown in Figure 11.6.

Figure 11.6.

(2) Then insert two cathodes joined as in Figure 11.7.

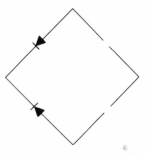

Figure 11.7.

(3) Now connect these cathodes to the anode of the x-ray tube, as in Figure 11.8.

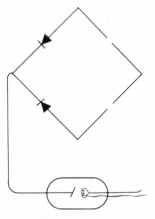

Figure 11.8.

(4) Next, insert two diodes on the opposite side of the circuit, with their anodes joined, and then connect them with the cathode of the x-ray tube, as in Figure 11.9.

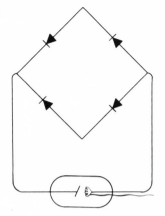

Figure 11.9.

(5) Finally, connect the remaining terminals to the terminals of the transformer, as in Figure 11.10.

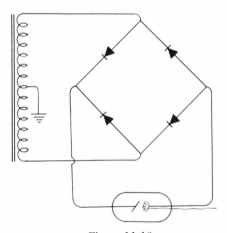

Figure 11.10.

The above rules are necessary because there is only one correct way to connect the rectifier diodes to each other and to the x-ray tube and transformer. If this relationship is altered in any way, the system will fail to rectify. Notice that in any particular half cycle, one parallel pair of rectifier diodes is conductive (see Figure 11.5).

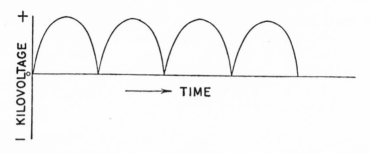

Figure 11.11. Wave form of a current rectified by four diode rectifiers. Note that all the values of kV are represented, from zero to the maximum value, or kVp. This is two-pulse rectification since there are two voltage peaks per full cycle.

The wave form of the full-wave rectified current is shown in Figure 11.1.

There is one disadvantage in four-diode rectification. Using the entire AC wave results in the production of a high percentage of low energy x rays, that is, low kV range. But these can be minimized either by using appropriate filters or by boosting the lower kV in the rectified wave form to higher kV by means of capacitors, as in constant-potential equipment. This applies especially to 250-kV therapy equipment.

Full-wave or two-pulse rectification permits a large increase in the tube rating or heat-loading capacity (relative to half-wave or single-pulse rectification), which means that larger exposures can be used without damaging the tube. But we must emphasize that a tube must be used in accordance with the rating furnished by the manufacturer for that particular tube.

QUESTIONS

1. Define rectification.
2. Why is it desirable to rectify the current for x-ray generation?
3. Name two main types of rectification.
4. How are x rays produced?
5. Show with the aid of a diagram: (a) single-diode rectification and (b) four-diode rectification. Draw the shapes of the current waves produced by each.

6. What is meant by a constant potential unit? Under what conditions, and why, is it desirable?
7. Draw and label the current curves in a self-rectified circuit; a single-diode rectified circuit; a four-diode rectified circuit. Which are half-wave rectified? Full-wave rectified?
8. Define inverse voltage; reverse bias; useful voltage. What is their importance?
9. What is meant by single-pulse rectification? Two-pulse rectification?
10. What property of diodes makes them suitable as rectifiers?
11. In what type of equipment might you find self-rectification used?
12. Why are valve tubes not conductive during the inverse half cycle?
13. Show by aid of a diagram a rectifier using four diodes. Draw the wave form of the rectified current. Why is it called full-wave or two-pulse?

CHAPTER *12*   X RAYS (ROENTGEN RAYS)

How X Rays Were Discovered

FOR A NUMBER of years before the discovery of x rays physicists had been observing high voltage discharges in vacuum tubes. In 1895 Wilhelm Konrad Roentgen, a German physicist, was studying these phenomena in a Crookes tube operated at high voltage in a darkened room. Suddenly, he noticed the *fluorescence* (glowing) of a barium platinocyanide screen lying several feet from the end of the tube. He soon realized that the fluorescence was caused by a hitherto unknown type of invisible radiation. Moreover, he found that this radiation could pass completely through solid materials such as paper, cardboard, and wood, since they did not prevent fluorescence when placed between the tube and the barium platinocyanide. However, the rays could be stopped by denser materials such as lead.

Thus, by the sheerest accident, Roentgen had discovered a new type of radiation which, upon leaving the Crookes tube, was capable of passing through certain solids that are opaque to ordinary light.

Roentgen quickly discovered the potentiality of the new radiation in medicine when he placed a hand (presumably his wife's) between the tube and a piece of cardboard coated with barium platinocyanide. Imagine his excitement on seeing the bones depicted on such a fluoroscopic screen for the first time!

Roentgen gave the name *x rays* to his newly found, invisible, penetrating radiation because the letter *x* represents the unknown in mathematics, although within the next few months he had ascertained most of the properties of x rays.

The discovery of x rays changed the course of medical history, to say nothing of its impact on science and industry. Roentgen's name is often directly linked with x rays in that they are also known as *roentgen rays*. *Roentgenology* is that branch of medicine dealing with the use of x or roentgen rays in diagnosis and treatment. The term *radiology* includes not only x rays but also natural and artificial radionuclides, computerized tomography, magnetic resonance imaging, and ultrasonography. *Radiography* deals with the art and science of recording x-ray images on film, paper, magnetic tape, and magnetic disc. *Fluoroscopy* includes the observation of x-ray images on a screen coated with fluorescent material, either directly or with the aid of an intensifying system.

Nature of X Rays

An x-ray beam consists of a group of rays that are related to white light, ultraviolet, infrared, and other similar types of radiant energy. They are all classified as *electromagnetic radiation*—wavelike fluctuations of electric and magnetic fields set up in space by oscillating (vibrating) electrons. A mechanical analogy would be, for example, the waves produced on the surface of water by a dropped stone.

The electric and magnetic fields fluctuate perpendicular to their direction as well as to each other, as shown diagrammatically in Figure 12.1. As they are identical in form, we usually depict only one of them as in Figure 12.2.

Figure 12.1. The electrical and magnetic components of an electromagnetic wave oscillate (vibrate) in mutually perpendicular planes. From J. Selman: *The Basic Physics of Radiation Therapy*, 2nd Ed. Springfield, Thomas, 1976.

All electromagnetic waves such as radio, heat, light, x rays and

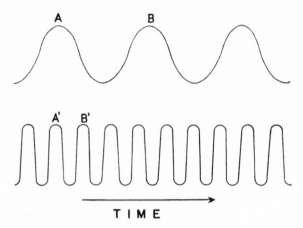

TIME

Figure 12.2. Electromagnetic waves. The upper and lower wave trains differ in wavelength, that is, the distance between two crests such as *A* to *B* and *A'* to *B'*. The lower wave thus has a shorter wavelength and therefore more crests or cycles in a given period of time, than does the upper wave, because their speeds are identical. Thus, the wave with the shorter wavelength has greater frequency or number of cycles per sec (hertz).

gamma rays have the same general form and travel with the same *constant speed* as light -3×10^8 meters, 3×10^{10} cm, or 186,000 miles per sec in a vacuum or air. However, they differ in *wavelength* — the distance between two successive crests in the wave, such as *A* to *B* in Figure 12.2. The number of crests or cycles per second is the *frequency* of the wave, the unit of frequency being the *hertz* defined as one cycle per sec. You can see, by comparing the upper and lower waves in Figure 12.2, that if the wavelength is decreased, the frequency must increase correspondingly. This can also be shown in another way. The speed with which the wave travels is equal to the frequency multiplied by the wavelength:

$$c = \nu\lambda \qquad (1)$$

where c = speed of x rays or light in vacuum or air
(3×10^8 m per sec)

ν (Greek *nu*) = frequency in hertz (cycles per sec)

λ (Greek *lambda*) = wavelength in m

Since c, the speed of all electromagnetic waves, is constant in a given material, an increase in frequency (ν) must always be accompanied by a corresponding decrease in wavelength (λ) and, conversely, a decrease in frequency by an increase in wavelength. *Frequency is inversely proportional to wavelength.*

The wavelengths of x rays are extremely short; for instance, in *ordinary radiography,* their useful range extends from about 0.1 to 0.5 Å (recall that 1 Å = 10^{-10} or one ten-billionth m!). These ultrashort wavelengths are associated with enormous frequencies—3 × 10^{19} to 6 × 10^{18} hertz (Hz).

The various kinds of electromagnetic radiation, ranging from radio waves with wavelengths measured in several thousands of meters, down to high energy x and gamma rays with wavelengths measured in thousandths of an Å, are shown in Figure 12.3.

Figure 12.3. Electromagnetic spectrum. Useful range of energies is as follows:

Radiography	0.1 to 0.5 Å (124 to 24.8 kVp)
Cobalt 60 gamma rays	0.01 Å (1.25 MeV)
Linac; betatron	0.0005 to 0.002 Å (25 MV to 6 MV)

As we shall attempt to explain in more detail later (see pages 170–172), each electromagnetic wave also behaves as a bit of energy that depends on the frequency of the wave. Such an energy bit is called a **photon** or **quantum.** It is preferable to designate x and gamma rays according to their photon energy rather than their wavelength.

Sources of X Rays

Whenever a stream of fast moving electrons suddenly undergoes deceleration (ie, reduction of speed), x rays are produced. While these conditions may prevail in nature, they can also be brought about artificially by means of an **x-ray tube.** Gamma rays, which are identical to x rays, are emitted by the **nuclei** of certain radionuclides.

The X-ray Tube

At this point we shall outline the main features of a typical x-ray tube, reserving a more detailed discussion of the subject for a later section.

Historically, the early x-ray tubes were cold cathode gas tubes. Such a tube consisted of a glass bulb in which a partial vacuum had been produced, leaving a small amount of gas. In it were sealed two electrodes, one negative (cathode) and the other positive (anode). The cathode terminal was **not** heated. Application of a high voltage across the terminals caused ionization of the gas in the tube with release of a stream of electrons which produced x rays upon striking the positive terminal (anode). The gas tube is now obsolete not only because of its inefficiency but also because tube mA could not be changed independently of kV, making it difficult to control x-ray quantity and quality.

In 1913 W. D. Coolidge, at the General Electric Company Laboratories, invented a new type of x-ray tube based on a radically different principle (Edison effect); this was the **hot cathode diode tube,** which revolutionized radiographic technic because it made possible the independent control of mA and kV. The principles of construction and operation are surprisingly simple and must be clearly understood by all those concerned with the use of x rays.

An x-ray tube has the following components (see Figure 12.4):

1. A *glass envelope* or *tube* from which the air has been evacuated as completely as possible. Air must be removed not only from the interior of the tube, but from the glass and metal parts as well, by prolonged baking before the tube is sealed. This process is called *degassing.* A high vacuum is necessary for two reasons:

a. To prevent collision of the high speed electrons with gas molecules, which would cause significant slowing of the electrons (see below).

b. To prevent oxidation and burning-out of the filament.

2. A *hot filament* supplied with a separate low voltage heating current. The filament serves as the *cathode,* or negative electrode, when the high voltage is correctly applied.

Figure 12.4. Model of an x-ray tube. *A* shows the two circuits and the general features. The inset at *B* indicates that x rays are emitted from the target in all directions, but only those approaching the port (window) pass out as the *useful beam,* the remaining x rays being absorbed in the protective housing.

3. A *target* which serves as the *anode,* or positive electrode, when high voltage is correctly applied.

4. A *high voltage* applied across the electrodes, charging the filament negatively and the target positively.

Notice that there are *two circuits in the x-ray tube:* one, a low voltage heating circuit through the cathode itself; and the other, a high-voltage circuit between the cathode and anode to drive the electrons (see Figure 12.4). However, at the cathode end the high voltage conductor is connected to one side of the filament circuit.

Conditions Necessary for the Production of X Rays

Whenever (1) *fast-moving electrons undergo rapid deceleration* or (2) *electrons drop from an outer shell to a hole in an inner atomic shell, x rays are produced.* The x-ray tube is a device for obtaining free electrons, then speeding them up, and finally stopping them. In addition to these basic processes, the electrons must also be concentrated on a small area of the anode known as the *focus.* These four conditions required for the production of x rays in a hot cathode tube will now be described in some detail because of their extreme importance.

1. **Separation of Electrons.** In common with all other atoms, the tungsten atoms in the filament have orbital electrons circulating around a central nucleus. How can these electrons be liberated from their atoms? The *filament current* supplying the filament causes it to become glowing hot or *incandescent,* with resulting separation of some of its outer orbital electrons. We may regard such electrons as escaping from the filament to form a cloud or *space charge* nearby. The electrons liberated in this manner are called *thermions,* and the process of their liberation through the heating of a conductor by an electric current is called *thermionic emission.*

2. **Production of High Speed Electrons.** If, now, a high potential difference, ie, kV, is applied across the tube, giving the filament a very high *negative charge* (cathode) and the target an equally high *positive charge* (anode), the resulting strong electric field causes the space charge electrons to rush at an *extremely high speed*

through the tube from cathode to anode, this electron stream constituting the **cathode rays** or **tube current.** *The speed of these electrons approaches one-half the speed of light,* and even more in some modern equipment.

3. **Focusing of Electrons.** The electron stream in the tube is confined to a very narrow beam and is concentrated on a small spot on the anode face — the *focus* — by a negatively charged metal focusing cup in which is suspended the filament; the narrower the electron beam the smaller the focus and the sharper the x-ray images.

4. **Stopping of High Speed Electrons in Target.** When the fast electrons enter the target of the x-ray tube, their **kinetic energy** changes to other forms of energy. The efficiency of ordinary radiographic equipment is such that *at 80 kV only about 0.6 percent of this energy is converted to x rays while the remaining 99.4 percent appears as heat.* (See page 167 for a discussion of efficiency of x-ray production.) In fact, only about one part in a thousand of the kinetic energy of the electrons eventually results in radiologically useful x rays! As shown in Figure 12.4B, x rays are emitted in **all** directions, but only those leaving the window of the x-ray tube comprise the **useful beam.**

You must avoid confusing the electrons flowing in the tube, with the x rays emerging from the tube. Imagine a boy throwing stones at the side of a barn. The stones are analogous to the electron beam in the x-ray tube, whereas the emerging sound waves are analogous to the x rays that come from the target when it is struck by electrons.

Electron Interactions with Target Atoms
X-ray Production

When the fast electron stream enters the tube target, the electrons interact with target atoms producing x rays by the following two processes:

1. **Brems Radiation.** Upon approaching the strongly positive **nuclear field** of a target atom, the negatively charged high-speed electron is deviated from its initial path because of the attraction between these opposite charges (see Figure 12.5). As a result, the

electron is slowed down or **decelerated,** thereby losing some of its kinetic energy; the *lost kinetic energy is radiated as an x ray of equivalent energy.* The term **bremsstrahlung** or *braking radiation* has been applied to this process. Brems radiation is *heterogeneous* or **polyenergetic,** that is, nonuniform in energy and wavelength because the amount of braking or deceleration varies among electrons according to their speed and how closely they approach the nucleus. With each different deceleration, a corresponding amount of kinetic energy is converted to x rays of equivalent energy; just as the deceleration varies, so does the energy of the x rays. An electron that happens to approach the nucleus head-on is completely stopped by the nuclear electrostatic field. In this special case of the brems effect, all of the kinetic energy of the electron is converted to an x ray of equivalent energy. The deceleration of electrons depends also on the atomic number of the target. Thus, targets of higher atomic number are more efficient producers of brems radiation (eg, rhenium with atomic number 75 as opposed to tungsten with atomic number 74). It should be pointed out that electrons also interact with, and are repelled by, the electrons swarming around the target nuclei. In this process heat is transferred to the target atoms; such heat production far exceeds x-ray production at ordinary values of tube potential (kV).

2. **Characteristic Radiation.** This is the other process of x-ray production in an x-ray tube. An electron with a sufficient minimum kinetic energy may interact with an *inner orbital electron* (for example, in K or L shell) of a target atom, ejecting it from its orbit (see Figure 12.6). To free this electron, work has to be done to overcome the attractive force of the nucleus. The atom is now unstable, being *ionized* (electron missing from atom) and in an *excited state* (electron vacancy in a shell). Immediately, the space or "hole" vacated by the electron is filled by electron transition from one of the outer shells. Since, in the first place, energy was put into the atom to free the electron, a like amount of energy must be given off when an electron from a higher energy level enters to fill the hole in the shell (satisfying the Law of Conservation of Energy). This energy is emitted as a *characteristic x ray* because its energy is characteristic of the target element and the involved shells. (In fact, there are series of characteristic rays

Figure 12.5. Production of bremsstrahlung (brems radiation). An electron with energy E, on approaching an atomic nucleus, experiences an attractive electrostatic force which causes it to change direction along a curved path. In changing direction the electron radiates energy h which must come from the kinetic energy of the electron. Therefore the electron moves away from the nucleus with energy E_2. The radiated brems photon energy $h = E_1 - E_2$.

because, for example, the replacing electron leaves a hole which must, in turn, be filled by an electron from a still higher energy level or shell.)

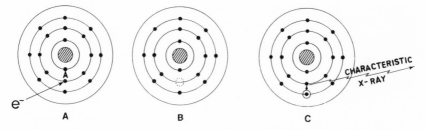

Figure 12.6. Production of characteristic radiation. In A, the incoming *electron* collides with an inner shell electron. In B, the atom is in an "excited state," an electron now being displaced from its shell. In C, an electron jumps from an outer shell to replace the ejected electron; this is accompanied by characteristic radiation, as the atom returns to its normal state.

We may now summarize the nature of the ***primary radiation,*** that is, the x rays emerging from the target:

a. **General Radiation** — "white," polyenergetic, or heterogeneous radiation with a continuous range of energies (and wavelengths) due to deceleration of electrons by strongly positive electric fields of nuclei in target atoms. This is ***brems radiation,*** constituting about 90 percent of emitted x rays when 80 to 100 kV is applied to the tube.

b. **Characteristic Radiation** — consists of limited, discrete energies (and wavelengths), constituting about 10 percent of emitted x rays when the tube potential is in the range of 80 to 100 kV. No characteristic radiation is produced at tube potentials less than 69 kV with a tungsten target.

Target Material

The target metal must be selected with two aims in mind. First, it must have a very ***high melting point*** to withstand the extremely high temperature to which it is subjected. Second, it must have a ***high atomic number*** because (1) the resulting ***characteristic*** radiation is of high energy and therefore more penetrating and (2) there is increased production of brems radiation. Tungsten, a metal with a melting point of 3370 C and an atomic number of 74, generally satisfies the above requirements. Rhenium (atomic number 75) and tungsten, coated on a molybdenum-tungsten disc, forms the target in rotating anode radiographic tubes for more efficient x-ray production. To facilitate the dissipation of heat from the anode in ***stationary*** anode tubes, a tungsten button is imbedded in a block of copper, which is a better conductor of heat than tungsten. The electron beam in the tube is focused on a small spot on this tungsten target.

Efficiency of X-ray Production

As already indicated, only a small fraction of the energy of the cathode-ray electrons undergoes conversion to x rays in the target. Most of the electrons' energy is degraded to heat as the result of collisions with outer shell electrons of the tungsten atoms. X rays are produced by the previously described process of brems radiation and, if the applied potential (kV) is high enough, by the additional process of characteristic radiation.

The efficiency of x-ray production may be defined as the percentage of the kinetic energy of the electrons that is converted to x rays. The efficiency is directly proportional to the atomic number of the target and the applied potential, as expressed in the following equation:

$$E = K \times Z \times kV_p \qquad (2)$$

where E is the efficiency in percent, K is a constant $= 1 \times 10^{-4}$, Z is the atomic number of the target, and kV_p is the peak kilovoltage. For example, with a tungsten target ($Z = 74$) and 80 kV_p

$$E = 1 \times 10^{-4} \times 74 \times 80$$
$$= 0.6\%$$

This means that of the total kinetic energy of the electron stream, only about 0.6 percent appears as x rays and the remaining 99.4 percent as heat in the anode when the applied potential is 80 kV_p.

Properties of X Rays

We shall now list some of the more important properties of x rays:

1. *Highly penetrating, invisible rays,* which belong to the general category of electromagnetic radiation and behave both as *waves and particles.*

2. *Electrically neutral,* so they cannot be deflected by electric or magnetic fields.

3. *Polyenergetic* or *heterogeneous,* having a wide span of energies and wavelengths; useful energy range in radiography is about 25 to 120 kVp (maximum photon energy 25 to 120 keV).

4. Liberate *minute* amounts of heat on passing through matter.

5. Travel ordinarily in *straight lines.*

6. Travel only at the *same speed as light,* 3×10^8 m per sec or 186,000 miles per sec in a vacuum.

7. Ionize gases *indirectly* because of their ability to remove orbital electrons from atoms.

8. Cause *fluorescence* of certain crystals, making possible their use in fluoroscopy, and in radiographic intensifying screens.

9. *Cannot be focused* by a lens.

10. *Affect photographic film,* producing a latent image which can be developed chemically.

11. Produce *chemical and biologic changes* by ionization and excitation.

12. Produce *secondary and scattered radiation.*

SPECIFICATIONS OF THE PHYSICAL CHARACTERISTICS OF AN X-RAY BEAM

One may describe a given x-ray beam on the basis of two properties—*intensity* and *quality.* Strictly speaking, the intensity of the radiation at a given point in the beam refers to the quantity of radiant energy flowing per second through a unit area of the surface perpendicular to the direction of the beam at the designated point. However, because of its simplicity and adequacy, the concept of *exposure rate* has been adopted in medical radiology. Furthermore, with the main interest in radiotherapy being centered on the interaction of radiation with the patient's tissues, another unit of quantity has had to be devised—the *absorbed dose.*

The *quality* of an x-ray beam refers to its penetrating ability. We shall now discuss the concepts of exposure and quality, leaving absorbed dose for a later section.

X-ray Exposure (Quantity)

Under certain controllable conditions, the degree of ionization (see pages 52–53) produced by radiation in matter is proportional to the quantity of radiation of a particular type. Therefore, ionization would be expected to serve as an appropriate basis for measuring x- and gamma-ray quantity in terms of exposure. Indeed, in 1928 the Second International Congress of Radiology established the *roentgen,* now symbolized by R, as the international unit of exposure *based on ionization in air.* Special instruments known as *ionization chambers* are used for the measurement of exposure (see pages 170–171).

In 1938 the roentgen was redefined as *"that exposure of x or gamma radiation such that the associated corpuscular emission per 0.001293 gram of air, produces in air, ions carrying one electrostatic unit of quantity of electricity of either sign."* This may be simply explained as follows: a roentgen is a definite radiation *exposure* which, in a standard quantity of air (chosen as 0.001293 g of air, which is really the weight of 1 cc of air at a temperature of 0 C and a pressure of 760 mm mercury), produces ionization consisting of a certain number of ions and electrons (called corpuscular emission in the definition). Eventually, all the usable energy of the corpuscles produced by one roentgen is spent in releasing pairs of oppositely charged ions. If the ions released by an exposure of 1 R are collected and measured, they will be found to carry one electrostatic unit (esu) of positive or negative charge. In other words, *1 R of x or gamma rays causes ionization in 1 cc of air under standard conditions, such that the ions of only one sign carry 1 esu of electric charge.* It should be pointed out that the roentgen is a valid unit only with x or gamma rays *up to 3 million volts.*

A revised definition of the roentgen as the unit of exposure was adopted by the International Commission on Radiation Units and Measurements (ICRU) in 1962, as expressed in the following equation:

$$X = \Delta Q / \Delta m \tag{3}$$

where X is the exposure in R, and ΔQ is the sum of all the electric charges on all the ions of *one sign* produced in air, when all the electrons released by photons (x and gamma rays) in a mass of air, Δm, are completely stopped in air.

Note that the most recent definition of exposure (equation [3]) implies two steps in the process: (1) photons first release electrons by interaction with atoms in the air, and (2) these primary electrons go on to produce ions whose total charge of one sign (positive or negative) is a measure of exposure in air. As specified in the definition, all the electrons released in (2) must give up all their kinetic energy in the formation of ions in air. Thus, the conditions laid down in the definition of 1938 were stated more precisely in 1962, so the value of the R is really unchanged in the newer definition. On this basis, the roentgen may be expressed as an amount of charge released per unit mass of air, specifically,

$$1 \text{ R} = 2.58 \times 10^{-4} \text{ coulomb/kg air}$$

In the modern International System of Units—SI—the *exposure unit* replaces the roentgen, and is an exposure of one coulomb per kilogram; this new unit is not yet in wide use.

The radiation exposure per unit time, for example R/min, at a given location is the *exposure rate:*

$$\text{exposure rate} = \frac{\text{exposure in R}}{\text{time in min}}$$
$$(R/min)$$

The *total exposure* in R is obtained by multiplying the exposure rate by the exposure time:

$$\text{exposure} = \text{exposure rate} \times \text{time}$$
$$(R) \qquad (R/min) \qquad (min)$$

In measuring radiation exposure, we must be careful that our instrument collects and measures all the produced ions; and that more ions are not accidentally lost to the surroundings than enter from the surroundings. The measuring instrument, designed to have a high degree of precision, is the *standard free air ionization chamber.*

For practical calibration of the roentgen output of an x-ray therapy unit, we may use a *thimble type ionization chamber* which has been calibrated initially against the more precise type of instrument. The thimble chamber was developed by H. Fricke and O. Glasser, and incorporated in the Victoreen R-meter (see Figure 12.7). Not only is this device convenient and simple to use, but it is sufficiently accurate for medical radiology if sent to the manufacturer or an approved standardization laboratory for calibration at regular intervals. However, its accuracy holds only for a limited span of x-ray or gamma-ray energies, so that outside this range, special caps must be placed over the thimble.

Other types of measuring devices have been introduced, such as the Baldwin-Farmer Sub-standard Dosemeter, as well as those

Figure 12.7. Diagram of a Victoreen-R-meter®, based on data furnished by the Victoreen Instrument Corporation. From J. Selman: *The Basic Physics of Radiation Therapy,* 2nd Ed. Springfield, Thomas, 1976.

using solid state circuits.

Radiation exposure as measured in roentgens is not the same as the total quantity of radiant energy in a beam. The former is of more practical value in radiology because the exposure in R is based on the ionizing ability which, after all, is responsible for biologic and radiographic effects.

The *exposure rate* of an x-ray beam may be altered by varying four factors: (1) tube current, (2) tube potential, (3) distance, and (4) filtration.

1. *Tube Current.* An increase in the filament current liberates more electrons *per second* at the filament. As a result, the tube current (mA) also increases and more electrons strike the target per sec, increasing the amount of x radiation emitted per sec. Thus, *the exposure rate is directly proportional to the mA,* if the other factors remain constant. It should be emphasized that a change in mA does not affect the quality of the radiation.

2. *Tube Potential.* A rise in *kilovoltage* (kV) increases exposure rate because the electrons in the tube are speeded up and produce more x-ray photons per sec at the target. The resulting x-ray beam also contains photons of higher energy than those produced at lower kV. Note that an increase in tube potential increases both

the exposure rate and penetrating ability of an x-ray beam, but that this relationship is not directly proportional. In fact, exposure rate is approximately proportional to kV^2. As will be shown later (see page 275), the exposure rate is higher with three-phase x-ray generators than with single-phase for the same applied kV.

3. *Distance.* In determining x-ray exposure rate, we must specify the distance from the target to the measuring device because the x rays emerge from the collimator in a spreading beam shaped like a cone. As the distance from the target increases, the number of rays in each square centimeter of the beam decreases; hence, the exposure rate decreases. Since the measuring device (eg, thimble chamber) has a definite size, it measures the exposure rate in a constant small volume of the beam. *The exposure rate is governed by the inverse square law of radiation,* to be discussed in detail in Chapter 18.

4. *Filtration.* The exposure rate of an x-ray beam may be altered by changing the thickness or type of filter placed in the beam — the thicker the filter and the higher its atomic number, the greater the reduction in the exposure rate beyond the filter. At the same time, *the beam is hardened due to the relatively greater removal of soft (low energy) than of hard (high energy) rays by the filter* except at the absorption edge (see page 207).

Quality of X Rays

Definition. The quality of an x-ray beam refers to its ability to penetrate matter. In radiology, we may define penetrating ability as the fraction of a particular x-ray beam that can pass through a given part of the body and onto an x-ray film; or that can enter the body and deposit energy in a tumor-containing volume at a particular depth.

However, we need a more precise concept of *penetrating ability* than that just stated. As shown in Figure 12.8A, for a diagnostic x-ray beam, suppose the measured exposure at the point where the beam enters the body were 1 R and the point where the beam leaves the body (at the film) were 0.2 R, then the transmission or penetrating ability would be $0.2/1 \times 100 = 20$ percent. With a more penetrating beam giving an exposure of 1 R at the entrance point as in 12.8B, the exposure at the film might be 0.4 R, giving a transmission or penetrating ability of 0.4/1 × 100 = 40 percent. Thus, the beam in 12.8B is more penetrating than that in 12.8A.

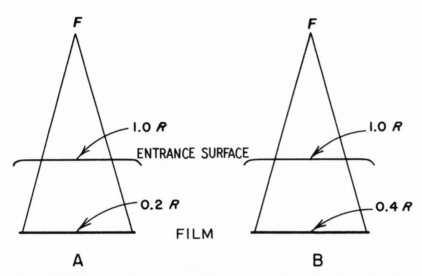

Figure 12.8. Concept of penetrating ability of an x-ray beam in radiography. In *A*, for an assumed exposure of 1.0 R at the entrance surface of the patient, the exposure at the film might be 0.2 R because of beam attenuation (absorption, scattering, distance) in the patient; this represents a transmission or *penetrating ability* of 0.2/1 × 100 = 20%. In *B*, for the same entrance exposure of 1.0 R, the exposure at the film might be 0.4 R, representing a transmission or penetrating ability of 40%. Thus, beam *B* is more penetrating than beam *A*.

X-ray Energy and Quality. To understand the relationship between x-ray energy and quality (ie, penetrating ability) we must first look into the meaning of x-ray energy. An individual x ray may be regarded as a bit of energy called a ***photon*** or ***quantum,*** represented by the equation

$$E = h\nu \qquad (4)$$

where E is the energy of the photon in ergs, h is a constant (Planck's constant), and ν (Greek *nu*) is the frequency of the x ray in hertz (cycles per second). This equation tells us that the ***energy of a particular photon is directly proportional to the frequency of its*** *associated wave;* therefore, x rays of high frequency have higher energy than x rays of low frequency. But since the frequency times the wavelength of an x ray equals a constant (speed of light), as shown in equation (1) on page 158, a wave of high frequency must have a short wavelength; and, conversely, a wave of low frequency must have a long wavelength.

Since the quality of x rays may be defined as their penetrating ability which, in turn, is determined by their energy, we may summarize the statements in the preceding paragraph as follows: a highly penetrating x-ray beam consists of photons which, on the average, have high energy, high frequency, and short wavelength. Conversely, a poorly penetrating x-ray beam consists of photons which, on the average, have low energy, low frequency, and long wavelength. This relationship is shown in Table 12.1.

TABLE 12.1
INTERRELATIONSHIP OF FACTORS IN RADIATION QUALITY SPEED
OF RADIATION IS CONSTANT
$c = frequency \times wavelength$

Frequency	Wavelength	Energy	Quality
high	short	high	good penetrating ability
low	long	low	poor penetrating ability

What influences the *energy* of x rays? We learned earlier that x rays consist of brems and characteristic radiation resulting from the interactions of high speed electrons with target atoms. The larger the kinetic energy of the electrons in the x-ray tube, the higher will be the energy of the resulting x radiation. Since the kinetic energy of the electrons depends on their speed which in turn depends on the potential applied to the tube, it follows that an increase in kV will ultimately produce x rays of higher energy. This discussion may be summarized as follows: the higher the kV, the greater the speed of the electrons, the greater their kinetic energy, the greater the energy of the x rays produced, and the greater the penetrating ability of the x-ray beam. We may therefore conclude that the *penetrating ability of x rays is increased by*

increasing the kilovoltage, and decreased by decreasing the kilovoltage.
However, this relationship is *not* a direct proportion.

How is the energy of an x-ray beam stated? Since the energy of x
rays depends on the speed of the electrons in the tube, which
depends on the applied potential, we customarily use the *peak*
(maximum) voltage to designate the energy of the beam. For
example, if the maximum potential applied across the tube is 100
kV, we then speak of a 100-kV x-ray beam. However, we must
bear in mind that the beam is actually *heterogeneous* or *polyenergetic*,
consisting of photons whose energies range from a minimum to the
peak value, in this case 100 kV (often stated as kVp).

On the other hand, since the energy of monoenergetic radiation
such as characteristic x rays and gamma rays is uniform for any
given beam, it may be expressed in units of electron volts. One
electron volt is the energy acquired by an electron when it is
accelerated through a potential difference of 1 volt. Thus, the
energy of monoenergetic radiation or of a particular photon is
stated in electron volts (eV) or in some multiple thereof, such as
kiloelectron volts (keV), million electron volts (MeV), or billion
electron volts (BeV); for example, the gamma rays emitted by
technetium 99m all have the same energy — 140 thousand electron
volts, usually stated as 140 keV.

Insofar as equivalence is concerned, an x-ray beam having a
particular kVp has a quality resembling a monoenergetic x-ray
beam of about one-third to one-half the peak energy. Thus, a
polyenergetic 120-kV x-ray beam is roughly equivalent to 50-keV
monoenergetic x rays.

Causes of the Polyenergetic Nature of an X-ray Beam. As we
have already noted, an ordinary x-ray beam is *polyenergetic*,
consisting of a tremendous number of photons that vary in energy
and penetrating ability. Since photon energy is directly proportional to frequency and inversely proportional to wavelength, we
may say that an ordinary x-ray beam is heterogeneous, consisting
of *innumerable rays of different energies and wavelengths.* Analogy
with white light may help clarify this. White light comprises a
mixture of various colors. When passed through a glass prism,
white light separates into its components which are identical to the
colors of the rainbow, or the *spectrum.* These colors differ in

frequency and wavelength. For instance, the wavelength of "red" is about 7000 Å, whereas the wavelength of "violet" is about 4000 Å. A light beam made up of a single pure color is called **monochromatic.** Similarly, an x-ray beam consists of different x-ray "colors"—energies or wavelengths—although they are invisible. X rays can be refracted by certain crystals and the photons separated according to their energy or wavelength.

We shall now explain the four major reasons for the polyenergetic nature of an x-ray beam:

1. *Fluctuating Kilovoltage.* The applied kV varies according to the wave form of the pulsating current (see Figure 9.4). Since changes in kV are manifested by changes in the energy of the resulting x rays, there must necessarily be a range of photon energies corresponding to the fluctuation of kV.

2. *Processes in X-ray Production.* The x-ray beam leaving the target consists of *general radiation* (brems radiation resulting from deceleration of electrons by target nuclear fields), and *characteristic radiation* (arising from electron transfers within the atoms of the target). The general and characteristic x rays constituting the primary beam, therefore, have a variety of energies.

3. *Multiple Electron Interactions with Target Atoms.* Electrons traveling from cathode to anode in the x-ray tube undergo varying numbers of encounters with target atoms before being completely stopped. In these encounters x rays are produced.

4. *Off-focus Radiation.* Some electrons may strike anode metal other than the focus (target), causing the emission of x rays. This *off-focus radiation* has been reduced by special design of modern tubes. Further decrease in off-focus radiation that happens to enter the x-ray beam can be achieved by special beam-limiting devices (collimators), which fit close to the tube aperture, thereby improving recorded detail (image sharpness).

X-ray Spectra. A particular x-ray beam can be precisely characterized by sorting out its photons according to their energy. This concept may be clarified by an analogy. Suppose we wish to classify a population of high school senior boys on the basis of height. We would first measure all the boys in the designated population and group them according to height. These data would then be set down as in Table 12.2 and plotted graphically as in

Figure 12.9, the number of boys in each group being the dependent variable, and the height the independent variable.

TABLE 12.2
HEIGHT DISTRIBUTION OF A CLASS OF SENIOR HIGH SCHOOL BOYS

Height	Number of Boys
in.	
63	1
64	2
65	4
66	7
67	13
68	14
69	15
70	15
71	14
72	10
73	7
74	1

Similarly, we can sort out the rays or photons in a given x-ray beam by means of a special instrument known as an x-ray spectrometer, determining the *spectrum*, or the range of intensities or relative numbers, of x rays of various energies. When these data are plotted as in Figure 12.10, a *spectral distribution curve* is obtained. In the figure, we have shown the spectral distribution curves for x-ray beams produced in a tungsten target by three different applied peak tube potentials — 30, 40, and 80 kV, respectively.

You can see that in each case the curve crosses the horizontal axis at a point corresponding to the peak or maximum applied kV. Thus, *the energy of the most energetic and most penetrating photons in a particular x-ray beam is governed solely by the applied peak kV.*

A comparison between these curves shows that an increase in kV causes not only an increase in the output of higher energy photons, but also an increase in output of photons of all other energies in the beam, as indicated by the areas under the respective curves. Thus, the higher the kV, the higher will be the exposure rate, and conversely.

If a sufficiently high kV (at least 69 kV) is applied across the

Figure 12.9. Distribution curve of a class of high school senior boys according to their height. Note that the peak incidence is at 68 to 70 inches.

Figure 12.10. Spectral distribution curves of x rays generated by peak tube potentials of 30, 40, and 80 kV, respectively. Those on the left show relative exposure rates as a function of wavelength, and those on the right as a function of photon energy. The latter is preferred. *Characteristic radiation* appears as a peak at *C* (actually, a group of closely spaced peaks), requiring an applied potential of at least 69 kV. The remaining curves (indicated by 30 kV, 40 kV, and 50 kV) represent *general radiation*. Note that in each case the maximum photon energy in the beam is the same as the applied peak kV (figure on the right).

tube, the curve is modified by the appearance of a sharp **peak** at 69 kV representing the **characteristic radiation** emitted by the tungsten target. This is shown in the 80-kV curve.

Although photons are preferably specified according to their energy rather than their wavelength, the following equation shows how they are related:

$$photon\ energy = \frac{12.4}{\lambda}\ keV \qquad (5)$$

where λ is the wavelength in angstroms (Å). For example, the energy of a photon $h\nu$ whose associated wavelength is 0.2 Å is obtained from equation (5):

$$h\nu = \frac{12.4}{0.2} = 62\ keV$$

The minimum wavelength λ_{min} of the radiation in an x-ray beam can be derived from the maximum photon energy by:

$$\lambda_{min} = \frac{12.4}{h\nu_{max}}\ Å \qquad (6)$$

In Figure 12.11 we see that if the kV is kept constant, an increase in mA simply increases the exposure rate. But, as shown in Figure 12.11, there is no shift in the curves—the maximum photon energy remains the same because it depends only on the applied peak kV. This is also evident from equation (5).

Specification of X-ray Quality—Half-value Layer and Kilovoltage. Because of the polyenergetic nature of the photons in an x-ray beam, the spectral distribution curves described in the preceding section depict most completely the distribution of photon energies in any given beam. However, this degree of precision is not required for our purpose in medical radiology. Instead, we use two methods of specifying beam quality, which include (1) the *half-value layer* and (2) the *accelerating potential* (applied voltage).

1. *Half-value Layer. The half-value layer (HVL) of an x-ray beam is defined as that thickness of a specified material (usually a metal) which reduces the exposure rate to one-half its initial value.* The material is used in a thin sheet called a *filter.* First we measure the exposure rate of the x-ray beam whose quality is to be specified. We then make a series of measurements with increas-

ing thicknesses of filter in the beam. That thickness of the selected metal which reduces the exposure rate 50 percent is the half-value layer. For example, if the exposure rate is initially 90 R/min and it requires 1.5 mm Cu (copper) to decrease the exposure rate by just one-half (ie, to 45 R/min), then the HVL = 1.5 mm Cu.

Figure 12.11. Effect of tube mA on relative exposure rate. With the kV held constant, a higher mA produces a larger exposure rate for all photon energies in the beam. However, the mA has no effect on the maximum photon energy, which is the same for both curves.

How is the *half-value layer of a beam measured?* A brief outline of the procedure will now be presented:

a. Select the x-ray technical factors of kV, mA, and filtration for the *initial beam whose half-value layer is being determined.* Collimate the beam to 10 cm × 10 cm.

b. Place a thimble ionization chamber in the center of the beam at a *fixed distance* from the focus of the x-ray tube. The thimble should be at least several feet from any possible scattering objects such as table, floors, or walls.

c. Determine the exposure rate in R/min (roentgens per minute) without any additional filtration of the beam (other than that which may already be present). Tabulate this exposure rate under *initial beam.*

d. Repeat the procedure after adding a 0.25 mm copper filter, if *orthovoltage* therapy is used, that is, 200 to 300 kV. All other exposure factors remain constant. (Different filters are needed for various photon energy ranges.)

e. Repeat the procedure for each of several further additions of copper filters. Assemble the results as in Table 12.3.

f. Plot the data **graphically** with exposure rate in R/min as the dependent variable and the thickness of added filter as the independent variable, as in Figure 12.12.

g. Locate the exposure rate corresponding to one-half the initial value on the vertical axis. Draw a horizontal line from this point to the curve, and then a vertical line from the point of intersection on the curve, to the horizontal axis, where the vertical line locates the thickness of copper responsible for the halving of the initial exposure rate. This halving thickness is the half-value layer. For an actual example, refer to Table 12.3 and Figure 12.12.

Depending on the kV of the initial beam, we use other metals to specify HVL. Thus, **aluminum** is used for superficial therapy beams, 50 to 150 kV; and **lead** for supervoltage therapy beams, above 500 kV.

2. *Applied Potential (Voltage).* The International Commission on Radiation Units and Measurements (ICRU) recommends that under certain conditions, the voltage applied to the source of radiation be included in the specification of beam quality. The following data are based on the ICRU report of 1963:

a. *For radiography,* the peak kV is customarily used to designate beam quality, since the HVL does not routinely serve a useful purpose. However, the HVL in aluminum for radiographic beams has an important application in patient protection (see pages 561–563).

b. *For x-ray therapy up to 2 million volts (MV), the kV or MV and the HVL should be stated* because in this range of radiation energy, filters cause significant changes in the quality of the beam.

c. *For x-ray therapy above 2 MV, the MV only need be stated* because in megavoltage therapy (2 MV and above) filters have very little effect on beam quality. With **gamma-ray beams** energy is stated in MeV.

Figure 12.12. Absorption curve of 220-kVp x rays in copper filters of increasing thickness based on data in Table 12.3. Half-value layers can be obtained from the curve. If, with no added filter, the exposure rate is 100 R/min, we must add a filter of 0.25 mm Cu to decrease the exposure rate to one-half its initial value, or 50 R/min. The half value layer (HVL) of this beam is therefore 0.25 mm Cu.

If the initial beam is then filtered by 0.5 mm Cu, we move the vertical axis to the 0.5 mm line. The corresponding exposure rate is found to be 37 R/min; half of this is 18.5 R/min, corresponding to a reading on the horizontal axis of 1.6 mm Cu. But the initial filter was 0.5 mm Cu. Therefore, the HVL of this particular beam is 1.6 mm − 0.5 mm = 1.1 mm Cu.

As more filtration is added, the beam becomes more homogeneous, that is, the HVL increases and becomes constant.

Table 12.4 gives the usual classification of radiotherapy beams. In addition, some dermatologists apply extremely low energy x rays, known as *Grenz* rays, having an energy of about 10 to 15 kV, in treating extremely superficial, noncancerous skin lesions. The German word Grenz means boundary, and refers to the fact that these rays are so soft that they lie between ultraviolet rays and ordinary x rays in the electromagnetic spectrum.

TABLE 12.3
EXPOSURE RATES WITH ADDED COPPER FILTERS
OF VARIOUS THICKNESSES. kV, mA,
AND DISTANCE CONSTANT THROUGHOUT

Added Copper Filtration	Exposure Rate
mm	R/min
0	100
0.25	50
0.50	37
1.0	25
1.5	19
2.0	15

TABLE 12.4
CLASSIFICATION OF RADIATION THERAPY BEAMS

Type of Therapy	Energy	Filter	Distance
			cm
Superficial X rays	50 to 120 kV	1 to 3 mm Al	5 to 25
Orthovoltage (deep) X rays	200 to 300 kV	1 to 2 mm Cu or 0.5 mm Sn	50
Megavoltage X rays	2 to 25 MV	—	100
^{60}Co gamma rays	1.25 MeV (av.)	—	80

Other methods, such as the equivalent constant potential and the photographic, can be used, but their application is limited and will not be described.

"Hard" and "Soft" X Rays

X rays may be roughly classified as *"hard"* or *"soft"* on the basis of their penetrating ability. This simply expresses the quality of a beam in nonscientific terms.

1. **Hard x rays** are higher energy photons with relatively high penetrating ability. Hard x-ray beams may be obtained with

    a. Higher generating voltage.

    b. Filters such as copper, which absorb relatively more of the less penetrating rays. The higher the atomic number of the filter and the greater its thickness, the greater is its hardening effect on the x-ray beam.

   2. **Soft x rays** are lower energy photons with relatively low penetrating ability. Soft x-ray beams may be obtained with

    a. Lower generating voltage.

    b. Filters of lower atomic number, such as aluminum.

THE INTERACTIONS OF IONIZING RADIATION AND MATTER

On passing through a body of matter, an x-ray beam undergoes *attenuation;* that is, its exposure rate gradually decreases. Attenuation consists of two related processes: (1) *absorption* of part of the radiation by various kinds of interactions with the atoms of the body in the path of the beam (see pages 186–192) and (2) emission of radiations comprising *scattered* and *secondary* radiation resulting from interactions in (1). A third factor is the *inverse square law.*

Scattered radiation refers to those x-ray photons that have undergone a *change in direction* after interacting with atoms.

Secondary radiation comprises the characteristic radiation *emitted* by atoms after having absorbed x-ray photons.

It must be emphasized that many of the x-ray photons do not interact with atoms at all, but pass through the body unchanged. This results from two factors: (1) x rays are electrically neutral so there is no electric force between them and orbital electrons, and (2) atoms contain mainly empty space.

Dual Nature of X Rays. The various types of interactions between x rays and atoms make up one of the most fascinating chapters in x-ray physics. To simplify the discussion, as well as to make it more accurate scientifically, we must regard an x-ray beam as consisting of discrete bits of energy traveling with the speed of light. Such a tiny unit of energy is called a *photon* or *quantum* (pl., quanta). This may seem to contradict the electromagnetic wave theory of radiation discussed earlier, but the phenomena of radiation absorption and emission can be explained only by the *apparently contradic-*

tory theories that a given x ray exists at the same time *both as a wave and as a particle of energy.*

This *dual nature* of electromagnetic radiation is now an accepted fact in physics. It tells us how characteristic radiation is produced in an x-ray tube when an electron drops from a higher to a lower energy level in the atom of the target metal (see Figure 12.6). Such a characteristic x ray is a quantum or photon of energy, and its energy and frequency are peculiar to the target element. Thus, an *atom of a given element can emit definite characteristic photons only,* and these are different from those of any other element. The energy of a characteristic photon represents the difference in the energy levels of the shells between which the electron has shifted.

On the basis of this concept, known as the *quantum theory,* an x-ray beam consists of showers of photons, or bits of energy, traveling with the speed of light and having no electric charge. Also known as the *corpuscular theory of radiation,* it applies equally to other forms of electromagnetic radiation such as light and gamma rays.

What determines the amount of energy in a given photon? Equation (4) cited above, formulated by the German physicist Max Planck, provides the answer:

$$\text{photon energy} = \text{a constant} \times \text{frequency}$$

$$E = h\nu$$

In this equation, h is Planck's constant (does not vary) and ν (Greek "nu") represents the frequency of the associated electromagnetic wave in cycles per sec (hertz = Hz). This equation tells us that the *quantum* or *photon energy is directly proportional to the frequency,* in agreement with the observation that the penetrating ability of x rays, which depends on their energy, increases as the frequency increases. And since the speed of x rays is constant and equals frequency times wavelength, an increase in frequency is associated with a decrease in wavelength. Thus, *highly penetrating x-ray photons have high frequency and short wavelength,* while, conversely, poorly penetrating x-rays have low frequency and long wavelength.

X-ray Interactions with Matter. As a basis for understanding the interactions of ionizing radiation and matter we must know something about the electronic *energy levels* or *shells* within the atom.

These are analogous to the mechanical model of the rock on the cliff (see pages 33–35). Since the nucleus carries a positive charge, it exerts an electric force of attraction on the orbital electrons, the force being greater the nearer the electron shell is to the nucleus. Hence, more work would be required to remove an electron from the K shell and out of range of the nuclear electric field than would be required to remove an electron from one of the outer shells. Inasmuch as work must be done in moving an electron away from the nucleus in the direction of the outer shells, *the shells are at progressively higher energy levels the farther they are located from the nucleus.* Thus, the K shell represents the lowest energy level, while the Q shell represents the highest.

The energy required to remove an electron from a particular shell and beyond the range of the nuclear positive electrostatic field is called the *binding energy* of that shell. Therefore, the binding energy is largest for K-shell electrons because of their proximity to the positively charged nucleus, and decreases progressively for successive shells. The binding energy is characteristic of a given element and shell; thus, it is about 70,000 eV for the K shell of tungsten, but only about 500 eV for the K shell of the average atom in the soft tissues of the body.

Owing to the relatively large amount of energy needed to remove an electron from an inner shell, such an electron is said to be *bound.* On the other hand, almost no energy is needed to liberate the outermost shell electrons, and they are therefore called *free* or *valence* electrons.

Let us examine in detail the possible sequence of events following the penetration of a body of matter by x-ray photons. Any of the four types of interactions may occur between the photons and atoms lying in their path: (1) photoelectric interaction, (2) coherent or unmodified scattering, (3) Compton interaction with modified scattering, and (4) pair production. Remember that many photons pass completely through the body without experiencing any type of interaction.

1. **Photoelectric Interaction (Photoelectric Effect).** This type of interaction is most likely to occur when the energy—$h\nu$—of the incident (incoming) photon is *slightly* greater than the binding energy (see above) of the electrons in one of the inner shells such

as the *K* or *L*. The incident photon gives up all of its energy to the atom; in other words, the photon is ***truly absorbed*** and disappears during the interaction. Immediately, the atom responds by ejecting an electron, usually from the *K* or *L* shell, leaving a ***hole*** in that shell (see Figure 12.13). Now the atom is ***ionized positively*** (why?) and in an ***excited state.*** Note that the energy of the incident photon ultimately went to (1) free the electron from its shell and (2) set it in motion as a ***photoelectron.***

Figure 12.13. Photoelectric interaction with true absorption. A. Incident photon loses all its energy on entering an atom, being *absorbed* in the process. The atom responds by ejecting an *inner shell* electron which becomes a photoelectron. B. Atom is in an *excited state* (also ionized—electron missing). C. Electron from a higher energy level fills vacancy or *hole* in the *K*-shell, a *characteristic* x-ray photon being emitted.

The energy exchange during a photoelectric interaction is beautifully expressed in Einstein's equation:

$$h\nu_{photon} = W_K + \tfrac{1}{2}mv_e^2 \qquad (7)$$

| energy of incident photon | binding energy of K shell | kinetic energy of K photoelectron |

where $h\nu$ is the energy of the incident (entering) photon, W_K is the binding energy or ***work function*** of the *K* shell of the element concerned, and $\tfrac{1}{2}mv_e^2$ is the kinetic energy of the photoelectron. The same equation applies to photoelectric interactions in other shells. However, when photoelectric interaction occurs with electrons in ***outer*** shells, the incident photons are more likely to be in the ultraviolet or visible light region; as indicated above, inner shell photoelectric interactions are more likely to occur with x or gamma photons.

What happens next? Suppose that a *K* electron has been ejected. The hole in the *K* shell is **immediately** filled by transition of an electron from one of the outer shells, usually the *L* shell, because they are at higher energy levels than the *K* shell (see pages 185–186). During the transition of an *L* electron to the hole in the *K* shell the energy difference between these shells is radiated as a photon known as a **fluorescent** or **characteristic x ray** because its energy (also its frequency and wavelength) is typical of the shells and the element concerned. Thus, the characteristic x rays of copper are different from those of lead.

In pursuing the sequence of events, you may ask, "What happens to the hole in the *L* shell?" It is promptly filled by an electron from an outer shell, that is, from a still higher energy level. This continues as each successive hole is filled by electron transition from some higher energy level, until the atom loses its excited state, returning to **normal** or **ground state.** The total energy carried by the characteristic photons in a single photoelectric interaction equals the binding energy of the shell from which the electron was initially expelled—in this case, the *K* shell.

In summary, then, the energy of the incoming photon in the **photoelectric interaction** involving the **K shell** has the following fate:

a. Photon enters atom and completely disappears.
b. A *K*-shell electron is ejected, leaving a hole.
c. Atom has excess energy—excited state.
d. A part of photon's energy was used to liberate electron and the rest to give it kinetic energy; ejected electron is a photoelectron.
e. Hole in *K* shell is filled by electron transition from a shell farther out, accompanied by emission of a characteristic x-ray photon.
f. Holes in successive shells are filled by electron transitions from shells still farther out, each transition being accompanied by a corresponding characteristic photon.
g. Sum of energies of all the characteristic photons equals binding energy of shell from which the photoelectron originated, in this case, the *K* shell.

Thus, the photoelectric effect gives rise to two kinds of secondary radiation — photoelectrons and characteristic x rays. Because of their negative charge, photoelectrons ionize atoms in their path. However, they usually have very low energy. For example, a 100-kV photon releases, in soft tissue, a 99.5-keV photoelectron which is absorbed in only about 1 mm of tissue. Still, this is one of the important ways in which x rays transfer energy to tissues and produce biologic changes in them. The characteristic x rays also have very low energy — about 0.5 keV — and are locally absorbed.

Because the absorption of x rays by photoelectric interaction depends strongly on the atomic number of the irradiated material, and on the energy of the radiation, the photoelectric effect is of utmost importance in radiography. The high atomic number of the elements in bone as contrasted with that of the soft tissues, together with the relatively long wavelength x rays used in radiography, contribute to a large difference in photoelectric absorption of these two kinds of structures. This is the major factor in *radiographic contrast* — the different degrees of darkness of various areas in a radiograph (see pages 359-361).

2. **Coherent or Unmodified Scattering.** If a *very low energy* x-ray photon interacts with a relatively bound orbital electron, it may set the electron into vibration. This produces an electromagnetic wave identical in energy to that of the incident photon, but *differing in direction* (see Figure 12.14). Thus, in effect, the entering photon has been *scattered without undergoing any change in wavelength, frequency, or energy.* Unmodified scattering occurs mainly with x rays whose energy is well below the range that is useful in clinical radiology.

3. **Compton Interaction with Modified Scattering.** If an incident (entering) photon of sufficient energy encounters a *loosely bound,* outer shell electron it may dislodge the electron and proceed in a different direction, as shown in Figure 12.15. The dislodged electron is called a *Compton* or *recoil electron.* It acquires a certain amount of kinetic energy which must be subtracted from the energy of the entering photon, in accordance with the Law of Conservation of Energy. Consequently, the energy of the incident photon is decreased, so it comes out of the atom with less energy

Figure 12.14. Unmodified scattering. The entering photon has undergone a change of direction only.

Figure 12.15. Compton interaction with modified scattering. *Part* of the photon's energy has been used up in removing a loosely bound orbital electron. Therefore, the emerging photon has *less energy,* and it has also undergone a *change in direction.*

(also, longer wavelength and lower frequency). This phenomenon, discovered in 1922 by the renowned physicist, A. H. Compton, is called the ***Compton Effect.*** The emerging photon, having undergone a change of direction, is called a ***scattered photon.*** The characteristic radiation, arising from electron transitions between outer shells, may be disregarded in radiology because of its extremely low energy.

The Compton Effect may be expressed as follows:

$$h\nu_i \quad = \quad E_r \quad + \quad h\nu_s \tag{8}$$

energy of	*energy given*	*energy of*
incident photon	*to recoil electron*	*scattered photon*

Thus, the frequency and energy of the scattered photon are less than those of the incident photon. A scattered photon, in turn, behaves in the same manner as other x rays on interacting with atoms. The recoil electrons cause ionization of atoms in the same way as other high speed electrons.

As the energy of the incident photon *increases,* the probability of occurrence of the Compton interaction *decreases.* But, at the same time, the *scattered photons* (1) have more energy and (2) tend to be scattered more and more in a forward direction, increasing the likelihood of their passing completely through the body and reaching the film. This constitutes the *scattered radiation* which, in radiography, impairs image contrast by an overall fogging effect and degrades recorded detail.

Despite the decreased chance of occurrence of the Compton Effect at higher photon energies, the probability of the photoelectric effect decreases even more sharply, so as the energy of the incident photon increases above 70 keV (about 180-kV x rays) the Compton Effect becomes the predominant type of interaction.

4. **Pair Production.** A *megavoltage* photon with energy of at least 1.02 million electron volts (MeV), upon approaching a *nucleus,* may disappear and give birth to a *pair*—a negative electron or *negatron,* and a positive electron or *positron* (see Figure 12.16). These charged particles share unequally, as kinetic energy, the photon's energy in excess of 1.02 MeV. The positron, as it comes to rest, combines with any negative electron and disappears giving rise to two photons with an energy of 0.51 MeV, moving in opposite directions. This is the *annihilation reaction.* The two processes exemplify, first, the conversion of energy to matter, and then matter to energy according to Einstein's equation $E = mc^2$. Note that the "magic" number 0.51 MeV is simply the energy

Figure 12.16. Pair production and annihilation reaction.

equivalent of the mass of an electron at rest. Pair production becomes significant at about 10 MeV, but not until about 24 MeV does it predominate over the Compton Effect insofar as energy absorption is concerned.

Secondary and Scattered Radiation Consists of:

1. Primary electrons
   a. Photoelectrons
   b. Compton or recoil electrons
   c. Positron-negatron pairs
2. Secondary and scattered x rays
   a. Characteristic
   b. Coherent or unmodified scattered
   c. Modified scattered (Compton Effect)
   d. Annihilation radiation

The secondary and scattered photons are less energetic (softer) than the incident photons, except for the relatively insignificant factor of unmodified scattering. The production of primary electrons accounts for the absorption of radiation by matter, since this removes energy from the primary beam. Hardening of an x-ray beam by a *filter* results mainly from photoelectric absorption of **relatively more low energy than high energy photons,** so that the emerging beam retains a relatively greater **percentage** of higher energy, more penetrating photons. A copper filter emits its own soft characteristic radiation which can be absorbed by an aluminum secondary filter. The aluminum also emits characteristic rays, but these are so soft that they are absorbed in a few centimeters of air.

Relative Importance of Various Types of Interaction in Radiology

The various types of interactions between x or gamma radiation and matter will now be discussed as they apply to diagnostic and therapeutic radiology, especially with regard to their relative importance.

1. **Diagnostic Radiology.** In the usual range of 30 to 140 kV, the photoelectric effect predominates insofar as energy absorption from the beam is concerned. Because photoelectric absorption is about four to six times greater in bone than in an equal mass of soft tissue in the radiographic kV range, this type of interaction is responsible for much of the *radiologic contrast* (manifested by differences in film darkness) between these tissues. Differences in density (grams/cc) of various tissues also contribute to radiologic contrast.

On the other hand, the Compton Effect makes its presence known mainly by the *scattered radiation* resulting from interaction with the atoms of the tissues, table top, etc. In fact, in the radiographic range, scattered radiation may comprise as much as 80 to 90 percent of the beam in soft tissues.

As will be shown later, the scattered radiation approaches the film from many directions and degrades radiographic quality, making it necessary to use grids and collimators. As kV is increased the scattered radiation becomes progressively more damaging to radiographic quality because (1) its energy increases and it is therefore more likely to pass completely through the body and reach the film and (2) it is scattered more and more forward toward the film. Note that the characteristic radiation arising in the photoelectric process is also scattered in many directions, but is so soft that it is absorbed locally in the tissues.

2. **Therapeutic Radiology.** When x or gamma radiation traverses the body, its interaction with the atoms of the tissues results in the absorption of energy through the liberation of electrons. The freed electrons, in turn, expend their energy in ionizing other atoms,

thereby causing tissue damage and concomitant therapeutic effects. This will be discussed more fully below.

The photoelectric effect predominates below about 140 kV. Primary photons in the incident beam are completely absorbed upon interaction with the tissue atoms, setting in motion photoelectrons which ionize atoms of the tissue along their paths.

As the applied voltage is increased from about 150 kV to 3 MV, the probability of the Compton interaction decreases, but the probability of the photoelectric interaction decreases even more, so that the Compton Effect becomes predominant.

Although pair production begins at about 1.02 MeV, it does not contribute significantly to energy absorption until about 10 MeV. Only at 24 MeV and above does ionization by negatrons and positrons become the main process of energy absorption.

Detection of Ionizing Radiation

There are several ways in which the effects of ionizing radiation make its presence known:

1. **Photographic Effect** — causes changes in a photographic emulsion so that it can be developed chemically.

2. **Luminescent Effect** — causes certain materials to glow in the dark. These include zinc cadmium sulfide, calcium tungstate, lead barium sulfate, and the newer rare earth phosphors such as lanthanum and gadolinium.

3. **Ionizing Effect** — ionizes gases and discharges certain electrical instruments such as the electroscope.

4. **Thermoluminescent Effect** — undergoes conversion to light in certain crystals after they have been heated.

5. **Chemical Effects** — changes the color of certain dyes.

6. **Physiologic Effect** — reddens the skin, destroys tissues, and causes genetic damage.

RADIATION DOSIMETRY

The changes produced in tissues by ionizing radiation result from the transfer of energy to the atoms and molecules of the tissues by the processes of *ionization* and *excitation.*

We must emphasize here that x and gamma rays represent *indirectly ionizing* radiation. While it is true that they liberate electrons by one or more of the interaction processes, it is these primary electrons which play, by far, the major role in causing subsequent ionization and excitation of atoms. In other words, the ionizing effect of x and gamma photons occurs indirectly by means of the *primary electrons* they first release in the tissues—photons transfer energy to orbital electrons, which, in turn, transfer energy to atoms to produce pairs of oppositely charged ions, or *ion pairs.* In pair production, electrons arise by materialization of very high energy photons.

The amount of energy transferred by ionizing radiation per unit length of path is called *linear energy transfer—LET.* We saw in the sections on the interactions of radiation with matter that they cause ionization. With a given type of radiation, such as x rays, the degree of ionization and the resulting tissue effects are related to the amount of energy absorbed at a particular site. This *absorbed dose* of radiation depends on the quantity (exposure in R) and quality (energy) of the radiation, and on the nature of the tissue (muscle, bone, etc). We know that more hard than soft radiation is needed for a given tissue effect as, for example, skin reddening (erythema). Such dependence on beam hardness or quality—so-called *wavelength* or *energy dependence*—is due to differences in the number and distribution of ions liberated by radiation of various energies, that is, differences in LET.

Exposure—the Roentgen

As described earlier, we use the *roentgen* (R) as the unit of *exposure,* based on the ionizing ability of the radiation. Thus, exposure is a measure of the amount of radiation delivered to a particular site. In addition, we must state the *quality* of the beam, namely, the peak kV applied to the tube as well as the half-value layer in the orthovoltage region, or the energy of the radiation in MV or MeV in the megavoltage region. The mA, time, and distance should also be included where applicable, although they have no bearing on the quality of the x-ray beam. The total duration of a therapy course in terms of days or weeks has a distinct influence on the effect of treatment, since a given radiation exposure at one sitting has a much more pronounced effect than the same total exposure given in fractions over a period of days or weeks.

Absorbed Dose—the Rad

The preceding paragraph dealt with exposure in roentgens, no mention being made of the dose *absorbed* in the tissues. Since only the energy actually transferred to the irradiated volume is responsible for the ensuing biologic changes, *we may define the absorbed dose as the amount of energy that ionizing radiation delivers per gram of irradiated matter.* The unit of absorbed dose is the *rad (radiation absorbed dose),* and is defined as an *energy absorption of 100 ergs per gram.* This applies to any type of radiation (x rays, gamma rays, beta rays, etc) and to any kind of matter, including tissues. In the new International System of units the rad is being replaced by the *gray* (Gy) = 1 joule/kg; thus, 1 Gy = 100 rads. On this basis, 1 centigray (Gy) = 1 rad.

The *roentgen,* it should be recalled, is limited to x rays and gamma rays up to 3 million volts (MV).

What is the relationship of the unit of absorbed dose—the rad—to the unit of exposure—the roentgen? The answer is not a simple one, because it depends on a number of factors. However, in the usual therapy range of 100 kV to 20 MV the *absorbed dose in soft tissues exposed to 1 R is approximately 1 rad,* with an error of only a few percent. In any case, this one-to-one conversion is not sufficiently accurate in radiotherapy of *soft tissues.*

On the other hand, absorption in other tissues such as *bone* depends on the energy of the incident radiation. For example, with an x-ray beam of half-value layer 1 mm Cu the absorbed dose bone is about twice that in soft tissues for the same exposure. Thus, 1 R would produce an absorbed dose of about 1 rad in soft tissue, and about 2 rads in cellular elements in compact bone. With beams of higher energy—HVL 4 mm Cu and above—the absorbed dose in bone and soft tissue is about the same. This is of practical importance in therapy when the beam has to traverse a bony structure; with the softer radiation, one must be careful not to exceed the tolerance of the bone cells while delivering a thera- peutic dose to the soft tissues. With the more energetic beams, having a half value layer of at least 4 mm Cu, the equal absorption per gram of bone and soft tissues decreases, but does not entirely prevent the possibility of serious bone damage.

Determination of Tissue Dosage

A simplified method of tissue or tumor dose determination will be covered under four headings: (1) in-air exposure, (2) backscatter, (3) given dose, and (4) tumor dose.

In-Air Exposure. When the exposure rate is measured at a given point in a beam, *with no scattering material in the vicinity of the measuring device* (other than air), it is called the *in-air exposure rate* and is usually expressed in R per min (abbreviated R/min). The total in-air exposure is obtained by multiplying the in-air exposure rate by the exposure time:

$$\text{in-air exposure} = \text{in-air exposure rate} \times \text{exposure time} \quad (9)$$
$$R = R/min \times time$$

This is, in fact, one method of calibrating a radiotherapy machine, the measuring device being either a Victoreen condenser-R-meter with a thimble chamber or some other type of radiation-measuring instrument. Several factors influence the in-air exposure rate in the orthovoltage region: it increases with an increase in kV, an increase in mA, an increase in beam cross-sectional area, a decrease in filtration, and a decrease in the source-skin distance (according to the inverse square law—see pages 204–206). Therefore, an ortho- voltage x-ray machine should be calibrated for every combination of treatment factors (kV, mA, filtration, and distance) that is to be used. With cobalt 60 gamma rays (1.25 MeV) we are concerned with source-skin distance and beam cross-sectional area in measur- ing in-air exposure rate. With megavoltage x rays, we must take into account beam energy, source-skin distance, and cross-sectional area.

Backscatter. If a radiation measuring device such as a thimble chamber is placed on the surface of the body (or some equivalent material such as Masonite® or water) the recorded exposure rate is larger than that in the absence of the body. In other words, the measured *entrance exposure rate* in R/min exceeds the in-air exposure rate. This results from *backscatter radiation* which is simply radiation scattered back from matter lying beneath the thimble chamber. Note that this increases the exposure to the skin and must be included in planning therapy. Another factor contributing to the in-air exposure rate is scattered radiation arising in the beam-limiting device (collimator).

We usually designate the degree of backscatter as the ratio of the measured entrance-R to in-air-R at the same point:

$$\text{backscatter factor} = \frac{\text{entrance-R}}{\text{in-air-R}} \qquad (10)$$

For example, if the entrance exposure is 125 R and, in the same time interval, the in-air exposure at the same point (in absence of body or phantom) is 100 R, then

$$\text{backscatter factor} = 125/100 = 1.25$$

Obviously, the larger the backscatter factor, the larger will be the entrance exposure for a particular in-air exposure.

Published tables give the backscatter factors obtained experimentally under various conditions, but it is preferable to have an experienced radiation physicist obtain this information directly.

The factors affecting the backscatter factor are as follows:

1. *Area of Treatment Field.* As this is increased, the backscatter factor increases due to the larger volume of irradiated tissue and the correspondingly larger source of scattered radiation.

2. *Thickness of Irradiated Part.* As this is increased, the backscatter factor increases for the same reason as in (1). However, beyond a certain critical thickness, further increase in thickness does not influence the backscatter factor.

3. *Energy of Beam.* Above 1 mm Cu, an increase of HVL decreases the backscatter factor because an increasingly greater percentage of the radiation is scattered in a forward direction, and less in a lateral or backward direction. It should be recalled that HVL increases with an increase in kV and filtration. With *megavoltage beams* of at least 1 MeV, backscatter is still smaller. However,

with megavoltage beams such as cobalt 60 gamma rays and linac x rays there is a ***buildup of electrons below the surface*** so that ionization and dosage reach a maximum at some depth below the surface. In fact, this buildup depth is 5 mm for cobalt 60 gamma rays, and 15 mm for 6-MV x rays, and 4 cm for 25-MV x rays.

It should be noted that the source-skin distance has no effect on the backscatter factor or electron buildup, although it does influence percent depth dose (see below).

Given Dose. In practice we express radiation dosage in terms of absorbed dose. Knowing the entrance exposure (including backscatter) we can convert this value to absorbed dose in rads. The conversion factor f published in *NCRP Report No. 66* (1981) for various photon energies in muscle and bone are given for three qualities of radiation in Table 12.5. To obtain the absorbed dose with radiation having an energy of less than 3 MeV, we simply multiply the exposure by the appropriate f value:

TABLE 12.5

SAMPLE VALUES OF AVERAGE CONVERSION FACTOR f RADS/R*

(Based on Measurement of Exposure in Air)

HVL	Muscle	Bone**
mm Cu		
1.0	0.929	1.95
1.7	0.943	1.46
Cobalt 60	0.958	0.927

*Adapted from NCRP Report No. 69 (1981).
**Cellular elements in compact bone.

$$\mathbf{\textit{exposure}} \times \mathbf{\textit{f}} = \mathbf{\textit{absorbed dose}}$$
$$\text{R} \qquad \text{rads/R} \qquad \text{rads}$$

Since we are dealing with beams that always enter the body through soft tissue, we use the f factor for muscle in converting entrance exposure to entrance dose. The latter is often referred to as the ***given dose.***

given dose = in-air exposure $\times f \times$ backscatter factor

Depending on the energy of the photon beam, the location of the given dose may be at the skin surface or at some depth below.

Given dose is often referred to as D_{max}. There being no electron buildup with orthovoltage x rays, maximum ionization (and dosage) occurs at the skin surface where the beam enters, and that is where the given dose is specified. But with megavoltage beams, depending on their energy, D_{max} is located at some depth below the skin surface because of electron buildup, and so the given dose is specified at the appropriate depth. However, it should be realized that buildup occurs rapidly before D_{max} is reached.

In summary, then, in the orthovoltage region, D_{max} is the sum of the entrance dose and the backscatter dose, there being no electron buildup. In the megavoltage region, D_{max} includes the entrance, electron buildup, and backscatter doses, the last being much less than that in the orthovoltage region.

Tumor Dose. As a beam of photons traverses matter the dose rate gradually *decreases.* There are three factors responsible for the weakening or *attenuation* of the beam.

1. Absorption
2. Scattering
3. Inverse square law

Absorption of radiation accompanies the various types of interactions between its photons and the atoms in the irradiated material (or tissues) as described earlier. Photoelectric interaction with true absorption predominates with radiation energy up to about 140 kVp. Compton interaction with partial absorption predominates in the energy region between 150 kVp and 10 MV. Above this limit, pair production with partial absorption begins to assume major importance.

Scattering occurs in matter (tissues included) mainly by the Compton process for radiation ranging in energy up to several million volts. In the pair production process radiation seems to be scattered, but this actually results from the annihilation reaction.

The *inverse square law,* a geometric factor, applies because the beam, on passing through the body, reaches points that are progressively farther from the radiation source. The exposure rate is inversely proportional to the square of the distance between the source of radiation and the point of interest, such as the tumor.

The *tumor dose* may be defined as the absorbed dose in rads at the location of the tumor. Ordinarily, this is determined for a point along the central axis (central ray) of the beam at the center of the tumor. Table 12.6 contains depth dose data for cobalt 60 gamma rays, and Table 12.7 for 6-MV linear accelerator x rays, obtained by measurement in a water phantom (a substitute for the human body). Refer back to Figure 12.8 which explains the concept of percentage depth dose. This is also expressed by the following equation:

$$\% \text{ depth dose at } x \text{ cm} = \frac{\text{dose rate at } x \text{ cm depth} \times 100}{\text{given dose rate}} \quad (12)$$

For example, suppose we are to treat a tumor whose center lies 10 cm below the skin surface where the beam enters the body. The field size measures $10 \times 10 \text{ cm}^2$ and we are to use a cobalt 60 beam (av. energy 1.25 MeV). In Table 12.6 for ^{60}Co at an 80-cm source-skin distance (SSD) we locate the 100 cm^2 column and find that at a depth of 10 cm the depth dose is *56.8 percent.* A total tumor dose of 6000 rads would require a given dose (GD) computed as follows:

$$\text{tumor dose} = \text{given dose} \times \% \text{ depth dose} \quad (13)$$

and rearranging,

$$\text{given dose} = \frac{\text{tumor dose}}{\% \text{ depth dose}} \quad (14)$$

$$\text{GD} = \frac{6000 \text{ rads}}{0.568} = 10,563 \text{ rads}$$

For linear accelerator 6-MV x rays, we use Table 12.7 where we find the 10-cm depth dose for a 100 cm^2 field and an SSD of 100 cm to be *68.8 percent,* so the GD would be

$$\frac{6000 \text{ rads}}{0.688} = 8721 \text{ rads}$$

Note that for the same tumor dose, the given dose is 17 percent smaller with 6-MV x rays than with cobalt 60 gamma rays at the usual SSD for these modalities.

The given dose in each example just cited is too large to to be delivered through a single field. In practice, therefore, it is divided

TABLE 12.6
PERCENT DEPTH DOSES*
COBALT 60

Square Fields	HVL 1.1 cm Pb				Source-skin Distance 80 cm				
Area (cm^2)	25	50	80	100	150	200	225	300	400
Dep. Factor	0.942	0.970	0.990	1.000	1.019	1.035	1.042	1.055	1.070
Depth (cm)									
0	23.5	26.8	30.1	31.9	35.4	39.0	40.8	44.5	50.1
0.5	100.0	100.0	100.0	100.0	100.0	100.0	100.0	100.0	100.0
1	98.2	98.1	98.3	98.3	98.4	98.5	98.5	98.5	98.5
2	92.3	92.7	93.1	93.2	93.4	93.6	93.6	93.7	93.9
3	86.7	87.6	88.2	88.3	88.6	88.9	89.0	89.2	89.5
4	81.3	82.7	83.4	83.6	84.1	84.4	84.6	84.9	85.2
5	76.2	78.0	78.9	79.2	79.7	80.2	80.4	80.7	81.2
6	70.9	72.7	73.9	74.3	75.0	75.6	75.8	76.2	76.8
7	65.7	67.7	69.1	69.6	70.5	71.2	71.4	71.9	72.6
8	60.8	62.9	64.5	65.1	66.2	66.9	67.3	67.8	68.6
9	56.1	58.4	60.1	60.9	62.0	62.9	63.3	63.9	64.7
10	51.6	54.1	56.0	56.8	58.0	59.0	59.4	60.1	61.0
11	47.9	50.3	52.2	52.9	54.2	55.3	55.7	56.5	57.5
12	44.4	46.6	48.5	49.2	50.6	51.7	52.2	53.0	54.0
13	41.1	43.3	45.1	45.8	47.2	48.3	48.8	49.6	50.7
14	38.0	40.0	41.8	42.6	43.9	45.1	45.5	46.4	47.6
15	35.0	37.1	38.9	39.7	41.1	42.2	42.7	43.5	44.7
16	32.2	34.3	36.2	36.9	38.3	39.4	39.9	40.8	41.9
17	29.8	31.8	33.6	34.3	35.7	36.8	37.3	38.2	39.3
18	27.5	29.4	31.1	31.8	33.2	34.3	34.8	35.7	36.8
19	25.4	27.3	29.0	29.6	31.0	32.1	32.6	33.5	34.6
20	23.4	25.2	26.9	27.5	28.9	29.9	30.4	31.3	32.4

Dep. factor is dependency factor, used to correct the given dose rate for field areas relative to 100 cm^2.

Adapted from original data by Frederick Hager, Physicist, East Texas Cancer Center, Tyler, Texas (by permission).

among two or more crossfiring beams centered on the tumor. For example, if we select a plan using three equally spaced beams around the body, and the tumor happens to be at a 10-cm depth for each beam, the total given dose for 6-MV x rays (for a 6000 rad tumor dose) is divided by three, giving

$$8721/3 = 2907 \text{ rads } \textit{for each field}$$

The total given dose for each field is fractionated over a period of about six weeks, all three fields being treated daily. Thus, for

TABLE 12.7

PERCENT DEPTH DOSES*

6 MV X RAYS

Square Fields	HVL 1.55 cm Pb				Source-skin Distance 100 cm					
Area (cm^2)	16	25	50	80	100	150	200	225	300	400
Output Factor	0.927	0.939	0.965	0.989	1.000	1.019	1.035	1.041	1.051	1.064
Depth (cm)										
1.5	100.0	100.0	100.0	100.0	100.0	100.0	100.0	100.0	100.0	100.0
2	99.9	99.9	99.9	99.9	99.9	99.7	99.6	99.5	99.3	99.1
3	95.7	96.1	96.1	96.0	96.0	96.0	96.0	96.0	95.9	95.8
4	90.9	91.5	92.0	92.0	92.0	92.0	92.0	92.0	91.8	91.8
5	86.0	87.0	87.9	88.0	88.0	88.0	88.0	88.0	88.2	88.3
6	81.5	82.4	83.4	83.7	83.8	84.0	84.1	84.2	84.2	84.4
7	76.6	77.6	78.9	79.7	79.9	80.4	80.6	80.7	80.8	81.0
8	72.2	73.3	74.7	75.8	76.2	76.8	77.0	77.1	77.1	77.4
9	67.9	69.0	70.8	71.9	72.4	73.1	73.6	73.7	73.8	74.0
10	63.9	65.1	66.9	68.2	68.8	69.4	70.0	70.1	70.2	70.5
11	60.6	61.8	63.7	65.0	65.4	66.2	66.8	66.9	67.1	67.5
12	56.9	57.3	60.2	61.7	62.1	63.0	63.5	63.7	63.9	64.3
13	53.7	54.7	56.7	58.0	58.6	59.5	60.2	60.6	61.1	61.6
14	50.5	51.7	53.7	55.1	55.6	56.6	57.3	57.8	58.2	58.9
15	47.8	48.8	50.8	52.1	52.8	53.8	54.5	54.9	55.4	56.1
16	44.8	45.9	47.8	49.2	49.9	50.9	51.8	52.0	52.7	53.3
17	42.3	43.4	45.1	46.5	47.1	48.1	49.0	49.4	50.0	50.8
18	39.5	40.8	42.6	43.9	44.5	45.6	46.4	46.9	47.5	48.2
19	37.5	38.6	40.4	41.9	42.4	43.5	44.3	44.7	45.4	46.1
20	35.4	46.4	38.0	39.4	40.0	41.0	41.8	42.3	42.9	43.7

Output factor is used to correct given dose for field areas relative to 100 cm^2.

*Adapted from original data by Frederick Hager, Physicist, East Texas Cancer Center, Tyler, Texas (by permission).

5-day per week schedule, the daily given dose to each field would be 2907/30 = 97 rads. The daily tumor dose from all three fields would be 6000/30 = 200 rads.

Applying similar calculations for a three-field plan with a ^{60}Co beam, the daily given dose would be 117 rads for each field. Although this daily given dose is larger than that with 6-MV x rays, it is well within skin tolerance. Actually, with megavoltage radiation the tolerance of normal organs in the vicinity of a tumor is much more of a limiting factor than skin tolerance.

Now let us examine the absorbed dose in **bone** lying in the path of the beam. In the case of **megavoltage** radiation such as ^{60}Co gamma rays, Table 12.5 shows the f values to be essentially the same in bone and soft tissue, so the absorbed dose in bone is practically the same as in soft tissue for a particular dose at a certain depth. On the other hand, with **orthovoltage** radiation the absorbed dose in bone is higher than in soft tissue, depending on the energy of the beam. Thus, in Table 12.5, with HVL 1.0 mm Cu, f is 1.95 for bone and 0.929 for soft tissue, so the absorbed dose in bone is about twice that in soft tissue under identical conditions.

Besides the central axis depth dose, we must know the doses at other points in the tumor to insure uniform irradiation so as to avoid undesirable over- or under-dosage. We must also know the doses to nearby normal organs to minimize radiation injury. Dosage to points away from the axis can be derived from **isodose curves,** which are computer-plotted percentage depth doses at various points in the beam (see Figure 12.17).

Factors Affecting Percentage Depth Dose

We have already shown how tumor dose varies with percentage depth dose (%DD). What conditions affect %DD?

The **percentage depth dose** increases with increasing (1) **half-value layer or beam energy,** (2) **treatment field area,** and (3) **source-surface distance.** The %DD decreases with increasing **depth of tumor.** These factors will now be discussed.

1. **Beam Quality.** As already noted, this is specified by the HVL and the kV or MV. The larger the HVL, the greater will be the penetrating ability of the beam and the %DD. In Tables 12.6 and 12.7, compare the %DD for ^{60}Co gamma rays (1.25 MeV) with 6-MV linac x rays for equal field areas. Examples of the application of %DD data in computing tumor dose are given on pages 201–203.

2. **Treatment Field Area.** As the area of the field increases, there is a corresponding increase in the volume of the irradiated tissue with resulting increase in the percentage of scattered radiation. The latter is added to the primary radiation reaching a given point below the surface and therefore contributes to an increased %DD.

3. **Source-Surface Distance (SSD).** As the distance between the

GAMMA-RAY
BEAM

Depth
in cm

COBALT 60 THERATRON ®
2 cm SOURCE
1.25 MeV (av.) - HVL 1.2 cm Pb - 80 cm SSD
10 x 10 cm² FIELD

Figure 12.17. Isodose curves. A specific set of curves should be obtained for each combination of treatment factors. The curved isodose lines connect all points receiving identical dosage, expressed in this case as a percentage of the given dose.

source (x-ray target; ^{60}Co) and surface is increased, the dose rate at the surface decreases according to the inverse square law. However, due to less divergence of the rays at the greater SSD (see Figure 12.18) a larger fraction of the surface exposure rate reaches a given depth below the surface; hence, the greater the SSD, the larger the %DD. This depends on the inverse square law and can be shown by an example based on Figure 12.18, aside from the other factors that influence %DD:

Figure 12.18. Percentage depth dose falls with decreasing source-surface distance, as shown by the greater divergence of the rays. This can be verified by the inverse square law.

Point P is located 10 cm below the surface

At SSD 70 cm

Point P is 10 cm + 70 cm = 80 cm from source F_1.
Dose rate at P, neglecting attenuation in tissue, is

$$\frac{70^2}{80^2} = 0.77 \text{ or } 77\% \text{ of given dose rate}$$

At SSD 100 cm

Point P is 10 cm + 100 cm = 110 cm from source F.
Dose rate at P, neglecting attenuation in tissue, is now

$$\frac{100^2}{110^2} = 0.83 \text{ or } 83\% \text{ of given dose rate}$$

4. **Depth of Tumor.** As the depth of the tumor increases, the %DD decreases because of the attenuation of the beam through absorption, scattering, and the inverse square law.

5. **Tissue Inhomogeneities.** The presence of tissues other than

those of water density will influence the %DD. For example, air filled lungs lying in the path of the beam will increase the %DD in the soft tissues beyond, due to the smaller attenuation per cm of path in the lung. On the other hand, bone will decrease the %DD because its greater density than soft tissue causes increased attenuation per cm of path; in other words, bone causes a "shadowing" effect on outlying tissue.

Modification of Orthovoltage X-ray Beams by Filters

The use of filters with orthovoltage beams has been mentioned several times, and a more complete discussion will now be presented. A filter is simply a sheet of metal placed in the path of a polyenergetic x-ray beam with an HVL up to about 4 mm Cu, to increase its average penetrating ability; that is, *a filter increases the average hardness of a beam.* This is brought about through the interaction of the x-ray photons with electrons in the atoms of the filter material (see section on interaction of radiation with matter). Recall that these interactions consist of absorption and scattering of photons. As a result, a *greater fraction of low energy* (long wavelength) *than of high energy* (short wavelength) x rays is *removed by a filter,* although some higher energy photons are also removed because of the "edge effect"—photons with energy close to the binding energy of the *K* or *L* shells are more likely to be absorbed by photoelectric interaction with *K* or *L* electrons than are photons of lower energy. In general, though, an orthovoltage x-ray beam undergoes an increase in half-value layer on passing through a filter.

Filters are not used to harden the cobalt 60 gamma ray beam because this is already virtually monoenergetic, having only two discrete energies—1.17 and 1.33 MeV. However, the steel capsule enclosing the source filters out the beta particles. Beam-flattening filters are used with cobalt 60 to provide more homogeneous exposure rate over the cross-section of the beam.

Notice that filtration does not change the maximum energy of a polyenergetic beam (see Figure 12.19); this depends solely on the *peak kilovoltage* applied to the tube. However, the smallest energy a photon can have in an x-ray beam leaving tube depends on the *inherent filtration* of the tube; that is, the filtration afforded by the glass envelope and the cooling oil layer through which the beam must pass after leaving the target.

Figure 12.19. Family of curves for an orthovoltage x-ray beam filtered by various added filters, as compared with an unfiltered beam. Note that the maximum photon energy is not altered since it depends on the peak kV only. The peak of the curve is shifted toward a higher photon energy as the atomic number of the filter increases; at the same time, the total exposure rate (area under the curve) decreases.

The inherent filtration of a tube is usually expressed in the equivalent thickness of aluminum or copper. Any additional filtration one chooses to place in the beam is called *added filtration.* The *total filtration* of an x-ray beam obviously represents the sum of the inherent filtration plus the added filtration.

total filtration = inherent filtration + added filtration   (15)

Filtration affects both the *exposure rate* and the *quality* (half-value layer) of an orthovoltage x-ray beam:

1. **Exposure rate** is always decreased by filtration because some photons are removed by absorption and scattering. In fact, the thicker the filter and the higher its atomic number, the smaller will be the exposure rate.

2. **Quality** is changed by filtration. An increase in either the

atomic number or the thickness of a filter increases the average penetrating ability of a beam; more specifically, the half-value layer increases. The type of filter should match the energy of the radiation. With radiation produced at 50 to 100 kV, aluminum is most suitable as a filter. Copper is used as the *primary filter* in the 120 to 400 kV range, but an aluminum filter must be placed between the copper and the patient as a *secondary filter* to absorb the characteristic radiation emitted by the copper. The resulting aluminum characteristic radiation, being soft, is absorbed in a few centimeters of air.

A special type of filter often used with 250- to 400-kV x rays is known as the *Thoraeus filter* (named after its inventor), a variety of *compound filter* consisting of three metals—tin, copper, and aluminum—placed in that order from the tube side to the patient side (see Figure 12.20). The chief advantage of the Thoraeus filter is that it provides a beam of the same half-value layer as a copper and aluminum filter, but with significantly less attenuation of the beam. Thus, for the same half-value layer, the Thoraeus filter provides about a 25 percent greater exposure rate than an equivalent copper and aluminum filter.

Figure 12.20. Schematic diagram of a Thoraeus compound filter, showing the relation of the component filters.

Comparison of Megavoltage and 250-kV Therapy

A number of years ago irradiation therapy of deep-seated tumors with 200 to 250 kV x rays was replaced by higher energy megavoltage beams such as cobalt 60 gamma rays (1.25 MeV) and 6 to 25 MV x rays. Several outstanding advantages relate to the use of radiation in this high energy range.

1. **Skin-sparing Effect.** As described before, the maximum dose with the higher energy radiation is located beneath the entrance skin surface. For example, cobalt 60 gamma rays deliver the maximum dose 5 mm, and 6-MV x rays 15 mm, below the surface. This shifts the skin reaction, ordinarily visible with 200-kV x rays, to a level below the skin, although the dose buildup occurs rapidly between the skin surface and the depth of maximum dose (D_{max}). While this permits a considerable increase in the total skin dose, still we must avoid excessive injury to the underlying tissues where it is not so readily apparent. In addition, we must avoid placing material in the path of the megavoltage beam any closer than about 15 to 20 cm from the skin, since Compton electrons liberated in such material and reaching the skin can significantly raise the dosage level there.

2. **Bone-sparing Effect.** An important advantage of megavoltage radiation is the nearly *equal absorption* occurring in bone and soft tissue, gram for gram. This permits larger doses to be delivered safely when there is bone in the path of the beam. However, there is "shading" of soft tissue beyond bone amounting to about 3.5 percent per cm of bone, up to 3 cm, for cobalt 60 gamma rays. This results from the greater attenuation of high energy photons in bone than in soft tissue for equal *thicknesses*. With 200-kV x rays and HVL of 1 mm Cu, absorption in bone is about two times that in soft tissue of the same mass, increasing significantly the likelihood of radiation injury to bone. At the same time, the lower energy radiation is severely shaded by the bone, so soft tissue beyond may be seriously underdosed.

3. **Greater Percentage Depth Dose.** The higher energy radiation provides a significantly higher percentage depth dose at a given treatment distance. In fact, this may be its greatest advantage over lower energy x rays. For example, according to Tables 12.6 and

12.7, at a 10-cm depth and with a 100 cm² field:

> Depth Dose with Cobalt 60 . . . . . 58.8% (SSD   80 cm)
> Depth Dose with 6-MV x rays . . . . 68.8% (SSD 100 cm)

This represents an increase in percentage depth dose of

$$100 \left(\frac{68.8 - 58.8}{58.8} \right) = \frac{100 \times 10}{58.8} = 17\%$$

with the higher energy radiation at the usual treatment distance for each modality. Even more striking is the 40 percent increase in percentage depth dose with megavoltage as compared with 200-kV x rays under similar conditions. At the same time, as we have just seen, the skin-sparing effect of megavoltage radiation further enhances the possibility of delivering an adequate dose to the tumor. It should be mentioned, however, that most authorities agree that the biologic effectiveness of cobalt 60 gamma rays relative to 250-kV x rays is about 85 percent; therefore, such gamma ray therapy requires a compensating increase in dosage of about 15 percent.

4. **More-forward Scatter.** Scattered radiation with high energy radiation is predominantly in a forward direction; that is, in the same direction as the primary beam. This results in less side scatter and a better defined beam edge, especially in the 6 to 25 MV range. Furthermore, the isodose curves can be flattened by suitably shaped filters, so there is more uniform irradiation of the selected volume.

QUESTIONS

1. Which properties of x rays led to their discovery?
2. What are roentgen rays? What are the two apparently contra-dictory theories as to their nature?
3. How are the frequency and wavelength of radiation related? What is the speed of x rays? Gamma rays?
4. How do soft rays differ from hard rays?
5. Describe the four essential components of a modern x-ray tube. Discuss the principles of x-ray production.

6. Discuss in detail the production of x rays when the electron stream hits the target.
7. What is characteristic radiation and how does it arise?
8. Discuss the differences between characteristic and general radiation. What is their relative importance in radiography?
9. Name ten properties of x rays.
10. What is meant by the quality of roentgen radiation? What factors influence it and in what manner? How can it be measured and specified (ICRU recommendations)?
11. Explain fully why a beam of x rays emerging from the target is heterogeneous. What are monoenergetic x rays?
12. What determines the maximum photon energy in an x-ray beam? State the equation that derives photon wavelength from energy.
13. Define and explain half-value layer and filters. What purpose does HVL serve?
14. Why is tungsten so widely used as the target material?
15. How is the quantity of radiation measured?
16. What factors influence exposure rate?
17. Discuss the four types of interactions of ionizing photon radiation and matter, showing how the corpuscular theory radiation applies.
18. What is the relative importance of the various interactions of photons with matter in radiography and radiotherapy?
19. Of what do scattered and secondary radiations consist?
20. How are tumor exposure and absorbed dose calculated?
21. Define absorbed dose. Name and define its unit.
22. What is the relationship between exposure rate and exposure? Exemplify this relationship by means of appropriate units.
23. Prove the statement in Figure 12.18 by application of the inverse square law.
24. Define percentage depth dose and explain the factors that influence it.
25. Define backscatter factor. What conditions affect it and how?
26. Describe a Thoraeus filter and discuss briefly its advantages in orthovoltage therapy.
27. What are isodose curves? Why are they used?

28. How does a filter influence the maximum photon energy in an orthovoltage or radiographic beam? The exposure rate?
29. Discuss the advantages of megavoltage therapy over 250-kV therapy.

THERMIONIC DIODE TUBES

IN CHAPTER 12 we learned that x rays are produced whenever a stream of fast-moving electrons undergoes rapid deceleration (loss of speed). These conditions prevail during the operation of a special type of *thermionic vacuum tube* — the hot filament or Coolidge x-ray tube. Before describing the detailed construction of such a tube, let us review its underlying principles:

1. *A hot metal filament gives off electrons* by a process called *thermionic emission.* The filament is heated by a separate *filament current.* The rate of electron emission increases with an increase in the temperature of the filament which, in turn, is governed by the filament current (measured in amperes).

2. *If no kilovoltage is applied,* the emitted electrons remain near the filament as an electron cloud or *space charge.*

3. *If kilovoltage is applied* between the filament and target so as to place a negative charge on the filament (cathode) and a positive charge on the target (anode), *space charge electrons are driven over to the anode at high speed by the large potential difference.* The maximum and average speeds of the electrons increase as the peak kilovoltage is increased. The electron stream crossing the gap between the cathode and anode constitutes the *tube current,* measured in milliamperes (mA).

4. *If the applied kilovoltage and resulting electron speed are high enough,* x rays are produced when the electrons enter the target, their *kinetic energy* being converted to heat (ordinarily more than 99 percent) and x rays (less than 1 percent).

A typical x-ray tube is a thermionic diode consisting of a tungsten filament cathode, a tungsten target anode, an evacuated glass tube enclosure, and two circuits to heat the filament and to drive

214

the space charge electrons to the anode. However, various important modifications of these tubes adapt them to special purposes. The structural and other details of radiographic, therapy, and valve tubes will now be described.

RADIOGRAPHIC TUBES

In this section we shall examine in detail the essential features of radiographic tubes used in medical x-ray diagnosis.

Glass Envelope

The working parts are enclosed in a *glass tube* or *envelope* containing as perfect a *vacuum* as possible. In fact, the tube is baked during manufacture to expel air and other gases that may have been trapped in the glass or metal parts, a process called *degassing*. As already noted, the vacuum offers an unobstructed path for the electron stream (tube current) and also prevents burning-out of the tube. Radiographic tubes are usually cylindrical in shape. Immersion in *insulating oil* in a suitable metal housing prevents high voltage sparkover between the terminals, thereby making possible the design of smaller tubes. The window through which the x rays leave is thinner than the rest of the tube.

Cathode

The negative terminal or *cathode assembly* consists of (1) the *filament*, (2) its *supporting wires*, and (3) the *focusing cup*. Loosely speaking, the terms "cathode" and "filament" are used interchangeably. The filament itself is a small coil of tungsten wire, the same metal that is used in electric light bulb filaments. In most radiographic tubes the filament measures about 0.2 cm in diameter and 1 cm or less in length, and is mounted on two stout wires which support it and also carry electric current. These wires lead through one end of the glass tube to be connected to the proper electrical source (see Figure 13.1). A low voltage *filament current* is sent through the wires to heat the filament, and one of these wires is also connected to the *high voltage source* which provides the high negative potential needed to drive the electrons toward the anode at great speed. A negatively charged concave metal cup behind the filament confines the electrons to a narrow beam and focuses them on a small spot on the tungsten target, known as the *tube focus* or *focal spot*.

GLASS ENVELOPE

CATHODE HOUSING

METAL FOCUSING CUP

FILAMENT

SUPPORTING WIRES FOR FILAMENT

Figure 13.1 Details of the cathode of an x-ray tube (side view).

The filament current, serving to heat the filament and provide a source of electrons within the tube, usually operates at about 10 volts and 3 to 5 amperes. An increase in the filament current raises the temperature of the filament and the rate of electron emission causing a sharp rise in tube current (mA) as shown in Figure 13.2.

Some tubes, such as those used in older mobile equipment, have a single filament. However, most modern radiographic tubes, in both stationary and mobile equipment, are provided with two filaments mounted side by side. The filaments usually differ in size, producing focal spots of two different sizes on the target. Such tubes are called *double focus* tubes, although they are really double filament tubes. Note that only one filament is activated for a given exposure, being selected at the control panel. Supporting the two filaments are three stout wires, one of which is connected in common with both filaments. In Figure 13.3, if terminals 1 and 3 are connected to the low voltage source, the large filament lights up. If, instead, terminals 2 and 3 are connected to the low voltage source, the small filament lights up.

The high voltage, applied through wire 3 which is common to both filaments, gives either one a high negative potential.

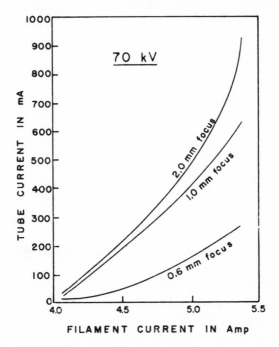

Figure 13.2. Relation of tube current (mA) to filament current. Note that a small increase in filament current produces a large increase in mA. Furthermore, mA is larger with a larger tube focus for a given filament current.

Filament Evaporation. As the tube ages, the filament gradually evaporates as the result of heating during use. Consequently, a number of changes take place in the tube.

1. *Thinning of the Filament.* Loss of metal (tungsten) by evaporation causes the filament to become progressively thinner. Its electrical resistance therefore increases (R inversely proportional to cross sectional area). However, filament circuitry is designed to maintain constant current (I). Thus, I^2R increases, thereby raising the filament temperature with resulting increase in tube current (mA). To correct this, the service representative adjusts the filament current *downward* just enough to obtain the proper electron emission for the required tube current. It will be found that *as the tube*

Figure 13.3. Simplified diagram of the connection of two filaments of an x-ray tube (double focal spot tube) to three wires, one of which is common to both filaments. The filaments are mounted side by side, facing the target.

ages, a progressively lower filament current setting is required for a desired tube milliamperage.

2. *Deposition of Tungsten on the Glass Envelope.* As the filament evaporates, some of the vaporized tungsten deposits on the internal wall of the glass tube. When this occurs on the window of the tube, it acts as an additional filter, reducing x-ray output. Furthermore, the tungsten deposit impairs insulation so that electrons may be attracted to this metallic coating and possibly puncture the tube.

Anode

There are two main types of anodes: (1) stationary and (2) rotating.

1. **Stationary Anode.** A gap of a few centimeters separates the cathode from the anode which consists of a block of copper in which is imbedded the target, a small tungsten button. These metals are selected for definite reasons:

a. *Tungsten* — so placed that it forms the actual target of the x-ray tube, the high speed electrons striking it directly. The target is the area on the anode in which useful x rays are actually produced. Since more than 99 percent of the electrons' kinetic energy changes to heat at the target, the *high melting point* of tungsten — 3370 C —

makes it especially suitable as a target metal. Furthermore, *tube efficiency*, that is, the percentage of the electrons' energy appearing in the form of x rays, is directly proportional to the atomic number of the target and the applied kV (see pages 367–368 for special mammographic tube with molybdenum target).

b. *Copper*—a much better conductor of heat than tungsten, carrying the heat away from the target more rapidly and thereby protecting it from overheating, within certain limits. Even greater heat-loading capacity can be achieved by circulating air, water, or oil around the anode, permitting larger exposures than would otherwise be possible.

Note again the electron stream bombards a limited area on the target called the *focus* or *focal spot*. X rays are emitted from the entire surface of the actual focus; in fact, there are innumerable points in the focal area from which x rays are projected in all directions.

As we shall see later, using the smallest practicable focus enhances the sharpness of the radiographic image. Therefore, radiographic tubes are provided with a small filament and a metal focusing cup. However, as the size of the focus decreases it experiences a greater concentration of heat with the attendant danger of overloading and melting the target. Tubes are so designed that the focus is small enough to give satisfactory radiographic detail, but not so small as to restrict their practical usefulness. Most stationary anodes have focal spot widths of 2 mm and 4 mm.

Anodes of radiographic tubes are constructed on the *line-focus principle* to provide a focus which, when projected toward the film, is smaller than is its actual area on the target. The line-focus principle can best be explained by a diagram, as shown in Figure 13.4. Here, the actual focus is a rectangle as in *B*. Assume this rectangle, *T*, to measure about 2 mm × 6 mm. In *A*, the side view of the tube, note that the anode is inclined, making an angle of 17° with the vertical. Since the film will be placed at some distance directly below the target, the *effective* or *apparent focal area* as projected toward the film is only *D*, which is about 2 mm × 2 mm. Perhaps it would become clearer if you were to imagine yourself lying supine in the position of the film and looking upward at the target—the focus would resemble a small square rather than a rectangle. In other words the focus is foreshortened, just as a pencil appears shorter when it is held obliquely in front of the eyes than it is when held parallel to the eyes. Furthermore, the effective size of the focal spot varies with the *direction* in which it is projected. As shown in Figure 13.5, it becomes smaller toward the anode end of the tube.

Figure 13.4. Line-focus principle. In *A* the target is shown in side view, and *D* is the *projected, apparent,* or *effective focus.* In *B* the target is shown in face view with the actual rectangular focus, *T,* at its center. The same principle is used in rotating anodes.

Another important relation is shown in Figure 13.6; the effective size of the focal spot diminishes as the anode angle becomes smaller (anode steeper). However, this also results in a more pronounced heel effect (see pages 421–422).

2. **Rotating Anode.** In 1936 there became available a radically different kind of anode of ingenious design—the *rotating anode.* As its name indicates, this anode, attached to the shaft of a small induction motor, *rotates during x-ray production.* Rotating anodes were previously constructed of solid tungsten in the form of a disc. Later, an improved type of rotating anode was introduced, consisting of a *molybdenum disc* coated with a *tungsten-rhenium alloy.* The addition of rhenium diminishes roughening of the focal area, thereby maintaining a high x-ray output (emissivity). The usual diameter of rotating anodes is about 7.6 cm (3-in.) although 12.7 cm (5-in.) models have been introduced for extra heavy duty. Speed of

Figure 13.5. Effect of angle of emission of x rays on apparent or effective focal spot size. An anatomic detail at *A* (toward the anode end of the tube) will have a sharper image because in this direction the effective focal spot size is smaller than at *C* where the effective focal spot size is larger. *A*, *B*, and *C* represent the effective sizes of the same focal spot projected at different angles, that is, in different directions with respect to the anode surface. Rotating anode shown.

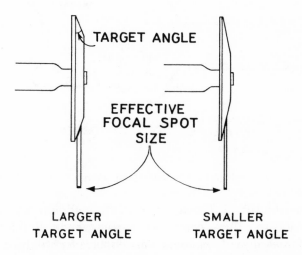

Figure 13.6. Effect of target (anode) angle on apparent or effective focal spot size. Note that a decrease in the target angle gives a smaller effective size when the actual focal spot size remains unchanged. Rotating anodes shown.

rotation is ordinarily 3300 to 3600 rpm (revolutions per min), but special high-speed models capable of 10,000 rpm are available for special procedures. A diagram of a rotating anode tube is shown in Figure 13.7.

As already mentioned, rotating anodes utilize the *line-focus principle*; they therefore have a beveled edge as shown in Figure 13.7. The cathode is so placed that the electron beam strikes the beveled edge of the anode, as shown in Figure 13.8, the degree of beveling being called the *target* or *anode angle.* Anodes are available with targets of various angles such as 10°, 12°, and 17°. These influence the size of the exposure that can be used in a very short exposure time without damaging the tube (see Table 13.1).

Figure 13.7. Rotating anode tube.

Outside the tube is the stator of the induction motor, the rotor being inside the tube, connected to the anode. Self-lubricating bearings coated with *metallic barium* or *silver* reduce friction, thereby prolonging tube life.

How does such an anode operate? During exposure the anode rotates rapidly while being bombarded by the electron stream. Although ordinarily rated at 3600 rpm, this is more likely to be

SIDE VIEW   FACE VIEW

FOCAL TRACK

EFFECTIVE
FOCUS SIZE

Figure 13.8. Line-focus principle with a rotating anode. The *focal track* is the actual area of impact of the electrons, or the actual focal area. Note how much smaller the apparent focal area is than the focal track. For example, a typical focal track is about 250 mm in length (circumference) and its width about 3 mm for a 1 mm^2 apparent focal spot. Thus, the area bombarded by electrons at any instant is $1 \times 3 = 3$ mm^2, while the heat is spread over an area of $3 \times 250 = 750$ mm^2.

Table 13.1
EFFECT OF TARGET ANGLE OF A ROTATING ANODE
ON SHORT-EXPOSURE RATING RELATIVE
TO THAT OF A STANDARD TARGET ANGLE OF 17°

Target Angle	Approximate Increase in Short Exposure Rating
12°	30%
10°	60%

3000 rpm due to slippage of the rotor. During rotation the anode constantly "turns a new face" to the electron beam, so that the heating effect of the beam does not concentrate at one point, as in the stationary anode, but spreads over a large area called the *focal track* on the beveled face of the anode as shown in Figure 13.8. However, the effective focus remains constant in position relative to the film because of the extremely smooth motion of the anode. As a result, it is possible to have an effective focus of 1 mm or even smaller—the 0.3 mm fractional focus tube. Furthermore, it becomes feasible to subject a tube to high milliamperage. For instance, with a stationary anode, the upper limit for a 4 mm focus is 200 mA, whereas with a rotating anode, the upper limit for a 2 mm focus is 500 mA, the maximum exposure time being approximately the same in both cases. Special tubes have been designed to tolerate a current as large as 1000 mA for very short exposures, operating on three-phase current.

Rotating anode tubes usually have two filaments to provide 1 and 2 mm focal spots; the smaller one is used to obtain fine radiographic definition, whereas the larger one can tolerate heavier loading in shorter exposure time to minimize motion in special radiographic procedures.

Special rotating anode tubes with 0.3 mm focal spots, and even smaller, have been designed for *magnification radiography*. Called *fractional focus tubes*, they permit placing the film at a distance from the part to permit direct magnification of the radiographic image. This is described on pages 374–380.

You can see from the preceding discussion that the modern rotating anode tube has successfully combined the extremely small focus with reasonably large heat-loading capacity. This has made possible the superb sharpness of detail in modern radiography.

Space Charge Compensation

The low-voltage current supplied to the x-ray tube filament heats it to incandescence (white hot), causing the emission of electrons (thermionic emission). The rate of electron emission, or the number emitted per second, depends on the temperature of the filament which, in turn, is governed by the current supplied to it. In fact, *a small increase in filament current produces a large increase in the rate of electron emission and resulting space charge.*

If *no* high voltage is applied across the tube, the electrons remain in the vicinity of the hot filament as a *space charge*. This gives rise to the *space charge effect* which may be simply explained as follows: since the space charge consists of electrons, it is negative and therefore tends to hold back the further emission of electrons (like charges repel). In fact, some electrons are actually repelled from the space charge back into the filament. At any particular value of the filament current, an equilibrium is reached between the rate of electron emission by the filament and the rate of return to the filament from the space charge. Thus, *the space charge has a definite size for a given value of the filament current in a given tube,* and as just indicated, a small change in filament current produces a large change in the size of the space charge.

If a sufficiently high voltage (kV) is now applied across the tube, imparting a large negative charge to the filament and an equally large positive charge to the anode, the space charge electrons are driven toward the anode at a speed that depends on the kV (but *not* directly proportional). When tube current (mA) is plotted as a function of tube voltage (kV) a family of *characteristic curves* is obtained as shown in Figure 13.9. As expected, there is a different curve for each value of filament current (amp). Furthermore, the larger the filament current, the greater will be the resulting tube current (mA).

Let us now examine the characteristic curves. Note that the lowest curve (representing a filament current of 4.2 amp) has an

Figure 13.9. Family of characteristic curves of a typical rotating anode tube (*Machlett Dynamax "60"®, Dunlee*). Note the progressive rise in mA as kV is increased. A space charge compensator is used to flatten the curves so that kV can be changed without a change in mA as explained in the text.

initial curved portion and then flattens out at about 100 kV, after which a further increase in kV causes no additional increase in mA. We can explain this as follows: a progressive increase in kV drives more and more of the space charge electrons per second to the anode; that is, there is an increase in mA. This is called the **space-charge limited region** of tube operation. But above 100 kV all of the space charge electrons are driven to the anode immediately after emission from the filament, so that further increase in kV cannot increase mA; hence, this portion of the curve is flat, representing **saturation current** or the **temperature-limited region.** Here the mA can be increased only by increasing the filament current and temperature.

The remaining curves in Figure 13.9 do not have a flat portion below 150 kV, so at the corresponding filament currents the tube operates only in the space-charge limited region. Operation of an x-ray tube in the space-charge limited region is undesirable in radiography because kV cannot be changed independently of mA—when the technologist changes the kV setting there is an unavoidable change in mA. To correct this situation a **space charge compensator** introduced into the filament circuit automatically lowers the filament current just the right amount, as the kV is raised, to keep the mA constant over the useful kV range. Now the technologist has full control of tube operation, being able to change kV without producing any appreciable effect on mA.

In modern automatic equipment with monitor-type mA selection, the space charge compensator has an additional function; it also selects the correct filament current to provide the desired space charge and resulting mA.

Factors Governing Tube Life

Overheating the filament or anode disc inevitably shortens tube life. While there are specific differences between the filament and anode in this regard, they have in common the tendency to vaporize and deposit tungsten on the glass wall of the tube. This leads to internal electrical stresses resulting in instability of operation and possible puncture of the tube wall. Furthermore, the tungsten deposit increases inherent filtration and so decreases x-ray output.

We shall evaluate the factors that influence tube life as they pertain to the filament, anode, and housing. The x-ray tube itself, as distinct from the housing, is often called the *insert*.

Filament Factors. The large tube currents (mA) often demanded in radiography require a large filament current and temperature. Failure of a radiographic tube may result from "burning out" of the filament due to application of excessive current which raises filament temperature beyond the rated limit. But tube failure can also occur from prolonged heating of the filament at normal current loads, just as an electric light filament burns out after a period of normal use. In most installations a special *booster circuit* limits filament current to a low or standby level until the x-ray exposure switch is closed. At this instant, the booster circuit automatically raises the filament current sufficiently to provide the desired tube current. This helps significantly to prolong tube life. At the same time, the technologist must avoid using the "boost-and-hold" method of making exposure (as in radiography of infants) unless it is absolutely necessary; excessive boost time unquestionably shortens tube life.

Undue heating of the filament, whether by current or time, or both, causes evaporation of the filament metal with resulting decrease in its diameter. A diameter reduction of only 10 percent will cause the filament to break and so end tube life. Furthermore, as mentioned earlier, the vaporized tungsten coats the glass wall of the insert and causes instability in the operation of the tube; eventually, the insert may be *punctured* by electrical spark-over, at present the most frequent cause of tube failure.

Anode Factors. The ability of the anode disc to accumulate, store, and discharge heat, limits the maximum allowable techniques. These three anode factors will now be taken up individually.

1. *Radiographic Tube Rating Chart.* If the rate of temperature rise in the anode disc exceeds a limiting value, localized melting or cracking occurs as a result of thermal stresses set up in the metal by the difference in temperature between the focal spot or track at the surface, and the depths of the disc. With a slower rate of temperature rise, enough time may elapse to permit heat conduction to equalize the temperature throughout the disc. Melting of the metal, short of actually destroying the disc, causes it to vapor-

ize and coat the glass wall of the insert, eventually resulting in its puncture. Furthermore, roughening of the focal track area and cracking of the anode disc reduces x-ray output because, as they leave the anode, the photons have to penetrate the uneven surface of the anode. Figure 13.10 shows the appearance of heat-damaged focal tracks and anode discs. Finally, warping of the anode disc causes noisy operation and decreased x-ray output.

New anode disc.

PITTING AND ETCHING OF FOCAL TRACK

CRACK

Frequently repeated overloading

SURFACE MELTS IN FOCAL TRACK

CRACK

Repeated overload with surface melts

LOCALIZED MELT

Overloading resulting in stopped anode and localized melt.

Figure 13.10. Surface appearance of anode disc under various conditions. *Adapted from Cathode Press, courtesy of the Machlett Laboratories, Inc.*

The safe limits of exposure factors for a "cold" anode can easily be found by referring to the radiographic tube rating chart provided by the manufacturer for each type of tube and for a given type of operation. Such a chart indicates the maximum "safe" exposure time for any selected combination of kV and mA for a single exposure and a relatively cool tube. The chart in Figure 13.11 is fictitious and is shown only by way of an example. It includes a series of curves representing various mA values of tube current. The vertical axis of the graph represents kV, and the horizontal axis maximum allowable exposure time in sec. Such a chart is quite simple to use. Assume that it applies to a particular tube of **given focus size**, and with a **given type of rectification**. Suppose we are to make an exposure of 300 mA and 65 kV, and we wish to determine the maximum allowable exposure time. Starting at 65 on the vertical axis, follow horizontally from this point to the point where it meets the 300 mA curve. Then from this point of intersection, follow vertically downward to the horizontal line, crossing it at three seconds, the maximum rating or tolerable exposure time with these factors.

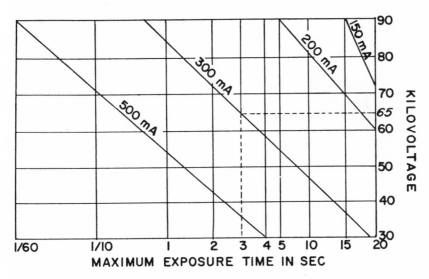

Figure 13.11. Tube-rating chart, arbitrary values. The chart for any particular tube must be obtained from the manufacturer.

It must be emphasized that the correct tube rating chart must be selected to avoid overheating the focal track, depending on the following conditions:

a. *Type of Rectification.* The maximum tube rating is less with half-wave (single-pulse) than with full-wave (two-pulse) rectification.

b. *Size of Tube Focus.* The maximum tube rating is less with a small focal spot or track than with a large one.

c. *Tube Design.* This affects the maximum tube rating; therefore the appropriate tube rating chart supplied by the manufacturer for the particular tube. For example, a tube with high-speed disc rotation has a higher rating than a conventional tube. Furthermore, smaller anode angles permit higher tube ratings for very short exposures.

d. *Cold versus Hot Tube.* The chart applies only to a relatively cold tube, one that has not been subjected to heavy loading just before use.

e. *Type of Power Supply.* Tube rating will be different for single phase and three phase, and for short or long exposures.

f. *Application.* A special chart must be used for rapid sequence radiography, as in angiography and tomography.

The tube rating chart for the particular tube in use should be mounted in the control booth, especially if the equipment lacks automatic exposure limiters. These devices make it impossible to activate the x-ray tube if it were to be overloaded by the selected technical factors.

2. ***Anode Storage Capacity.*** With multiple exposures the anode assembly gradually accumulates heat. (This is not the same as the maximum exposure factors for a "cold" anode, as determined from a tube rating chart.) We must therefore deal with the capacity of an anode to store heat without cracking, melting, or warping, any of which may reduce x-ray output (see above). Overheating and vaporization of disc metal result in coating of tungsten on the glass wall of the insert with the attendant harmful effects described earlier. Furthermore, excessive accumulation of heat may reach the anode stem and rotor bearings. The latter may become sufficiently deformed to slow down or stop the rotor, a condition that is obviously fatal to the insert. Heat storage capacity of the anode is measured in ***heat units,*** defined by the following equation for single-phase operation:

$$\textbf{Heat Units (H.U.)} = \textbf{kV} \times \textbf{mA} \times \textbf{sec} \qquad (1)$$

For three-phase, six-pulse operation, equation (1) must be multiplied by the factor *1.35;* and for three-phase, twelve-pulse, by *1.41.* However, these factors should *not* be used to convert single-phase charts to three-phase operation; the applicable tube rating chart must be used for each type of tube and equipment as noted on page 229.

Note that heat units are not fictitious, but really represent energy:

$$1 \text{ kV} \times 1 \text{ ma} \times 1 \text{ sec} = 1 \text{ watt-sec } (nominal)$$

which is a unit of energy. (Actually, 1 H.U. is equivalent to an energy of 0.71 watt-sec, where 0.71 is the RMS conversion factor.) The *heat storage capacity* of the anodes of various diagnostic tubes ranges from about 70,000 H.U. to about 400,000 H.U., depending on the *size of the anode* (ie, anode mass) and the cooling method. The cooling characteristics of anodes are specified by the *heat dissipation rate,* which must be determined from cooling curves supplied by the manufacturer of that particular tube (see Figure 13.12). If the anode has been heated to its full storage capacity by a large number of exposures, additional exposures are limited by the cooling rate of the anode.

The equation defining heat unit storage also demonstrates that an x-ray tube operates more efficiently at higher kilovoltages. For example, a given radiographic technic calling for an exposure of 60 kV, 100 mA, and 1 sec would develop the following number of heat units in the anode:

$$\text{H.U.} = 60 \times 100 \times 1$$
$$\text{H.U.} = 6000$$

If the kV is increased by 10 (ie, about 15 percent) and the time reduced one-half, the exposure in terms of visible radiographic effect would remain essentially the same, but now let us see how many heat units would be developed in the anode:

$$\text{H.U.} = 70 \times 100 \times \tfrac{1}{2}$$
$$\text{H.U.} = 3500$$

Thus, with an increase in kV the heat units in the anode have been decreased almost one-half, even though the exposure has remained virtually unchanged.

The **short-exposure rating,** or the ability of a focal track to withstand a large heat input in a small fraction of a second, does not necessarily follow the heat storage capacity of the anode. For example, as described on page 276, the short-exposure rating is higher with three-phase than with single-phase current for a tube with the same heat storage capacity. Furthermore, as shown in Table 13.1, the short-exposure rating of a rotating anode tube increases significantly as the target angle decreases. Still a third factor in this problem is the speed of rotation of the anode; thus, with high speed anodes — 10,000 rpm — the short-exposure rating is increased about 70 percent over that of conventional rotating anode speed of 3000 rpm.

In general, *an increase in the actual area of the focal spot or track increases the instantaneous rating of the anode, whereas an increase in the anode mass increases its heat storage capacity.*

After prolonged use, or with minor overloading, the anode disc becomes roughened by *pitting* or *etching.* When severe, this reduces the x-ray output of the tube. The use of *rhenium-tungsten-molybdenum* instead of pure tungsten as the anode material aids in minimizing this problem.

In the ordinary oil-immersed tube, adequate *cooling* results from the transfer of heat to the oil, tube, housing, and surrounding air by simple convection and conduction. For heavier loads, as in chest surveys, special procedures, and high voltage radiography, cooling is improved by mounting a small fan outside the tube housing. Some specially designed tubes are cooled by a forced oil circulating system, the oil flowing into the hollow anode and then between the tube and housing; this provides a very high rate of heat dissipation. Heat storage capacity may be enhanced by the use of rotating anodes with surface areas 100 percent greater than usual. The oil incidentally provides efficient insulation, while the metal housing helps make the tube rayproof by shielding out unwanted radiation.

3. *Anode Cooling Curve.* The rate at which the anode cools, starting at any particular value of heat storage (heat units), is given by the anode cooling curve appropriate to the tube under consideration. Figure 13.12 shows a typical anode cooling curve. At no time should another exposure be made if the additional heat

produced in the anode would increase the stored heat beyond the instantaneous rating. Thus, starting with a known amount of heat already present in the anode, we must allow enough time to elapse for it to cool down sufficiently to permit the additional heat load. An example is given in the legend to Figure 13.12.

Housing Factors. Often overlooked, the ability of the metal housing to store and dissipate heat contributes to tube life. Thus, the temperature of the housing must be kept below 90 C (200 F), both to prevent damage to the housing itself and to permit adequate cooling of the insert. In fact, excessive heat may bring the oil to the boiling point and even cause the housing to explode. This is a real hazard with rapid serial exposures in angiography and cineradiography. An air blower may help cool the housing, but is effective only if the housing cools more slowly than the anode disc. Regular servicing of the blower is mandatory to assure proper function, especially for an under-table tube. Special cooling curves, similar to those for anode cooling rate, are available for the housing.

Figure 13.12. Anode cooling curve. With this tube, if the anode has the maximum 200,000 heat units already stored, then at the end of two minutes the stored heat will have decreased to 120,000 H.U. It would then be safe to load the anode with additional 80,000 H.U. for a total maximum of 200,000 H.U. For complete evaluation, a housing cooling curve should also be consulted. (*Based on data furnished by courtesy of Machlett Laboratories, Inc.*)

Angiographic Rating Chart. Because of the rapid sequence exposures needed in angiography, special rating charts must be consulted to avoid anode damage. A typical angiographic rating chart appears in Figure 13.13. Knowing the total number of exposures in a particular series, for example twenty, we move vertically upward from this point on the horizontal axis, to the curve for the desired number of exposures per second, say four per second. From this point of intersection we move horizontally to the vertical axis where the maximum allowable combination of kV × mA × sec for a single exposure is indicated—in this case, about 3700. In other words, the product of the three technical factors must be less than 3700 to remain within the safe limits for this particular tube under these operating conditions (three-phase, 1 mm focal spot, 60-cycle stator operation). To simplify the use of angiographic rating charts it is advisable to have posted in the control booth a table showing the maximum number of exposures that can safely be made with the usual technique and number of exposures per second, and the cooling off times between successive runs of exposures. Furthermore, there should be posted specific recommendations for *initial warm-up* of the tube before angiography is started; this helps minimize thermal stress engendered by a large load applied to a cold tube.

Cineradiographic Rating Chart. Rapid sequence exposures in cineradiography present a high thermal load to the anode disc just as in angiography. Figure 13.14 is a typical cineradiographic rating chart. It gives the maximum allowable kV × mA × sec combination for a desired over-all cine run time in seconds, with a particular sequence of exposures. For example, if we wish to make a cine strip over a period of ten seconds with 1/60 second exposures at a rate of thirty per second, we start at 10 on the horizontal axis and move up to the appropriate curve, then from the point of intersection horizontally to the vertical axis where the product of the three factors turns out to be 250 per exposure. Since this is three-phase operation, we must multiply 250 by 1.35, giving 340 H.U. per exposure. With a tube having an anode heat storage capacity of 200,000 H.U., 300 exposures (30 per sec × 10 sec) would give a maximum allowable load of 700 H.U. per exposure, so the value 340 H.U. turns out to be well within the tube rating.

Summary of Practical Steps in Extending Useful Tube Life. A

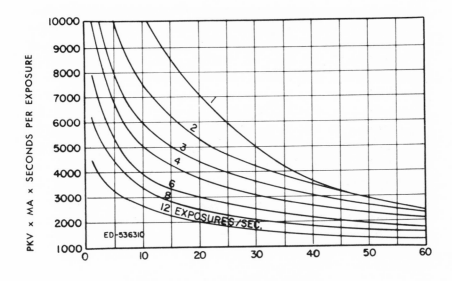

TOTAL NUMBER OF EXPOSURES

Figure 13.13. Typical angiographic rating chart, applicable *specifically* to the Dynamax "61" rotating anode tube with a 1 mm effective focal spot, and three-phase, 60-Hz operation. (*Courtesy of the Machlett Laboratories, Inc.*)

number of precautions in the use of radiographic tubes contribute significantly to prolongation of their useful life. These have been described in detail but will now be summarized:

1. *Filament life* is shortened by application of large filament currents (and resulting high temperatures). Therefore the "boost" or preparation time during which the filament temperature is held at full value should be kept as short as possible.

2. *Instantaneous ratings,* as derived from tube rating charts, should never be exceeded. Be certain to use the correct chart for the particular tube, focal spot size, type of rectification, and type of current (single or three-phase).

3. The *anode should be warmed up* before being subjected to a large load; use warmup times suggested by the manufacturer. Heat produced by a large power load on a cold anode causes uneven expansion that may crack the anode disc.

4. The *life of the bearings* in a rotating anode tube is shortened as the total rotation time is increased. Therefore the anode should

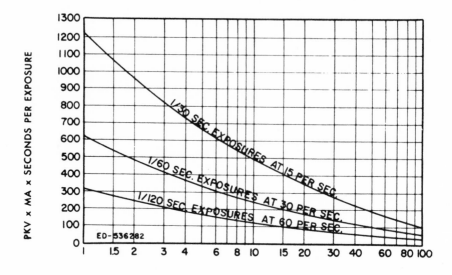

Figure 13.14. Typical cineradiographic rating tube, applicable *specifically* to the Dynamax "61" rotating anode tube with a 1 mm effective focal spot, and three-phase, 60-Hz operation. (*Courtesy of the Machlett Laboratories, Inc.*)

not be run unnecessarily. This becomes a special problem in radiography of infants when the rotor is kept activated while the technologist awaits the opportune instant to make the exposure. In addition, the bearings may be damaged by heat overload of the anode.

5. *Excessive temperature of oil in the tube housing may shorten tube life.* Therefore adequate cooling of the tube housing must be provided; for example, by use of an auxiliary fan which may be provided at the time of installation.

6. *Rapid sequence exposures* as in angiography and cineradiography may easily exceed the tube rating. Therefore the proper rapid sequence rating charts and anode cooling curves should be consulted. In fact, it is good practice to work up a chart showing the maximum number of exposures in the time intervals for various procedures which may pose a hazard for the x-ray tube; this chart should be posted in the control booth for ready reference.

7. *Avoid overheating the filament and anode.* Even minor overheating, if repeated a sufficient number of times, causes evapora-

tion of tungsten which is deposited on the glass wall of the insert. Eventually the insert may be punctured by spark-over, especially with application of high kV. In fact, tube puncture ranks high as a cause of tube failure in ordinary routine radiography, whereas anode warping or cracking occur more often in rapid sequence radiography.

X-RAY THERAPY TUBES

These are x-ray tubes designed exclusively for use in clinical radiation therapy. Such tubes, operating at relatively low mA values of tube current, are manufactured in various models for the desired kV range.

In x-ray therapy, four main kV energy ranges are available for treatment at different depths in the body.

1. **Low Voltage.** This includes a range of about 50 to 120 kV and is used to treat lesions in the skin. It is also known as *superficial therapy.*

2. **Intermediate Voltage.** This is about 130 to 150 kV and is used mainly in treating lesions a few centimeters below the skin.

3. **Orthovoltage.** The usual range of 160 to 300 kV provides x rays of relatively high penetrating power, applicable in deep x-ray therapy for the treatment of lesions below the surface; now replaced by megavoltage except for special indications.

4. **Megavoltage.** Operating at potentials of mV and more, the specially designed tubes for this type of equipment, the *linear accelerator* or *linac,* will not be described here.

In general, an orthovoltage therapy tube differs from a radiographic tube in having a larger filament, a stationary anode, and a larger focal spot; the last permits greater heat loading for continuous operation. The anode consists of a tungsten mass imbedded in a large block of copper, its face usually being inclined at an angle of about 30° to generate a beam of reasonably uniform intensity. As is true of radiographic tubes, therapy tubes have a separate filament current to heat the filament and produce a space charge; and a high voltage to drive the electrons to the target at high speed. Such tubes operate in the space-charge limited region of the characteristic curve.

Since there may be a tremendous amount of heat liberated in the anode, particularly in the orthovoltage region, special means of cooling the tube must be provided. Superficial therapy tubes are usually cooled in the same manner as radiographic tubes, depending on the anode heat load. On the other hand, intermediate and orthovoltage therapy tubes most often have hollow anodes cooled by circulating oil between the tube and housing. A pump then transfers the hot oil to a special tank where it is cooled by water circulating in coils.

The oil serves another purpose. Because it is highly refined and moisture free, it has superb insulating ability. Such insulating oils permit a reduction in the size of the tube housing, thereby making it more easily maneuverable.

VALVE TUBES (VACUUM DIODE RECTIFIERS)

The use of valve tubes in rectification has already been described. They are *thermionic diode tubes* having the same general construction as x-ray tubes, but differing from them in certain details to serve a specific function. We shall now describe their structural components and operation; while they are still widely used in radiographic equipment, they are being superseded by solid state rectifiers in modern radiographic units.

Cathode

The filament of a valve tube consists of a coil of tungsten wire which is longer and thicker than the filament of an x-ray tube. It lies in the *longitudinal axis* of the tube, supported by a large molybdenum spiral as shown in Figure 13.15. Modern valve tube filaments are *thoriated* for more efficient release of electrons, and for greater durability. The filament of a valve tube is heated through its own filament circuit, and is also provided with a connection to the high voltage circuit. Thus, the valve tube as well as the x-ray tube has two circuits.

Figure 13.15. Cathode of a valve tube (vacuum diode rectifier).

Anode

As shown in Figure 13.16, the valve tube anode, having a *large surface* and a *cylindrical shape* (resembling a metal can), surrounds the filament. This makes it possible for a large current (many electrons per sec) to pass from the cathode to the anode, thereby assuring a *small voltage drop* across the valve tube.

Figure 13.16. Diagram of a valve tube (vacuum diode rectifier).

Principles of Operation

A valve tube normally operates *below saturation;* that is, in the space-charge limited region (see page 226). Because of its large size, the filament emits a generous space charge when heated by its current, thereby making available enough electrons for any reasonable combination of kV and mA. The superabundance of space-charge electrons, together with the large cylindrical anode, is responsible for the *low electrical resistance* and consequent *small voltage drop* in the forward direction across the valve tube; for example, with a 500 mA current in the x-ray tube, the voltage drop in each valve tube should not exceed 3 kV. Since the speed of the electrons in the tube varies with the kV drop across the tube, the electrons do not gain significant speed with a drop of only 3 kV, and therefore lack sufficient energy to produce x rays during normal operation. However, in a defective valve tube in which thermionic emission decreases, the resistance may increase until the voltage drop becomes large enough to accelerate the electrons to the point of x-ray production. Furthermore, a large fall in kV across the valve tube would decrease the kV available for the operation of the x-ray tube.

Bear in mind that the mA in a valve tube must equal that in the x-ray tube because they are connected in series and *all parts of a series circuit carry an identical current.* Since current is defined as the rate of flow of electric charge one may say that an electric current represents the flow of a certain *number of electrons per second.* During operation, the same number of electrons per second pass from cathode to anode in the x-ray tube as in the valve tube. But in the valve tube, the individual electrons move less rapidly and in a larger group, while in an x-ray tube the same number of electrons move in smaller groups, but at a very high speed. For example, suppose that in the valve tube 1 trillion electrons were passing to the anode in one second; with only a 3-kV drop, each electron would move slowly but at the end of the second, 1 trillion would have reached the anode. Now consider 1 trillion electrons in an x-ray tube. Under the large kV drop, each electron moves at a very high speed, taking only a tiny fraction of a second to reach the anode, but at the end of a second, 1 trillion have reached the anode, the same number per sec as in the valve tube.

The valve tubes are placed within the oil in the transformer casing for the sake of convenience. Incidentally, this affords protection from x radiation that might be emitted in the event of valve tube failure as described above (page 240). Furthermore, this arrangement decreases the bulk of the x-ray apparatus, at the same time making the valve tube assembly shockproof.

SOLID STATE RECTIFIERS

In recent years, intensive investigation of a class of materials known as semiconductors has led to the development of an entirely different type of high voltage rectifier—the *solid state diode rectifier.* To understand its basic principles we must look into the conduction of an electric current in solids from a slightly more advanced point of view than in Chapter 6.

One of the ways in which we can classify matter is on the basis of its *conductivity,* defined as the ease with which electrons move about within it. Accordingly, there are three classes of solids: (1) *conductors* (excellent conductivity—electrons can be made to drift readily from point to point), (2) *nonconductors* or *insulators* (very poor conductivity—high resistance to movement of electrons), and (3) *semiconductors* (intermediate conductivity).

What accounts for the difference in conductivity of these three classes of matter? Energy-state diagrams come to our aid. An *energy state* is the energy of a particular electron, corresponding to its energy level in the atom. In Figure 13.17 we see the energy states that an electron may have in a single atom. Since a piece of matter is an aggregation of a fantastic number of atoms usually arranged in a crystal lattice, that is, a regular pattern, their energy levels merge into a series of *energy bands.*

Figure 13.17. Possible energy states of an electron in a single atom. The higher energy states are in the direction of the arrows.

There are three types of energy bands—*valence, forbidden,* and *conduction.* No electron can remain in the forbidden band; this band represents the energy needed to raise an electron from the valence band to the conduction band where the electron can move freely. The various bands are shown in Figure 13.18.

Figure 13.18. Energy level diagrams of three types of matter. In a conductor (A) electrons move freely from the valence band to the conduction band. In an insulator (B) there is a large energy gap between the valence and conduction bands preventing free movement of electrons. In a semiconductor (C) there is a small energy gap between the valence and conduction bands making it possible to raise electrons to the conducting band, thereby controlling resistance.

In a *metallic conductor*, shown in Figure 13.18A, the outermost or *valence* electrons are very loosely bound; in fact, the valence band actually overlaps the conduction band. Thus, an extremely weak electric field (applied emf) causes the electrons in the valence band to drift in a particular direction as an electric current. Because electrons can be made to flow in a metal with the application of so little energy, electric current in a conductor is not easily controllable (as it is in a semiconductor).

In an *insulator*, shown in Figure 13.18B, all electron-containing bands are completely filled. Since a very large energy gap exists between the valence band and the conduction band in insulators, an extremely large electric field would be needed to raise an electron to the conduction band, so that, for all practical purposes, an insulator does not conduct an electric current (we may say that it has virtually infinite resistance).

Now we come to the third class of solids—*semiconductors*. These are intermediate between conductors and insulators in their ability to conduct an electric current. In Figure 13.18C you can see that a small energy gap exists between the valence band and the conduction band. Thus, only a small amount of energy is needed in semiconductors to raise the valence electrons to the conduction band. Note that this energy gap is much smaller in semiconductors than in insulators (compare Figure 13.18B with 13.18C). Because the valence and conduction bands do not overlap in semiconductors, current flow can be regulated; for example, the addition of carefully measured amounts of certain impurities to a semiconductor modifies its conductivity. In fact, its conductivity is controllable by the kind and amount of impurity.

Of the available semiconductors, we shall limit our discussion to *silicon* (an element in ordinary sand—silicon dioxide) because it is now being used in the manufacture of solid state rectifiers for x-ray equipment.

VALENCE
ELECTRONS

SYMBOL FOR SILICON
WITH 4 VALENCE ELECTRONS

Figure 13.19. The silicon atom has four valence (outer shell) electrons as indicated by the broken lines.

Basic to an understanding of semiconductors is the rule that, in combining chemically, most atoms share their valence electrons in such a way that the outer shell of each contains eight electrons. This is known as the *octet rule.*

The silicon atom has four valence electrons (in its outermost shell) as shown in Figure 13.19. Silicon atoms aggregate into crystals by sharing these valence electrons with each other—socalled *covalent bonding*—as shown in Figure 13.20. Such bonds, in effect, saturate the outer or valence shells, thereby satisfying the octet rule and enhancing the stability of the crystal structure. Pure silicon is an example of an *intrinsic* semiconductor.

If a small amount of *arsenic* is added to silicon, it contributes to the crystal lattice an *extra* electron, not needed for bonding silicon and arsenic atoms (see Figure 13.21). This is a loosely bound electron which can easily be raised to the conduction band by a small applied electric field. Arsenic is known as a *donor* atom because it furnishes electrons. Silicon "doped" with arsenic is called *n-type silicon* (*n* stands for negative). Its conductivity can be controlled by the amount of arsenic doping—the more arsenic, the

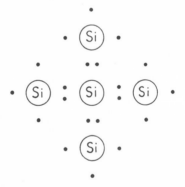

Figure 13.20. Diagram of the crystal lattice of silicon atoms which share valence electrons in pairs by means of *covalent bonds.* Each silicon atom is surrounded by four others (actually, in three dimensions). Note that the central Si atom, by electron sharing, now has an *octet*—eight valence electrons. In a real crystal there are tremendous numbers of Si atoms forming covalent bonds.

more electrons available and the greater the conductivity.

On the other hand, if *gallium* with its three valence electrons is added to the silicon as shown in Figure 13.22, there is a shortage of one electron in the crystal structure called a "*hole.*" Such a hole *behaves like a positive charge,* gallium-doped silicon being known

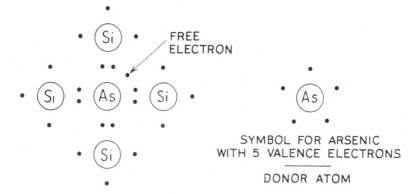

Figure 13.21. *N*-type silicon. Addition of a minute amount of arsenic with its five valence electrons introduces a free electron into the crystal. Under the influence of an applied emf, this free electron can be raised to the conduction band and made to drift through the crystal as part of an electric current.

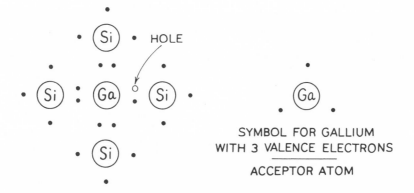

Figure 13.22. *P*-type silicon. Addition of a minute amount of gallium with its three valence electrons results in a deficit of one shared electron in the crystal lattice. An absent electron is equivalent to a positive charge, here called a "hole"; this can accept an electron.

as *p-type silicon* (*p* stands for positive). Since the hole can accept an electron, gallium is an *acceptor* atom.

How do these two types of semiconductors behave? In Figure 13.23A, representing an n-type semiconductor, electrons drift in

an applied electric field just as they do in a conductor. But in a
p-type semiconductor, shown in Figure 13.23B, an applied electric
field causes electrons to move toward holes, at the same time
leaving new holes which are then, in turn, filled by other electrons.
Thus, the holes, in effect, drift in the opposite direction from that
of the electrons as though the holes were positive charges.

Suppose, now, we were to combine n-type and p-type silicon at
a *junction* as in Figure 13.24. Some electrons from the n-type
silicon combine with holes of the p-type near the junction, leaving
positive and negative ions, respectively, as shown in the figure. A
potential difference exists between these oppositely charged ions,
called the ***barrier voltage*** or ***potential hill.***

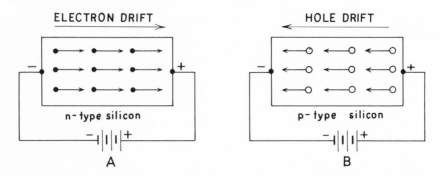

Figure 13.23. *A,* behavior on *n*-type silicon when an electric field (emf) is
applied. Free electrons are raised to the conduction band and drift through the
crystal just as in a conductor. *B,* in *p*-type silicon, electrons enter from the
negative terminal of the battery and combine with holes which may be regarded
as drifting toward the negative terminal.

Let us see how an n-p junction rectifies—that is, ***conducts current in only one direction.*** Suppose we apply an emf across this
junction in the direction shown in Figure 13.25A, with the negative terminal of the source at the n-end, and the positive terminal
at the p-end. Electrons in the n-type silicon move toward the
junction and, at the same time, holes in the p-type silicon also
move toward the junction where the electrons and holes combine.
As a result, the n-type silicon accepts electrons from the negative
terminal of the battery, while the p-type silicon passes electrons to

electrons and holes
combine at n-p junction

n-type silicon   p-type silicon

potential hill

Figure 13.24. Behavior of an *n-p* junction. When *n*-type and *p*-type silicon are brought into contact, holes and electrons combine near the junction leaving, respectively, negatively and positively charged ions. A potential "hill" (potential difference) is built up at the junction.

the positive terminal. Thus, the diode (ie, the n-p junction) continues to conduct current as long as the battery terminals are connected in the manner shown. This is called a ***forward biased diode.***

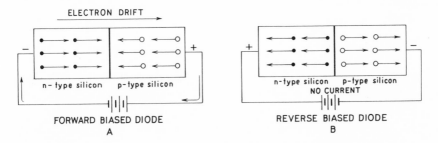

ELECTRON DRIFT

n-type silicon   p-type silicon

FORWARD BIASED DIODE
A

n-type silicon   p-type silicon
NO CURRENT

REVERSE BIASED DIODE
B

Figure 13.25. Effect of an applied electric field (emf) of an *n-p* junction. In *A*, with the negative terminal connected to the *n*-type silicon, electrons drift toward the junction where they combine with holes. The net effect is that the electrons enter the *n*-type silicon and leave the *p*-type silicon. In *B* the battery terminals have been reversed; now electrons are withdrawn at the positive end, and holes at the negative end. Both are immediately depleted and no current flows. When AC is applied, current flows only during the forward-biased half of the cycle; in other words, the *n-p* junction behaves as a *rectifier.*

Now if the battery terminals are reversed, as in Figure 13.25B, electrons leave the n-type silicon, and holes leave the p-type silicon; that is, electrons enter the latter. This causes an increase in the number of positive ions on the n-side of the junction, and an increase in the number of negative ions on the p-side of the junction, thereby increasing the barrier voltage. As a result, the barrier voltage instantaneously becomes equal and opposite to the applied voltage and no current flows across the diode. This is now a *reverse biased diode.* Thus, if an alternating current is applied to an n-p junction it undergoes rectification, being conducted across the junction only when the negative half of the AC cycle is directed from *n* to *p*. The symbol for a solid state diode rectifier is shown in Figure 13.26.

Figure 13.26. Symbol of a solid state diode rectifier.

A practical silicon rectifier for x-ray equipment consists of a stack of individual diodes, each containing an n-p junction. These diodes, called *modules,* are connected in series. The complete assembly is enclosed in a sealed ceramic tube containing an insulating liquid. Each module is capable of withstanding a maximum of 1000 volts, so that for a 150-kV generator, 150 modules are required. The rectifier stack is of the *controlled avalanche type* to minimize breakdown of individual modules. A silicon rectifier for x-ray equipment is shown in Figure 13.27.

What are the advantages of the silicon rectifier over the valve

Figure 13.27. Silicon rectifier for x-ray equipment. Various sizes are available, from about 8 to 10 inches in length.

tube? They may be listed as follows:

1. Compact size.
2. No filaments, hence no filament transformers needed for solid state rectifiers. This is especially important in three-phase equipment where twelve rectifiers are ordinarily used.
3. Low forward voltage drop—less than 300 volts at maximum current rating of 100 mA.
4. Low reverse current—0.002 mA at maximum voltage.
5. Long life due to rugged construction.

Because of these advantages, solid state rectifiers are gradually replacing valve tubes in modern radiographic units.

RECTIFIER FAILURE

The technologist should form the habit of checking for satisfactory operation of the rectifier diodes during each exposure. This can be done by simply watching the milliammeter, which indicates *average mA*. With four diode (full-wave) rectification, the *peak mA* is actually about one and one-half times the reading of the milliammeter. Whenever one rectifier diode in such a system fails, the system operates as a two-diode (half-wave) rectifier, producing a drop in the milliammeter reading to about one-half the normal value, and causing radiographic underexposure. With pushbutton selection of mA there is no compensation for half-wave rectified operation, and so the average mA drops to one-half the normal value.

The simplest device for testing the competence of any type of rectifier diode is the *spinning top*. This is a flat metal top which has a small hole punched near one edge (see Figure 13.28). It is placed on a film exposure holder containing an x-ray film, and made to spin during an x-ray exposure of one-tenth second. If all four diodes are operating, the circuit is fully rectified and there should be 120 pulses per sec with 120 corresponding peaks of x-ray output on 60-cycle current. Therefore, in one-tenth second there will be twelve peaks and the image of the spinning top on the radiograph will show twelve spots, as in Figure 13.29A. If only six dark spots appear in the radiograph of the top, as in Figure 13.29B, there were only six pulses in one-tenth second or sixty pulses per second, indicating that the circuit is half-wave rectified, provided the exposure timer is known to be operating correctly.

Figure 13.28. Diagram of a lead spinning top used to determine the integrity of the rectifiers in a full-wave rectified circuit.

As a valve tube nears the end of its useful life, sufficient evaporation of its filament has occurred to decrease electron emission. This entails an increase in resistance of the valve and an accompanying larger voltage drop ($V = IR$) across it. A lower kV now remains to operate the x-ray tube, thereby reducing x-ray output during that half cycle. Under these conditions, with full-wave (two-pulse) rectification, alternate dots show less density, as in Figure 13.29A, and complete failure of the valve tube can occur momentarily.

The spinning top may be used to test the accuracy of the x-ray exposure timer if all four rectifier diodes are known to be functioning properly, in single-phase equipment. However, with 12-pulse three-phase equipment, the image produced by a spinning top is a dark band with intermittent indistinct darker pulses that do not permit accurate evaluation of the timer. An oscilloscope should be used with such equipment, as it provides an image of the actual pulses; in a properly operating 12-pulse circuit, there will be 12 pulses in 1/60 sec.

QUESTIONS

1. Describe the main features of a thermionic diode tube.
2. Compare the structural details of radiographic, therapy, and valve tubes.

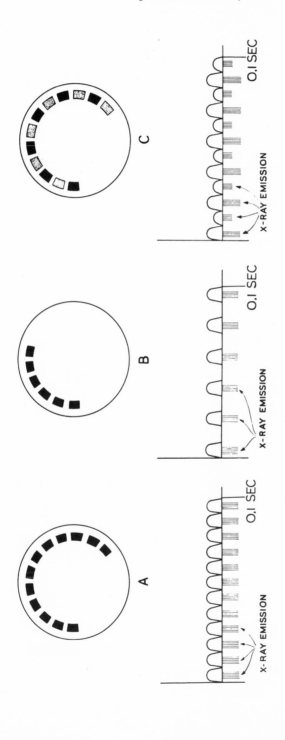

Figure 13.29. Spinning top test. In *A*, the radiograph of the spinning top shows twelve spots in 1/10 sec, representing 120 kV peaks per sec; this is full-wave single-phase rectification. In *B*, there are six spots in 1/10 sec, representing 60 kV peaks per sec; this is half-wave single-phase rectification, which may occur when one diode rectifier is completely inoperative. In *C*, one rectifier diode is malfunctioning (ie, partly operative), so there is less voltage left for the x-ray tube; therefore, every other spot appears lighter (data kindly furnished by Willis R. Preston).

3. Describe, with aid of a diagram, a double focus, stationary anode tube.
4. Explain the principle of the rotating anode tube and show its important structural features by means of a simple diagram. Enumerate its advantages over a stationary anode tube.
5. As a radiographic tube ages, what adjustment must be made in the filament current, and why?
6. What effect does evaporation of the filament have on tube operation? tube life? x-ray output?
7. Describe the line focus principle and discuss its importance in radiography. To what types of tubes does it apply?
8. Discuss saturation current.
9. How does the space charge effect influence the operation of a radiographic tube? How does a change in filament current affect space charge?
10. To what part of the tube does heat storage refer? In what units is it expressed?
11. Using the chart in Figure 13.11, determine the tube rating ("safe" exposure time) at 70 kV and 500 mA.
12. Discuss the importance of anode heat storage; anode cooling rate; housing cooling rate; anode pitting; anode evaporation.
13. Why does a radiographic tube anode have a greater heat loading capacity with full-wave rectification than with half-wave rectification?
14. Summarize the steps that should be taken to prolong tube life.
15. Compare the values of peak milliamperage and milliammeter readings in a full-wave and half-wave rectified circuit.
16. Show by a labeled diagram the construction of a vacuum diode rectifier. Why must it operate below saturation conditions?
17. Compare the current in an x-ray tube and valve tube connected in the same circuit. Compare the kV drop in each under normal conditions.
18. How are radiographic and deep therapy tubes cooled?
19. Describe the spinning top method and state its purpose. What is used instead of a spinning to check timer accuracy in twelve-pulse three-phase equipment, and why?

20. What are the main causes of x-ray tube failure? How can they be minimized?
21. What are semiconductors? How is their conductivity controlled?
22. Describe the principle of the n-p junction.
23. What intrinsic semiconductor is most often used in solid state rectifiers in medical radiography?
24. Discuss solid state rectifiers on the basis of principle and construction. List their advantages and disadvantages relative to valve tubes.
25. Prove that kV × mA = watts.
26. Show how heat units are related to energy according to equation (1).

CHAPTER *14*   *X-RAY CIRCUITS*

THE MAJOR ITEMS of an x-ray unit have been covered in some detail, but they have been discussed individually without relation to each other. There now remains the task of combining them to create a functioning x-ray machine. A number of auxiliary devices are necessary for the proper operation of x-ray equipment, and these will also be described.

Source of Electric Power

The electric power company supplies a high voltage alternating current to the *pole transformer* outside the building. The transformer, which is mounted atop a pole, is a step-down transformer. It reduces the high voltage to 120 to 240 volts, depending on the type of equipment to be served. The voltage supplied to the radiology department is called the *line voltage*.

A *three-wire system* conducts the current into the building, the two outer wires being "hot" and the middle one "grounded" (neutral), as shown in Figure 14.1. At the instant that one hot wire is 120 volts above ground, the other is 120 volts below ground, thereby producing a potential difference of 240 volts. Thus, connection to the two hot wires provides a 240-volt source, whereas connection to either hot wire and the neutral wire provides 120 volts.

Most x-ray units now operate on 240 volts, although some of the less advanced equipment, and especially the older mobile units, require only 120 volts.

Note that the current delivered to the Radiology Department is *alternating current* (AC) because it is necessary for the operation of the x-ray transformer. Under unusual circumstances when only direct current (DC) is available, it must first be converted to AC so that it can be stepped up by the transformer.

254

Figure 14.1. Three-wire system which brings electric power into the building. By connecting the electrical appliance or equipment to the appropriate wires as indicated, one may obtain 120 volts or 240 volts.

The Main X-ray Circuits

To simplify the discussion of the electrical connections of an x-ray unit, we may regard the circuit as being divided at the x-ray transformer. The part of the circuit connected to the primary coil of the transformer is the *primary* or *low voltage* circuit, whereas the part connected to the secondary coil is the *secondary* or *high voltage* circuit. This scheme is perfectly natural, since the two coils of the transformer are electrically insulated from each other, and since the profound difference in voltage in the two circuits requires separate consideration. However, some parts of the equipment are connected to both the low and high voltage sides.

1. **Primary Circuit.** Included in this portion of the circuit is all the equipment that is connected between the electrical source and the primary coil of the x-ray transformer. Each essential component will be described in proper sequence.

a. *Main Switch.* This is usually a double-blade, single-throw switch, illustrated in Figure 14.2.

b. *Fuses.* Each wire leading from the main switch is provided with a *fuse*—an insulated cylinder with a metal cap at each end, in the center of which a thin strip of metal of low melting point connects the caps. Overloading the circuit with excessive amperage causes the metal strip within the fuse to melt because of the heating effect of the current, thereby breaking the circuit. Figure 14.3 shows the construction of such a fuse and its electrical connection. Fuses protect the equipment and reduce fire hazard.

A blown fuse is easily replaced, but the underlying cause should first be ascertained and corrected.

Figure 14.2. Double-blade single-throw switch. When the switch is closed toward the left, the metal blades contact the corresponding wire and the circuit is completed to the x-ray machine.

Figure 14.3. Diagram of a fuse (left), and its connection in a circuit. When the circuit is overloaded (excessive amperage) the wire in the center of the fuse melts, breaking the circuit.

c. *Autotransformer.* Discussed in detail in Chapter 10, the auto-transformer changes the voltage supplied to the primary of the transformer, thereby providing various kilovoltages for the x-ray tube.

d. *Prereading Kilovoltmeter.* Since kV selection must be made (by means of an autotransformer) before a radiographic exposure, we must have a metering device that can indicate the desired kV. This function is served by the prereading kilovoltmeter which is an AC voltmeter connected in parallel with the autotransformer, that is, across the primary circuit between the autotransformer and the transformer (see Figure 14.12). How, then, is it possible for a voltmeter in the primary circuit to indicate kV across the secondary circuit? The answer lies in the calibration (standardization) of the prereading kilovoltmeter in the primary circuit by the manufacturer, against actual peak kV values in the secondary circuit by means of spark gap measurements. These depend on the fact that a given kV will cause a spark to jump between two metal spheres separated by a particular distance or *air gap* (at standard temperature, atmospheric pressure, and relative humidity). The kilovoltages obtained by such spark gap measurements are recorded directly on the scale of the prereading kilovoltmeter for each corresponding autotransformer setting. In other words, the prereading kilovoltmeter, since it is in the primary circuit, does not measure kV directly, but rather indicates what the kV will be in the secondary circuit because it has been initially calibrated to do so at the factory. The main advantage of the prereading kilovoltmeter is that *slow* fluctuations in line voltage can easily be corrected. If, for instance, the line voltage should drop, the autotransformer controls are adjusted manually until the correct kV shows on the prereading kilovoltmeter.

Some types of x-ray equipment do not employ a prereading kilovoltmeter. Instead, the desired kV is obtained by means of kV-labeled *pushbuttons* which select the appropriate transformer settings. The calibration of these settings is similar to that of a prereading kilovoltmeter. But these fixed pushbutton settings indicate kV accurately only if the line voltage is the same as it was during the actual calibration. Since the line voltage may fluctuate slowly, depending on the other electrical equipment in use, a means of detecting such fluctuation is provided by a *compensator voltmeter* connected in parallel across a portion of the primary side of the autotransformer. A mark on the compensator voltmeter scale indicates the correct line voltage. If the pointer is above or below this mark on the meter, a *line voltage compensator* permits adjustment of the line voltage to the correct value. The compensator varies the number of turns on the primary side of the autotransformer until the compensator meter needle indicates that the correct line voltage has been restored; only then will the correct kV be obtained.

e. *Timer and X-ray Exposure Switches.* These switches control the current to the primary coil of the transformer, serving to complete the x-ray exposure. The switches themselves are modifications of an ordinary pushbutton, as shown in Figure 14.4, and can be used for either hand or foot operation. But these are not designed to withstand the high amperage in the primary circuit (as high as 90A with a 200 mA unit), or to prevent electrical shock. Therefore, these switches operate a *remote control switch,* which in turn closes the primary circuit.

Figure 14.4. Pushbutton switch. Depressing the button brings the metal contactors together, thereby closing the circuit.

f. *Remote Control Switch.* Operated by either hand or foot switch, its basic design can best be appreciated by studying Figure 14.5.

g. *Timer.* Included in the exposure switch circuit is a timer which can be set to start and stop an exposure of preselected duration. There are six main types of manual exposure timers. They include (1) *synchronous timer,* (2) *motor-driven impulse timer,* (3) *simple electronic timer,* (4) *electronic timer (modern type),* (5) *milliampere-second timer,* and (6) *phototimer.*

(1) *Synchronous Timer*—consists of a small synchronous motor rotating at a fixed speed that depends on the AC frequency, but turning a disc at a slower speed through a system of reduction gears. The disc operates "make" and "break" contacts—the farther the disc is set to rotate, the longer the time between the closing and opening of the timer circuit and, hence, the longer the exposure. Synchronous timers are reasonably accurate for exposures of 1/20 to 20 sec, but have been replaced by timers permitting shorter exposures to a high degree of precision.

Figure 14.5. Remote control switch. The pushbutton, *P*, when depressed, completes the circuit through the coil of the remote control switch. This magnetizes the core, *C*, which attracts the metal button, *B*, on the insulated bar. This closes the primary circuit by bringing together the contacts at *S*. When the pushbutton is released, the reverse occurs, breaking the circuit.

(2) ***Motor-driven Impulse Timer***—also activated by a synchronous motor, but operates at a higher speed to provide exposures of $1/120$ or $1/60$ sec to $1/5$ sec. It is so designed that the contactors open and close the timing circuit at or very near a zero point of the AC cycle, so that it actually measures the time in impulses; hence its great accuracy.

(3) ***Electronic Timer (Simple Type)***—provides a range of $1/30$ to 20 sec in less advanced equipment. However, it opens and closes the timing circuit within one-fourth cycle from the zero point. While sufficiently precise for exposures longer than $1/10$ sec, it introduces an unpredictable and significant error in exposures of $1/20$ sec or less. Virtually obsolete, it is mentioned only because of its use in old-style radiographic units.

(4) ***Electronic Timer (Modern Type)***—provides extremely accurate exposures down to 1 millisecond ($1/1000$ sec). Its circuitry, shown in Figure 14.6, consists essentially of a rheostat (variable resistor), a capacitor, and a ***thyratron*** which is a special gas-filled triode that becomes conductive at a particular, critical voltage. When the x-ray exposure switch is closed, switch *S* is simultaneously opened, allowing current to build up a charge on the capacitor. When the capacitor charge reaches a critical value, discharge suddenly occurs through the thyratron, activating the exposure-terminating switch and thereby ending the exposure. The time required to build up the necessary charge on the capacitor governs

the time of the x-ray exposure; it depends on the product RC (resistance × capacitance) and can be varied by adjusting the resistance of the circuit by means of the rheostat. The capacitance C remains constant in this particular circuit. In six-pulse and twelve-pulse three-phase equipment the thyratron, and the electromagnetic relay with its mechanical contactor, are replaced by a *thyristor,* which is a solid state device that functions like a thyratron but can provide much shorter and more accurate exposures. These may be as short as 1 millisecond with a 1-millisecond delay (1 millisec = $1/1000$ sec) between activation of the exposure switch and the actual start of the exposure.

Figure 14.6. Simplified circuitry of an electronic timer. When switch S is closed, charge cannot build up on the capacitor. Activation of the exposure switch (in another part of the circuit) starts the exposure and opens switch S, allowing a charge to build up on the capacitor. When this reaches a preset value, the capacitor suddenly discharges through the thyratron tube, activating the exposure termination switch. This may be either an electromagnetic switch, as shown, or a *thyristor,* a solid state device functioning like a thyratron but allowing exposures as short as 1 millisec, with a 1-millisec delay. The time for buildup of capacitor charge depends on RC, which is the product of resistance by capacitance. Since C is constant, we select the exposure time by adjusting R by means of a rheostat.

(5) *Automatic Exposure Control*—includes a phototimer circuit. With this system, originated by Morgan and Hodges, a film is exposed to the x-ray beam and as soon as it has received the correct amount of radiation for the desired degree of film darkening (density), the exposure terminates automatically. This requires a

special type of diode known as a ***phototube;*** its cathode is coated with an alkali metal such as potassium or cesium, which has the peculiar property of ***giving off electrons when struck by light.*** If the anode of the phototube has, in the meanwhile, been given a positive charge from an outside source, the electrons emitted by the cathode are attracted to the anode, constituting a current in the phototube. By placing a fluorescent screen between the photo-tube and the x-ray source, we can make the phototube indirectly sensitive to x-rays, the brightness of the screen depending on the intensity of the x radiation. As shown in Figure 14.7, the phototube-fluorescent screen combination is placed behind the cassette whose back is radiotransparent (x-ray transmitting). When a predetermined quantity of radiation has reached the fluorescent screen, depending on the part being radiographed, the resulting current in the photo-tube operates a capacitor, thyratron, and relay circuit which acti-vates a contactor to terminate the exposure. Automatic exposure control (see Figure 14.7) makes possible extremely accurate reproduction of radiographic density, provided the anatomic part is carefully centered. The most useful application of automatic exposure control is in spotfilm and chest radiography, and in photofluorography, although it is also available now for general radiography.

h. ***Backup Timer and Minimum Exposure Time.*** Modern equip-ment designed for automatic (phototimed) exposure control has a special manual backup timer that is set to terminate the exposure in the event of failure in the automatic circuit, to eliminate the danger of overloading the tube or overexposing the patient. Accord-ing to Department of Health, Education, and Welfare (HEW) regulations, which must be observed by all manufacturers: (1) no phototimed exposure shall exceed the tube limit (ie, tube anode rating), and (2) a maximum phototimed exposure shall not exceed 800 mAs. In more advanced radiographic equipment with pushbut-ton selection of the anatomic part, the backup timer is set auto-matically for each selection by internal circuitry but HEW regulations still apply as above.

A manual ***backup timer*** is set for a specific time, usually about 0.5 sec. As an example, if the exposure called for 140 mAs at a 200 mA setting, the time would be 140 mAs/200 mA = 0.7 sec,

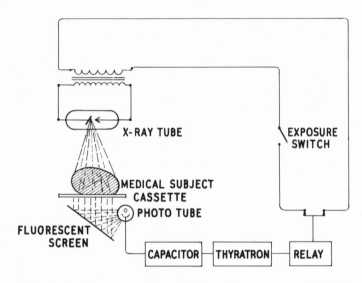

Figure 14.7. Automatic exposure control. When the exposure switch is closed, x rays passing through the patient and reaching the fluorescent screen of the phototimer assembly cause the screen to emit light which activates the phototube. Current then flows in the phototube and charges the capacitor while the exposure is in progress. When the predetermined voltage is built up on the capacitor, the thyratron becomes conductive, activating the relay which opens the exposure circuit and terminates the exposure even while the manual exposure switch is still closed.

and the exposure would would be terminated at 0.5 sec by the backup timer. Thus, the film would be underexposed.

Radiographic equipment timer circuits have a ***minimum exposure time,*** which varies with the type of equipment, ranging from about 0.05 sec (50 millisec) in older equipment, to 0.005 sec (5 millisec) in later models. (With the introduction of thyristors, minimum exposure times will be in fractions of milliseconds.) For example, with a equipment having a 0.05 sec minimum exposure time, if the exposure required 2 mAs at 200 mA, the time would be 2 mAs/200 mA = 0.01 sec. Since this is less than the minimum exposure time (0.05 sec), the exposure would terminate at 0.05 sec and the film would be overexposed. But if the exposure required 12 mAs, the time would be 12 mAs/200 mA = 0.06 sec; as this is longer than the minimum exposure time (0.05 sec), the exposure time would terminate correctly after a total of 0.06 sec.

i. *Circuit Breaker.* Additional protection against overloading the circuit is provided by a circuit breaker which can easily be reset, while a blown fuse has to be replaced. It is usually connected in series with the exposure switch, timer, and remote control switch. Figure 14.8 illustrates schematically the operation of a magnetic circuit breaker, shown in the exposure circuit, 2. When the exposure switch is closed, circuit 2 is completed through the timer, the electromagnet of the remote control switch, and the circuit breaker contacts which are in the closed position. This activates the electromagnet of the remote control switch closing the primary circuit, 1, that leads to the primary side of the x-ray transformer. If there should be a momentary surge in the primary current, this will, through circuit 3, increase the strength of the electromagnet in the circuit breaker to the point where it will open circuit 2, thereby interrupting the current to the electromagnet of the remote control switch, opening the remote control switch, and breaking the primary circuit, 1. The circuit breaker must then be reset manually before another exposure can be made.

Figure 14.8. Magnetic circuit breaker together with the magnetic remote control switch, as they are connected in the primary circuit.

j. *Filament Circuit of X-ray Tube.* The primary circuit supplies the *heating* current for the filament of the x-ray tube, but this current must first be reduced to 3 to 5 amp and 6 to 12 volts by a *rheostat* (variable resistor); in accordance with Ohm's law, the greater the resistance, the smaller the current (amp). Most radiographic units are equipped with *pushbutton type* mA selectors which also choose the desired focal spot size. The pushbuttons operate through individual preset resistors which provide the correct filament current for each tube current, such as 100, 200, and 500 mA. Another type of filament current regulator is an electromagnetic device called a *saturable reactor* (see page 140). In series with this is an *oil immersed step-down transformer,* which further reduces the voltage to the required value, as shown in Figure 14.9. Because this *filament transformer* has its secondary coil in the high voltage circuit and its primary coil in the low voltage circuit of the x-ray unit, it must be oil immersed to provide sufficient insulation between these two circuits.

Figure 14.9. Filament circuit. The rheostat varies the filament current (and voltage), thereby controlling filament temperature, electron emission, and tube current (mA). Thus, it is an *mA selector.* A saturable reactor is being used instead of the rheostat in advanced design equipment. The step-down transformer further helps reduce the voltage and also insulates the primary circuit from the high voltage in the secondary circuit.

There is often included in the filament circuit a *filament stabilizer* for the x-ray tube because a relatively small change in the filament voltage or current causes a large change in electron

V:JR Q:J'R

emission and consequent tube current (mA). The filament stabilizer corrects for instantaneous fluctuations in line voltage that may be caused by momentary demand elsewhere on the line, such as in the starting of an elevator or air conditioner. It may be so effective that a variation in line voltage of 10 percent will cause no greater change than $1/2$ percent in the filament voltage. The stabilizer consists of a capacitor and a small, modified split transformer which are so arranged that they compensate for a rise or fall in line voltage and provide a more uniform filament voltage, maintaining the filament current more nearly constant.

k. *Filament Ammeter.* In order to measure the filament current, and hence the amount of heat developed in the filament, an ammeter is connected in series in the *filament circuit* of old style equipment. By previous calibration, we can establish the readings of this meter that correspond to desired mA in the x-ray tube at a given kV. In modern radiographic units a *space charge compensator* automatically adjusts the filament current to maintain constant mA over a wide range of kV; furthermore, pushbutton selection of mA automatically provides the correct filament current for the desired tube current.

l. *Primary Coil of X-ray Transformer.* Although the high voltage transformer operates as a unit, we may regard its primary winding (coil) as a component of the primary circuit. Both the primary and the secondary coils are immersed in special transformer oil for added insulation.

In general, the wires in the primary circuit must be relatively large, because of the high amperage. Circuit breakers and fuses should be conveniently located for easy resetting or replacement.

2. **Secondary Circuit.** This includes the secondary coil of the transformer and all devices to which it is connected electrically. The wire conductors in the secondary circuit have a smaller diameter (than those in the primary circuit) because they carry a smaller current (mA).

a. *Secondary Coil of X-ray Transformer.* As we have indicated earlier, this consists of many turns of electrically insulated wire that is thinner than the wire in the primary coil because of the very small current in the secondary circuit. The transformer *steps up* the primary voltage to provide the high voltage required to operate the x-ray tube, the step-up ratio being about 500:1.

b. *Milliammeter.* In order to measure the mA in the x-ray tube, a *milliammeter* is connected in series in the high voltage circuit. Since the milliammeter is grounded together with the midpoint of the secondary coil of the x-ray transformer, it is at zero potential and can therefore be safely mounted in the control panel without hazard to personnel.

Attention must be called to the fact that the *tube current is measured in milliamperes by the milliammeter placed in the high voltage circuit, while the filament current is measured by an ammeter placed in the low voltage filament circuit.* The milliammeter measures average values and gives no indication of the peak values of tube current.

c. *Milliampere-second or mAs Meter.* It is desirable to have in series with a regular ammeter, a mAs meter. Due to the large mass of the rotating mechanism, it turns slowly so that the attached indicator needle registers the product of mA and time, that is, it indicates *milliampere-seconds* (mAs). This device is needed because the ordinary milliammeter does not have time to register the true mA at exposures of less than 1/10 sec. The ballistic meter therefore serves to measure mA at very short exposure times; and because of its great sensitivity, it must be used in conjunction with an impulse timer or an electronic timer. At exposure times longer than 1/10 sec, the ordinary milliammeter will register the correct average mA.

d. *Rectifier.* In all but self-rectified units, a system of rectification is included to change AC, supplied by the transformer, to DC. As we have already noted, rectification increases the heating capacity of the x-ray tube, safely permitting larger exposures.

e. *Cables.* These conduct the high voltage current from the rectifier to the x-ray tube. The *midpoint of the secondary coil of the transformer is grounded.* However, the total kV across the ends of the transformer secondary remains unchanged because one-half is below, and the other half above, ground potential (see Figure 14.10). For example, if there is 90 kV across the transformer and the center is not grounded, the kV will fluctuate between 90 kV above ground and 90 kV below ground according to the AC sine wave. If the center of the secondary coil is grounded, the peak kV

will still be 90, but in this case one-half or 45 kV will be above
ground and one-half will be 45 kV below. The difference between
45 above zero and 45 below zero is still 90. Under these conditions
each cable has to be insulated for only 45 kV (rather than 90 kV),
representing a significant saving in weight and cost.

Figure 14.10. In *A* the transformer secondary has been grounded at its midpoint.
With the upper end of the secondary coil positive, and the lower end negative,
final kV = *45 kV* − (−*45 kV*) = *90 kV.* Each cable needs insulation for only 45
kV above or below ground. A similar situation prevails when the polarity of the
secondary reverses in the next half cycle (values in parenthesis).

In *B* the secondary has not been grounded at its midpoint. Total secondary
voltage is again 90 kV, but it now represents the difference between 90 kV at one
end of the secondary, and 0 at the other end. Each cable must therefore be
insulated for the full 90 kV above or below ground.

The cables are designed to eliminate the danger of shock,
provided the insulation remains intact. Ordinarily, very heavy
insulation would be required to prevent the high voltage from
sparking over to the patient or other objects near the cable.
However, the grounded woven wire sheath surrounding the cable
obviates the danger of sparkover. Figure 14.11 shows a shockproof
cable in cross section with its standard three conductors. The same
type of cable is used for both terminals of the x-ray tube. When the
cathode cable is connected to the cathode end of a double-focus

x-ray tube, all three conductors make contact with the two fila-ments (see Figure 13.3). The other end of this cable makes contact with both the filament circuit and one end of the transformer secondary. When the ***anode*** cable is connected to the anode, connection is made with only one of the conductors within the cable. At the other end of the cable, the three conductors join a single conductor which connects with the opposite end of the transformer secondary. Thus, the three conductors in the anode cable serve as a single conductor, which is all that is needed for the anode.

Figure 14.11. Cross section of a shockproof cable.

f. ***X-ray Tube.*** The ultimate goal of the x-ray equipment is the operation of an x-ray tube, the last piece of equipment connected in the high voltage circuit.

Completed Wiring Diagram

In order to visualize clearly the relationship of the various parts of the x-ray unit, we must connect them correctly in the circuit. Figure 14.12 presents schematically a full-wave rectified x-ray unit employing four rectifier diodes (these may be valve tubes or solid state diodes). Most of the auxiliary items, though desirable or even necessary for proper operation, have been purposely omitted to avoid complicating the diagram. The hook-up of these accessory devices has been indicated in the preceding sections. We can readily modify this basic diagram; thus, for self-rectification we simply omit the rectifier and connect the transformer to the tube terminals.

X-ray Control Panel

An x-ray machine requires not only suitable control devices for easy selection of kV, mA, and time, but also readily accessible meters to check the operation of the equipment. The controls and meters are mounted compactly in a *control panel*—a separate unit which is connected electrically to the x-ray equipment and is comparable in function to the dashboard of an automobile.

X-ray control panels vary greatly in complexity, depending on the design of the individual x-ray machine. If we realize that all control panels, regardless of their intricacy, are similar in their basic design, the problem of operating unfamiliar equipment becomes a relatively simple matter. The more complicated units are variations of the basic pattern.

In Figure 14.13 is shown a simple, nonautomatic control panel comprising all the essential items; familiarity with this diagram will make it much easier to understand the operation of the more complex types of equipment. The three meters shown in the figure include the milliammeter, filament ammeter, and kilovoltmeter. The milliammeter registers, in mA, the current in the secondary circuit, including the x-ray tube.

A filament ammeter indicates filament (heating) current, which ultimately determines mA. Turning the control knob in the lower left hand corner of the diagram, labeled "filament control," varies the filament current. This control actually operates a rheostat in the filament circuit to vary resistance.

A kilovoltmeter does not actually measure kV directly, but is connected across the primary circuit and therefore measures volts. However, these readings have been calibrated beforehand against known tube kilovoltages and the meter scale has been marked accordingly in kV (see pages 256–257). A kilovoltmeter serves also as a compensating voltmeter because any drop in the line voltage produces a lower kV reading on the meter. The technologist can adjust this manually by turning the "major" and "minor" kV

Figure 14.12. Simplified wiring of a single phase x-ray unit, with full-wave four-valve tube rectification. Note that the filament circuits of the valve tubes have been deliberately omitted to avoid complicating the diagram.

Figure 14.13. The essential components of a primitive x-ray control panel. The filament control knob regulates the rheostat in the filament circuit, varying the filament current and consequently controlling the tube current (mA). The filament ammeter measures the current in the filament circuit. The kV control operates the autotransformer in steps of 10 kV (major) and 1 kV (minor). Actually, the autotransformer varies the primary voltage which is registered on the prereading kilovoltmeter in "kilovolts." The milliammeter indicates the average tube current in mA.

controls which operate the autotransformer, a device that varies the voltage input to the primary of the x-ray transformer. The major control varies the kV in steps of ten, while the minor varies it in steps of one.

An important modification of this basic plan is found in the type of control panel in which the kilovoltmeter is replaced either by *kilovoltage selector* control knobs or *pushbuttons* operating through the autotransformer to provide a range of kV. The appropriate kV settings have been arrived at by previous calibration at the factory. In other words, when the settings read "56," it means that if the kV were actually measured it would be 56 kV, provided the line voltage corresponds to that at the time of original calibration. With this system a line voltage meter and a line voltage compensator must be included to correct for variations in line voltage.

Modern radiographic equipment includes a ***milliamperage selector.*** Instead of a filament control knob, there is an array of pushbuttons which activate the proper resistor to obtain the correct filament current for the desired mA. The pushbuttons also select the focal spot. For example, the pushbutton setting for large focal spot and 200 mA should automatically activate the large focal spot and deliver a tube current of 200 mA.

The timer, indicated in the lower righthand corner of the diagram, controls the duration of the x-ray exposure which is initiated by the pushbutton x-ray switch. In addition, there is a main switch; when this is in the "on" position, the primary voltage is applied to the autotransformer, and also to the kilovoltmeter which is connected in parallel across the primary circuit. At the same time, the current also flows through the ***filament only*** of the x-ray tube and registers on the filament ammeter. Thus, ***when the main switch is closed, only the filament ammeter and the kilovoltmeter should normally be activated.*** Then, when the x-ray switch is closed, the primary voltage applied to the primary side of the x-ray transformer is stepped up by the transformer, and current finally passes through the x-ray tube as indicated on the milliammeter. Thus, ***the milliammeter does not register until the x-ray switch is closed.***

The construction and operation of the circuit breaker have already been discussed.

Most diagnostic equipment is supplied with a special radiographic-fluoroscopic ***changeover switch,*** enabling the radiologist to do spotfilm work automatically. Shifting the spotfilm device into the radiographic position activates the ***changeover switch*** and automatically selects the exposure factors for radiography. When the spotfilm is withdrawn from the radiographic position, the exposure factors automatically return to fluoroscopy. Phototiming is essential for timing spotfilm exposures.

You will find it advantageous to correlate the sections on the various items of x-ray equipment with the operation of the basic control panel, thereby developing a much clearer concept of the function of the various parts.

THREE-PHASE GENERATION OF X-RAYS

Available for a number of years in Europe, three-phase generators are being installed in the United States in ever increasing numbers. This trend has paralleled the growth of angiography with its need of large tube currents and very short exposure times.

The circuitry of three-phase equipment is necessarily more complex than that of single-phase. At present, there are three main types of three-phase circuits: six-pulse-six-rectifier, six-pulse-twelve-rectifier, and twelve-pulse-twelve-rectifier. All use *solid state diode rectifiers.*

A three-phase generator operates on three-phase current, which consists of three single-phase currents out of step with each other by one-third cycle or 120° (see Figure 14.14). Therefore, the transformer primary and secondary coils must each have three windings. These are arranged in either a *delta* or a *star* configuration (see Figure 14.15). Three-phase circuits all have delta-wound primary coils, but differ in the form of the secondary windings. In Figure 14.16 is shown a wiring diagram of a twelve-pulse-twelve-rectifier generator having a balanced circuit.

With three-phase equipment, three autotransformers are needed for kV selection, one for each phase. Furthermore, because of its nearly constant value, the high voltage circuit cannot be closed and opened at or near zero potential as in the conventional single-phase unit. This introduces the danger of power surge which can damage the equipment. Therefore, special thyratron timer circuits have been designed to make the contactors open and close sequentially instead of simultaneously. Power surge is further suppressed by the solid state rectifiers themselves. In more modern equipment thyratrons and mechanical contactors have been replaced by solid state *thyristors* to improve further the accuracy of exposure timers (see pages 259-260).

At present, three-phase generators are available with ratings up to 1600 mA at 150 kV and with exposure times as short as 1 millisec (1/1000 sec). Furthermore, as shown in Figure 14.17, the voltage is the resultant of three out-of-phase single-phase voltages and never reaches zero. In fact, the voltage shows a small fluctuation or *ripple* and may be regarded as nearly *constant potential.*

Figure 14.14. Voltage curves for three-phase power supply. In the upper diagram, phase *1* lags phase *2* by 120°, and phase *2* lags phase *3* by 120°. In the lower diagram the three-phase current has been rectified to give six pulses in 1/60 sec, with a 13 percent variation in voltage, or *ripple*. Special circuitry (not shown) provides twelve pulses in 1/60 sec with a ripple of only 3 percent, giving virtually constant potential.

Figure 14.15. Types of windings used in transformers for three-phase equipment.

Although the effective kV at the transformer is about 95 percent with a 12-pulse, and 87 percent with a 6-pulse generator, the effective kV during operation is actually 95 percent with either generator because of the voltage-smoothing effect of the capacitance in the high tension cables. The resulting ripple is about 3 to 5 percent in both instances, contrasted with about 70 percent in single-phase full-wave rectification.

Figure 14.16. Simplified wiring diagram of a twelve-pulse-twelve-rectifier generator in a balanced circuit. Note the delta winding of the transformer primary, and the delta and star windings of the secondaries.

Comparison of radiographic technics with the two systems shows that with the same mAs, 85 kV three-phase is equivalent to 100 kV single-phase generated x rays. On the other hand, if one uses 100 kV with both types of equipment, the mAs for three-phase will be about 0.4 that of single-phase for equal radiographic density. However, in this case the contrast will be less with the three-phase generator because of the greater half-value layer of the x-ray beam. When technics are adjusted to obtain the same density and contrast, the ***radiation exposure of the patient is the same with both types of equipment.*** Hence, from the standpoints of radiographic quality and patient exposure, there is no appreciable improvement with the three-phase generator.

Probably the single most important advantage of the three-

Figure 14.17. Rectified voltage curve with three-phase twelve-pulse x-ray generator. The voltage remains nearly constant throughout the alternating current cycle, the slight variation being called *ripple;* in this case, ripple is 3.5 percent. Note the twelve peaks or pulses per cycle of $1/60$ sec.

phase system is the higher tube rating at ***very short exposures*** allowing the use of very high mA with exposure times as short as one millisecond. Figure 14.18 shows tube rating curves comparing the maximum mA that can be used with three-phase and single-phase equipment at various exposure times (Dynamax® "61" tube, 1 mm focus, 100 kV). Note that at $1/120$ sec the maximum ratings are 1000 mA with three-phase, and 860 mA with single-phase. On the other hand, at five seconds the situation is reversed; now the maximum ratings are 190 mA with three-phase, and 230 mA with single-phase. The reason for this is that with very short exposures, heating occurs mainly at the anode surface and is readily dissipated. But with long exposures with three-phase equipment the large power input heats the anode to a greater depth and thereby decreases tube rating.

Because of the complex circuitry of three-phase equipment, changeover from fluoroscopy to spotfilm radiography is slow — 1.5 to 2 sec. This can be overcome by introducing a device known as a Q stator into the circuit; it reduces changeover time to 0.5 sec.

In summary, then, the advantages of the three-phase generation of x rays are as follows:

1. High mA at very short exposures, especially useful in angiography, spotfilm radiography, and tomography.
2. Nearly constant potential characteristics.
3. Higher effective kV.

Figure 14.18. Comparison of tube rating curves with typical single-phase and three-phase x-ray generators. Note the higher rating with three-phase for short exposures, and the slightly higher rating with single phase for long exposures.

SPECIAL MOBILE X-RAY EQUIPMENT

Battery Powered Mobile X-ray Units

Ordinary mobile x-ray units, operating on 120 or 240 volts, require heavy cables to avoid excessive voltage drop, especially with long cables. Furthermore, in the event of a power blackout such equipment may be useless.

Self-contained mobile apparatus powered by storage batteries eliminates the need of an external power supply except to recharge the batteries. Depending on the particular model, these batteries may be either of the wet cell or the nickel-cadmium type.

One type of heavy-duty mobile unit* operating on a recharge-

---

*General Electric CMX-110 Cordless Mobile X-ray Unit.®

able nickel-cadmium battery pack provides a reasonably high mA for a rotating anode tube with 1 and 2 mm focal spots. If the rotor does not run for more than ten seconds, exposures totaling *10,000 mAs* are obtainable at 100 kV! Output is at virtually constant potential. Furthermore, x-ray exposures range from 1.0 to 300 mAs in 24 steps. Since the tube current is fixed at 100 mA, a separate timer is unnecessary, the exposure time being obtained by simply dividing the mAs by 100 mA. Thus, exposure times range from 0.01 sec at 1 mAs, to 3 sec at 300 mAs.

Maximum tube ratings are as follows:

kV	mAs
110	200
100	250
50–90	300

In operation, the battery direct current is converted to high frequency alternating current, and the voltage is stepped up by a transformer and rectified by four silicon rectifiers. A meter indicates battery condition at any instant. Recharging the battery requires an ordinary 105 to 125 volt, 50 to 60 cycle, 5 amp current, and stops automatically when the battery pack is completely recharged.

Capacitor (Condenser)-Discharge Mobile X-ray Units

One of the early methods of generating x rays utilized the principle of storing a quantity of electric charge in a capacitor (condenser) and then discharging it through an x-ray tube. At this point review the capacitor on pages 84–85. For our present purpose, we may say that the *capacitor stores mAs.* (Note that mA is a measure of charge per sec, so mA times sec should represent charge.) Although capacitor discharge mobile apparatus is no longer widely used, its basic features should be of general interest.

The voltage and charge on a capacitor are related by the following equation:

$$Q = CV \qquad (1)$$

where Q = charge in coulombs

V = potential in volts

C = capacitance in farads (constant for a particular capacitor)

By selection of appropriate units, equation (1) is readily adapted to x-ray equipment; thus, with a capacitance of 1 microfarad (μF),

$$mAs = \mu F \times kV$$

In other words, if the capacitor is designed to have a capacitance of 1 μF, then 1 kV of potential is acquired for every mAs quantity of electric charge stored in the capacitor. For example, at a potential of 75 kV, it will have a charge of 75 mAs, so a total of 75 mAs will be available to the x-ray tube. To charge the capacitor in ten seconds requires only 75 mA/10 sec = 7.5 mA, a small current, indeed.

The time it takes a ***capacitor*** to discharge to 37 percent of its initial charge is called the ***time constant***, τ (Greek letter, *tau*), which is determined by the equation

$$\tau = RC \tag{2}$$

where R and C are the resistance and capacitance of the circuit, respectively. By selecting the proper capacitance for a particular circuit we have a means of controlling the discharge time.

In practice, we should avoid too great a drop in kV during exposure, a situation that would exist if the capacitor were allowed to discharge completely. Instead, some type of interval timer must be used to control the duration of the exposure. The term ***wave-tail cut-off*** refers to the process of stopping the discharge of the capacitor at some preselected point on the discharge curve (see Figure 14.19). The first portion of the diagram shows the charging curve as the capacitor is charged to a desired peak kV, V_τ, in time, T_p. At *time* T_0 the exposure is initiated and the capacitor discharges along the discharging curve which, in this case, is cut off at time T_r. The tube current decreases along a similar curve. Wave-tail cutoff is represented by the dotted portion of the discharging curve.

If we were to start with 100 kV and a tube current of 500 mA, and used 30 mAs for an exposure, the exposure time, t, would be obtained from

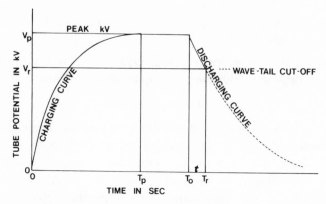

Figure 14.19. Charging and discharging characteristics of a capacitor discharge radiographic unit. V_p is peak kV; V_r is residual kV after capacitors have discharged during exposure time $(T_r - T_o)$; and T_p is time required to charge capacitors to peak kV.

$$mAt = mAs \tag{3}$$
$$500t = 30$$
$$t = 30/500 = 0.06 \text{ sec}$$

During this exposure time the tube potential will have dropped from 100 kV to 70 kV (a loss of 30 kV accompanying a loss of charge of 30 mAs), when the total capacitance is 1 μF.

How do we start and stop the discharge of the capacitors, thereby activating and deactivating the x-ray tube? This requires a **grid-controlled x-ray tube** (see Figure 14.20). An ordinary x-ray tube is a diode, having two electrodes. On the other hand, a grid-controlled tube has a third electrode or **grid,** making this type of tube a **triode.** The grid consists of several crisscrossed wires bridging the cathode's focusing cup which is completely insulated from the filament. When a relatively small negative potential is placed on the grid, it prevents electrons from passing to the anode. The negative potential on the grid is called **grid bias.** A grid bias of −2 kV with the equipment under discussion will prevent the capacitors from discharging through the x-ray tube; thus, the grid bias functions as a switch that interrupts the circuit through the tube. When the exposure switch is activated, grid bias is instantaneously reduced to almost zero, permitting the applied kV to drive the space charge electrons to the anode as in an ordinary diode x-ray tube. When the preselected mAs value has been reached in the exposure (determined either by an mAs control device or a phototimer) a grid bias of −2 kV is automatically applied and wave-tail cutoff achieved, thereby stopping the exposure.

Figure 14.20. Simplified diagram of a grid-controlled x-ray tube. Exposure is started by removing the negative charge on the grid (nearly to zero); it is stopped by restoring a negative charge to the grid.

Figure 14.21 shows a simple block diagram of a capacitor-discharge unit. For those who may be interested in greater detail, Figure 14.22 contains a wiring diagram of such equipment. As shown, one capacitor is charged during each half cycle of the alternating current to one-half the desired kV. The two capacitors in series discharge almost continuously through the tube during exposure, with a relatively small ripple in kV. Note the summation of the kV of the two capacitors in series.

Figure 14.21. Block diagram of a capacitor discharge radiographic unit.

In actual radiography with capacitor discharge apparatus, after the main switch is turned on, the line voltage is adjusted and the kV selected. Next, the capacitors are charged by depressing the

Figure 14.22. Simplified wiring diagram of a capacitor discharge radiographic unit. *A* is autotransformer. *H.V.* is high voltage transformer. *S* is solid state diode (rectifier). C_1 and C_2 are capacitors.

charger button. When the preselected kV has been acquired by the capacitors, charging automatically stops. The mAs is selected by another control, although this step is omitted with phototiming (optional). Finally, the exposure button is activated, causing the capacitors to discharge through the x-ray tube.

Note that after completion of the exposure, kV may not return immediately to zero because of a residual charge on the capacitors. Because of electric shock hazard the high voltage cables cannot be disconnected while any charge remains. Another warning should be sounded here—if a charge remains on the capacitors, leakage may cause generation of x rays without activation of the exposure switch.

Some Advantages of Newer Mobile Type Apparatus

Unlike ordinary mobile x-ray units, battery-powered equipment is not subject to troublesome line voltage fluctuations. Another advantage is their constant potential output. Radiographs are equivalent in quality to those produced at high kV; for example, 85 kV at constant potential is equivalent to about 100 kV with conventional full wave rectification.

The decision as to which type of mobile equipment to purchase depends on several factors, such as use, cost, and availability of service, just as in the case of other equipment.

Field Emission X-Ray Equipment*

Electronics deals mainly with the behavior and use of orbital electrons that have been given off by metals. However, such electron emission is ordinarily prevented by an electric *potential barrier* or *hill,* acting as a sort of electric fence, present on the surface of the metal. Thus, electrons can be emitted only when given sufficient energy — for example, 4.5 eV for tungsten — to penetrate the potential barrier.

We learned earlier that liberating energy can be imparted to orbital electrons in three ways: (1) *heat* — thermionic emission as in an ordinary x-ray tube, (2) *light* — photoelectric emission as in a photocell, and (3) *bombardment with other radiation* such as electrons, other particles, x rays, and gamma rays.

The field emission principle is still another way of bringing about electron emission. This requires the application of very strong electric fields; that is, high voltage, great enough to make electrons leave the surface of a *cold* metal (Schottky effect). For a particular metallic element, the probability of an electron's escaping the potential barrier depends very strongly on the applied field or voltage. For example, an increase in field strength of only 1 percent causes a 10 percent increase in current density (amp per sq cm of emitter surface).

In general, the emitted electrons have nearly uniform energy, for only electrons at the highest energy level (ie, valence electrons) in the emitter atoms are likely to escape the potential barrier.

Note that field emission occurs *without* heating the metal, thereby permitting the design of a *cold cathode* vacuum diode x-ray tube. To dispel any doubts about this, you should know that field emission of electrons has been accomplished at a temperature of 4 K— (−269 C)!

---

*Manufactured by Hewlett-Packard.

†Kelvin or absolute zero = †273 C.

One of the exciting prospects of field emission, aside from the elimination of the hot cathode, is the extremely high current densities obtainable. Since there are about 10^{22} free electrons per cc of metal (swarming around in the lattice structure), a tremendous number will strike the potential barrier when a high voltage is applied. In fact, about 1 percent escape, yielding a current density of about 1 million amp per sq cm of emitter surface steadily, and about 10 times this value in pulses. Nowhere near this current density is obtainable with pure thermionic emission in a conventional x-ray tube, in which current density is about 100 amp/cm^2.

Unfortunately, there is a pronounced space charge effect that limits the ultimately achievable current density. However, in practice the emitter can function well at current densities below those causing a strong space charge effect.

The emitter or cathode is, in its *simplest* form, a tungsten needle measuring about 1 to 0.01 micron (1/thousandth to 1/100 thousandth of a millimeter) in diameter because this tiny dimension— many times smaller than a pin point—provides a very intense current at a reasonable voltage. The hemispheric needle tip consists of a single crystal of tungsten. A cone-shaped, divergent beam of electrons is produced, arising from only a small area of the tiny tip.

Our interest naturally centers around the application of the field emission principle to a functional x-ray tube. But first recall that in an ordinary x-ray tube the information carried by the x-ray beam in "bits" per sec is proportional to the number of electrons striking the target per second; or, stated differently, proportional to the current density in the cathode ray beam in, say, mA per cm^2. Generally, we use a 1 or 2 mm focal spot and a tube current ranging up to a few hundred mA.

On the other hand, in a field emission x-ray tube the *cathode* or emitter consists of several rows of electron-emitting needles resembling combs, surrounding a *conical anode* (see Figure 14.23). While the anode presents a large surface to the emitted electrons to improve heat dissipation, it gives off a symmetric beam of x rays from a very small area. It need not be explained further that x rays are produced when the fast electrons strike the anode,

ANODE
X-RAY EMISSION
CATHODE

Figure 14.23. Diagram of a field emission x-ray tube. Data furnished by courtesy of Hewlett-Packard.

in the same way as in an ordinary x-ray tube.

Several advantages of field emission tubes should be mentioned. They are smaller than conventional x-ray tubes, and less expensive to manufacture. No separate filament circuitry is needed. The focal spot size remains constant with change in kV and mA, whereas ordinary x-ray tubes are subject to "blooming;" that is, the focal spot enlarges appreciably with increased loading of the tube. Furthermore, because of the uniform and symmetrical emission of the x-ray beam from the end of the anode, there is no heel effect so that intensity and resolution are virtually constant over the surface of the film area.

Field emission medical radiographic equipment is no longer available, but the principle has application in industrial and biologic research, especially in high-speed radiography and photography.

QUESTIONS

1. Describe with the aid of a diagram the overload circuit breaker.
2. What is the function of a fuse and how does it work?
3. Discuss the principle of the prereading kilovoltmeter.
4. Why is a remote control switch necessary? How is it constructed?
5. Describe the four main types of exposure timers. Describe automatic exposure control.
6. What is the advantage of a circuit breaker over a fuse?

7. Show by diagram the filament circuit and its important components.
8. Why can a milliammeter be safely mounted on the control panel? What is a ballistic mAs meter and under what conditions is it an essential part of the control apparatus?
9. Explain why the center of the transformer secondary coil is grounded.
10. Explain how the kilovoltage control knob varies the kilovoltage. Which device does it operate in the primary x-ray circuit?
11. Which device in the filament circuit is operated when the filament control knob is manipulated? What function does it serve?
12. Describe a shockproof cable with the aid of a diagram.
13. Prepare a simple wiring diagram of an x-ray machine, including four-diode rectification.
14. Of what does a three-phase current consist?
15. How does the design of a three-phase transformer differ from that of a single-phase? What type of rectifiers is used with three-phase equipment?
16. What is meant by ripple? Discuss its importance in radiography.
17. What are the advantages and disadvantages of the three-phase over the single-phase generator?
18. Name two types of mobile apparatus other than the conventional kind.
19. Discuss briefly the principle of the capacitor discharge unit. How is exposure time controlled?
20. What is meant by field emission? State some of its advantages over other methods of generating x rays.

CHAPTER *15*   *X-RAY FILM, FILM HOLDERS, AND INTENSIFYING SCREENS*

O N PASSING THROUGH THE BODY, an x-ray beam interacts with the constituent atoms by photoelectric and Compton processes. As a result, the beam emerging from the body—the **exit beam**— consists of a pattern in which different areas have different numbers of photons corresponding to the pattern of tissue thicknesses, atomic numbers, and densities through which the beam has passed. The term **aerial image** refers to such an exit beam, since it contains information about the tissues through which the beam has passed. This information pattern can be revealed by various image receptors such as film, film-screen systems, and fluoroscopic screens.

In the early days of roentgenography, glass photographic plates coated with an emulsion sensitive to light were used to record the radiologic image. The disadvantages of plates included the danger of breakage, the hazard of cutting one's hands, the difficulty in processing, and the inconvenience in filing these plates for future reference. With the introduction of flexible films, these disadvantages were eliminated. This chapter deals with the use of films and intensifying screens—one type of image receptor system whose purpose is to display the aerial image.

Composition of X-ray Film

There are two essential components: the **base** and the **emulsion.**

1. **The Base.** Modern safety film has a base about 0.2 mm (7 mils or 0.007 in.) thick, consisting of a transparent sheet of **polyester plastic** which is usually tinted blue. It is called "safety" because it is nonexplosive, being no more inflammable than the same thickness of paper.

2. **The Emulsion.** This consists of microscopic crystals of **silver**

bromide suspended in *gelatin.* A small amount of sodium iodide may also be present. The gelatin, a transparent material similar to that used in cooking, is obtained mainly from cattle skins and bones treated with mustard oil to improve the sensitivity of the emulsion by providing *traces of sulfur.* To the gelatin dissolved in hot water are added, in total darkness, silver nitrate and potassium bromide to produce *silver bromide,* and a much smaller amount of silver nitrate and potassium iodide to produce *silver iodide.* Silver bromide and silver iodide are examples of *silver halides.* Heating the mixture to a temperature of 50 to 80 C—a process called digestion—further improves the sensitivity of the emulsion. After cooling, it is shredded, washed, reheated, and mixed with additional gelatin. Not only does the gelatin keep the silver halides uniformly dispersed in the emulsion, but it is also readily penetrated by the processing chemicals and by the water used in the final wash.

Finally, the emulsion is spread in a layer about 0.35 to 0.5 mils thick on both sides of the polyester base which has previously been coated with a special adhesive agent. Cooling is then carried out under strictly controlled conditions. Such double coated or *duplitized* film is the type most widely used in routine radiography. Single coated film is available for special purposes such as mammography. It must be emphasized that from the moment the ingredients are brought together in the emulsion until the finished sheet film is packed in boxes, the entire process must be carried out in *total darkness.*

Film Emulsion Characteristics. Emulsions have been designed to respond to certain regions of the color spectrum such as blue or green light emitted by intensifying screens, as well as to x rays. Furthermore, an emulsion should display the radiologic image of a variety of tissues with optimum recorded detail, density, and contrast, qualities that will be discussed later.

An ordinary film contains the silver halide crystals clustered in the form of irregular microscopic pebble-shaped grains. The speed of such emulsions can be increased only by increasing the size of the grains and the thickness of the emulsion. This inevitably impairs recorded detail or image sharpness because of the coarser overall granular pattern. Such pebble-shaped grains vary in size and shape, measuring about 1 to 1.5 microns in width.

A new type of emulsion called ***T-grain*** (Eastman Kodak Company) has appeared on the market, in which the grains of various sizes and shapes are flat, with the flat side facing the x-ray tube. Their size is similar to that of conventional silver halide grains. The flatness of the grains, as well as the addition of special sensitizers, allows them to capture more light without the need of thickening the emulsion. Consequently, the films display increased speed without sacrificing recorded detail. Since the T-grain emulsion is sensitive mainly to the light from green-emitting screens, a magenta dye is added to the emulsion to minimize crossover (see pages 305–306) and further improve recorded detail.

To be suitable for radiography, an emulsion should have two important characteristics:

1. ***Speed or Sensitivity***—the relative ability of an emulsion to respond to radiation such as light and x rays. An emulsion is said to be fast or have high speed if a small exposure produces a radiograph of adequate density (darkening).

2. ***Latitude***—the ability of an emulsion to display a radiographic image with a reasonably long tonal range, from white, through various shades of gray, to black. This is ***long scale*** or ***low contrast***, to be discussed later in more detail. Another aspect of latitude is ***exposure latitude***—the range of exposure factors that will produce an acceptable radiograph. Obviously, an emulsion should have sufficient latitude to allow a reasonable degree of error in exposure without serious impairment of radiographic quality. Both aspects of latitude—long tonal range and permissible margin of exposure error—are closely related. However, excessive film latitude may impair image visibility, that is, the ability to see fine recorded detail.

Another type of latitude is ***subject latitude***, which depends on subject contrast (see pages 359–361). This has to do with the range of densities resulting from contrast in the subject being radiographed; with higher subject contrast, latitude decreases and so does the margin of exposure error.

Types of Films

There are three main types of x-ray films in use at the present time in medical radiography.

1. **Screen Film** is the type most often used in radiography. Although sensitive mainly to the blue light emitted by ordinary (calcium tungstate) or certain rare earth intensifying screens, this film also responds to the direct action of x rays. Some film emulsions are designed to have maximum sensitivity to the green light emitted by certain types of rare earth screens. Thus, screen film is used chiefly in cassettes with intensifying screens, a combination that has made possible the high speed and excellent quality of modern radiography. Film manufacturers produce screen films having a variety of speeds and contrasts to suit the fancy of almost any radiologist, both for general radiography and for special examinations.

2. **Nonscreen or Direct-exposure Film** had a thicker emulsion than screen-type film and was used without intensifying screens to obtain fine recorded detail. This type of film is no longer available, but ordinary film can be used in cardboard holders to obtain superb recorded detail of small anatomic parts such as fingers or toes.

3. **Mammography Film** is a modified single-emulsion industrial film characterized by *slow speed,* high contrast, and extremely fine grain; however, radiation dosage to the breast is excessive. Low dose systems are available, using special single-emulsion film with a single screen.

4. **Duplicating Film** is used to copy radiographs. The original radiograph is inserted into a cassette whose opaque front has been replaced by a pane of clear glass. A sheet of special duplicating film is then placed, with emulsion side down, onto the radiograph and the cassette lid closed. An exposure is made to an ordinary illuminator at a distance of 12 in. (30 cm) for 6 sec and the film is processed as usual. When necessary, the density of the copy may be improved by adjusting the exposure time; a longer exposure will decrease image density, and conversely. Duplicating films, when properly exposed, produce excellent copies of the original.

Practical Suggestions in Handling Unexposed Film

1. Films deteriorate with age; therefore, the expiration date stamped on the box should be observed, the older films being used first.

2. Since moisture and heat hasten deterioration, films should be stored in a cool, dry place.

3. Films are sensitive to light and must be protected from it until processing has been completed.

4. Films are sensitive to x rays and other ionizing radiations, and should be protected by distance and by shielding with protective materials such as lead.

5. Films are marred by finger prints, scratches, and dirty intensifying screens, and by crink marks due to sharp bending.

6. Rough handling causes black marks due to static electricity. These appear as jagged lines, black spots, or tree-like images after development.

Film Exposure Holders

Each x-ray film must be carried to the radiographic room in a suitable container which not only protects it from outside light but also allows it to be exposed in radiography. Film holders are available in standard film sizes.

There are two types of film holders used in general radiography: *cardboard holders* and *cassettes.*

1. **Cardboard Film Holder**—an enclosed light-proof envelope into which the film is loaded *in the darkroom.* The film *with its paper wrapping* (if it is provided with such a wrapper) is placed in the folder and the long flap of the envelope is folded over it, followed by the two shorter side and end flaps. After being closed and secured by the hinged clip, the holder is ready to be taken to the radiographic room for exposure. During exposure, the front of the film holder must face the tube, the back cardboard being lined with lead foil to prevent fogging of the film by x rays scattered back from the table. Figure 15.1 shows a cardboard film holder in cross section. Cardboard holders are seldom used, except for extremely fine recorded detail of small parts.

2. **Cassette** — a case measuring about one-half inch in thickness and having an aluminum, stainless steel, or plastic frame, a hinged lid with one or more flat springs, and a bakelite or light metal front. One of a pair of intensifying screens is mounted on the inside of the cassette front, and the second screen is mounted on the inside of the lid. As will be shown below, intensifying screens convert the energy of x-ray photons to light photons, thereby speeding up the radiographic process. The front of the cassette faces the x-ray tube during exposure. We load the cassette by raising the hinged lid *in the darkroom,* slipping a film gently into the cassette of the same size, and closing the lid by means of the springs. The film is thus sandwiched between two screens and in close contact with them. Figure 15.2 shows a cassette in cross section. Lead foil cemented to the lid behind the back screen helps absorb radiation scattered back toward the screen.

Figure 15.1. Cross section of a cardboard film holder.

Intensifying Screens

We have already mentioned the use of intensifying screens and shall now describe their structure and function.

Figure 15.2. Cross section of a cassette with intensifying screens and film.

1. **Composition.** An intensifying screen (see Figure 15.3) consists of microscopic crystals of a *phosphor* (luminescent material), incorporated in a binding material, and coated on one side of the white reflecting surface of a sheet of high grade cardboard or Mylar® (plastic, 250 microns or 10 mils thick) called the *base.* The phosphor coating is the *active layer;* it usually measures about 100 microns or 4 mils thick in medium speed screens. It is, in turn, coated with a thin, smooth, abrasion-resistant material, its edges being sealed against moisture. For years calcium tungstate was the most widely used phosphor because it:

Figure 15.3. Magnified cross-sectional diagram of an intensifying screen.

a. Emits blue and violet light to which ordinary x-ray film is particularly sensitive.
b. Responds well in the kV range ordinarily used in radiography.
c. Does not deteriorate appreciably with use or with age.
d. Does not have significant afterglow or lag (see pages 295, 307).
e. Can be used to manufacture screens of uniform quality. As will be seen below, other phosphors (eg, rare earth types) are rapidly gaining favor because of their greater efficiency (see pages 299–300).

2. **Principle.** Phosphors are crystalline materials that have the unique ability to *luminesce* or give off visible light when struck by x rays. While the process is incompletely understood, we do know that it involves the transition of electrons between *energy bands* in the crystal lattice, shown diagrammatically in Figure 15.4. (Note the similarity to the concept of semiconductors, pages 241–243.) The *valence band* contains atomic valence electrons and is usually filled, the *forbidden band* normally remains unoccupied by elec-

trons except at certain points, and the **conduction band** allows free movement of electrons. An imperfect crystal results from faults or metallic impurities which serve as **traps** for electrons in the forbidden band; in fact, the minute amount of impurities added to the phosphor crystals in intensifying screens produce traps that usually contain electrons.

Figure 15.4. Schematic concept of a phosphor crystal. Note the similarity to a semiconductor crystal.

There are two kinds of luminescence—*fluorescence* and *phosphorescence*—classified, respectively, according to whether immediate or delayed emission of light occurs following exposure to x rays. A brief, simplified discussion of these processes will now be given.

a. *Fluorescence*—light emitted *promptly*, within 10^{-8} sec after absorption of an x-ray photon by photoelectric or Compton interaction. The resulting primary electron raises one or more valence electrons to the conduction band, leaving a "hole" in the valence band (see Figure 15.5). Immediately, in less than 10^{-8} sec, a trapped electron drops from the forbidden band into the hole in the valence band, giving off visible light. The trap is reset, so to speak, when it is refilled by transition of an electron from the conduction band. A much less common event in radiographic phosphors is the direct transition of an electron from the conduction band to a hole in the valence band without preliminary trapping. As a result of fluorescence, such as that occurring in a pair of medium speed calcium tungstate screens, *one incident x-ray photon causes the emission of about 300 light photons,* about one-half of which reach the film (see Ter-Pogossian). The ability of a particular phosphor to change x-ray photon energy to light energy is called its *conversion efficiency.*

Figure 15.5. Process of fluorescence. An incoming photon (not shown) initiates a photoelectric or Compton interaction in the valence band (*VB*), releasing a primary electron which, in turn, imparts energy to a number of secondary electrons and raises them to the conduction band (*CB*). In *1*, a secondary electron has been raised to the *CB*, leaving a hole in the *VB*. In *2*, any electron previously trapped in a flaw in the forbidden band (*FB*) immediately falls into a hole in the *VB* and a photon is emitted as fluorescent light. In *3*, an electron from the *CB* finally drops into the empty trap, resetting it. Note that fluorescent light emission occurs *promptly*, in less than 10^{-8} sec.

b. *Phosphorescence*—light emitted after a delay of 10^{-8} sec or more after the absorption of an x-ray photon. Such *delayed emission* of light is also known as *afterglow.* Here, absorption of x-ray photons causes elevation of electrons to the conduction band, leaving many holes in the valence band (see Figure 15.6). However, in crystals subject to intense phosphorescence, such as zinc sulfide, the traps in the forbidden band are normally empty of electrons. When the newly arrived electrons drop from the conduction band into traps in the forbidden band, they remain there for a variable length of time. Heat from the kinetic energy of the atoms then lifts the trapped electrons back to the conduction band, whereupon

PHOTON
PHOSPHORESCENT LIGHT

Figure 15.6. Process of phosphorescence. Here, traps are normally empty. In *1* we have the same sequence of events as in fluorescence (Figure 15.5). But in *2*, electrons drop from the conduction band (*CB*) into empty traps, one of which is shown here. Electrons remain in the traps for variable lengths of time before a small amount of energy, such as the heat present in the crystal, raises them back to the *CB* as in *3*. Finally, they drop into holes in the *VB*. Note that *delayed* emission of light occurs in phosphorescence.

they may drop into holes in the valence band, accompanied by the emission of visible light.

Thus, there are two types of luminescence occurring in certain crystals following the absorption of x rays. One is the ***prompt emission of light*** by the process of ***fluorescence.*** The other is the ***delayed emission of light*** through ***phosphorescence.*** In both cases the tiny phosphor crystals absorb energy in the form of x rays and convert this energy to visible light which is emitted in all directions. Phosphorescence is virtually nil in intensifying screens, but is strong in fluoroscopic screens. The total amount of light emitted in a particular region of the active layer depends on the quantity of x rays striking that region, and is a summation of the light given off by the innumerable, closely packed crystals.

In the object being radiographed, those parts which are readily penetrated by x rays will appear on the ***screen*** as brighter areas than those parts which are poorly penetrated. Thus, the screen registers, although temporarily, the *aerial image* and includes zones of various degrees of brightness. These, in turn, ultimately produce corresponding differences in darkening of the radiograph. Since the film emulsion is specially sensitive to the particular color of light emitted by the screens, this *photographic effect* is of major importance. In fact, *as much as 98 per cent of the recorded density (blackening) in a film exposed with intensifying screens may be photographic in origin,* that is, due to light emitted by the screens, the remaining 2 percent resulting from direct x-ray exposure. Thus, screens greatly intensify the effect of x rays on the film emulsion, thereby reducing the exposure needed to obtain a particular degree of film blackening and, at the same time, substantially decreasing patient exposure. Intensifying screens have made possible the use of grid radiography of thick anatomic parts such as the abdomen, skull, and spine, and have led to the development of high speed radiography.

To summarize this discussion, we may say that the *exit* or *remnant radiation* (radiation that has passed through the patient and carries the aerial image) passes through the front of the cassette and impinges on the front intensifying screen. This emits light which varies in brightness depending on the amount of radiation reaching any particular area of the screen. In fact, there is a light and dark pattern on the screen corresponding to the relative transmission of x rays through the various body structures in the path of the beam; the screen image represents the aerial image in the form of light. The image in light emitted by the screen photographically affects the film emulsion with which it is contact, recording the light and dark pattern, although this is reversed on the finished radiograph. X rays also pass on directly to the film causing a variable, though small, photographic effect. Some x rays reach the back screen which fluoresces and affects the film emulsion nearest it in the same manner as the front screen. Thus, a film is coated on both sides with a sensitive emulsion so that one side receives light from the front screen, and the other from the back screen, as shown in Figure 15.7.

3. **Screen Speed.** A screen is said to be fast or to have high speed when a relatively small x-ray exposure produces a given output of

Figure 15.7. Schematic representation of the principle of the intensifying screen. X-ray photon *1* strikes the front screen causing it to fluoresce at that point. Another x-ray photon such as *2* may pass directly to the film and affect it at that point. Or a photon such as x ray *3* may pass through the front screen and the film, striking a crystal in the back screen and exciting fluorescence in it. Actually the screens and film are in close contact. Not shown here is *crossover* from one screen to the emulsion on the opposite side of the film (see Figure 15.11).

light and causes a certain degree of blackening of a film. Conversely, a screen is said to be slow when a relatively large exposure is required for a given amount of film blackening. *The speed or intensifying factor of a pair of intensifying screens may be defined as the ratio of the exposure required without screens to the exposure required with screens to get the same degree of blackening of x-ray films.* Another name for intensifying factor is *speed factor.*

$$\text{intensifying factor} = \frac{\text{exposure without screens}}{\text{exposure with screens}}$$

Since the denominator is always less than the numerator, the intensifying factor of a pair of screens always exceeds unity, which means simply that the exposure with screens is less than that without screens for the same amount of film blackening.

At present, screen speed is rated according to arbitrarily assigned numbers as follows:

Screen Speed Number	Generic Name
less than 100	detail
100	medium speed
more than 100	high speed

On this basis, screens with a speed of 200 require 50 percent less exposure than screens with a speed of 100, for equal radiographic density. It is expected that the generic names for screens will eventually be discontinued, and screen speed will be identified by number alone. Note again that these numbers are arbitrary, and not obtained according to the definition of intensifying factor as stated above.

But we must take into account the speed of the *film-screen system,* since different speeds pertain to a particular type of screen depending on the speed of the film being used. Thus, high-speed screens with slow films may be no faster than slower screens with high-speed films. So, choice of radiographic image receptors for a particular application should be based on a *film-screen system* that provides the requisite speed and image quality, rather than on screen speed alone.

The *speed* of intensifying screens depends on two main classes of factors—intrinsic and extrinsic.

a. **Intrinsic Factors** are those inherent in the composition of the screens and include the phosphor, the thickness of the active layer, the size of the phosphor crystals, and the reflectance of the backing.

(1) *Phosphor.* The speed conferred on an intensifying screen by a particular phosphor depends on its *conversion efficiency* which is determined by two factors: (1) its ability to absorb x-ray photons, and (2) its ability to convert the absorbed x-ray energy to light energy, but this is a very inefficient process. Actually, only about 5 percent of x-ray energy in ordinary calcium tungstate, and 20 percent in rare earth phosphors, is converted to light energy (see Christensen et al.). Conversion efficiency can be enhanced by the addition of special activators; for example, activated calcium tungstate has twice the conversion efficiency of ordinary calcium tungstate (activated calcium tungstate is the phosphor in DuPont High Plus screens®).

Note that not all the light emitted by the phosphor reaches the film—about 50 percent is absorbed in the screen itself. *Screen efficiency* refers to the ability of light given off by a phosphor actually to leave a screen and expose a film. Thus, the intensifying factor of a screen depends on both phosphor conversion efficiency and screen efficiency.

Some of the newer phosphors with intrinsically higher conversion efficiency include **barium strontium sulfate** (Kodak X-omatic Regular Screens®) which fluoresces at shorter wavelengths than calcium tungstate and gives screen speed about 1.5 times that of par speed screens. Another phosphor, **barium fluorochloride** (DuPont Quanta II Screens®), provides screen speed about four times that of par speed screens, but with moderate increase in mottle.

An entirely new class of **rare earth phosphors** comprising mainly salts of **gadolinium** and **lanthanum** displays significantly greater conversion efficiency than calcium tungstate while retaining excellent image resolution. Rare earth screens such as Lanex Regular® (Kodak) and Alpha 4® (3M Trimax) have a speed factor about four times that of medium or par speed calcium tungstate screens. However, they emit light mainly in the **green** region of the spectrum and so require special green-sensitive film and a special darkroom safelight. Recorded detail is nearly as good with these rare earth screens as with the par speed type. Even greater speed is possible with Alpha 8® (3M Trimax) screens, but with significant impairment of recorded detail and increase in mottle. Still another type of rare earth screens—Blue Max 1® and Blue Max II® (General Electric) and Quanta III® (DuPont)—contain **lanthanum oxybromide** activated by terbium as the phosphor; its most attractive feature is the emission of violet and blue light to which ordinary film is maximally sensitive, so special film is not needed. Blue Max I screens have about twice the speed of par speed screens without effect on recorded detail, whereas Blue Max II and Quanta III screens have about four times the speed of medium speed screens, but they slightly impair recorded detail and increase mottle. In practice, these 400-speed screens produce high quality radiographs with a large reduction in patient exposure. Table 15.1 gives the speed factors of some typical screens relative to medium speed.

(2) *Thickness of Active Layer.* For a given phosphor, the thicker the active layer the greater will be the speed. In fact, this contributes more to screen speed than does crystal size.

(3) *Size of Phosphor Crystals.* Larger crystals impart greater speed to intensifying screens than do smaller ones for two reasons. First, more light is emitted by larger crystals because they receive more x-ray photons. Second, larger crystals scatter less light within

the screen's active layer, increasing screen efficiency.

(4) *Reflectance of Backing.* The more light reflected back to the active layer by the cardboard or plastic backing, the greater will be the speed. However, this may be undesirable with thick active layers because of the detrimental effect on image sharpness caused by the diffusion (spread) of light in the screen.

TABLE 15.1
PHOSPHOR COMPOSITION AND LIGHT EMISSION
OF VARIOUS SCREENS, AND THEIR SPEED FACTORS
RELATIVE TO MEDIUM OR PAR SPEED SCREENS

	Screen	Phosphor	Principal Light Emission	Relative Speed Class
	Par Speed (Du Pont)	Calcium tungstate	Blue	100
	High Plus (Du Pont)	Calcium tungstate	Blue	200
	Quanta II (Du Pont)	Barium fluorochloride	Blue	400
	X-omatic Regular (Kodak)	Barium strontium sulfate	Blue	150
Rare Earth Phosphors	Lanex (Kodak)	Gadolinium and lanthanum compounds	Green	400
	Alpha 4 (3M Trimax)	Rare earth compounds	Green	200 or 400°
	Alpha 8 (3M Trimax)	Rare earth compounds	Green	400 or 800°
	Blue Max 1 (General Electric)	Lanthanum oxybromide and terbium	Blue and Violet	200
	Blue Max 2 (General Electric)	Lanthanum oxybromide and terbium	Blue and Violet	400
	Quanta III (Du Pont)	Lanthanum oxybromide	Blue and Violet	400 or 800°

°Depending on special type of film.

Thus, a faster screen would probably incorporate a more luminescent phosphor, such as specially activated calcium tungstate in a thicker layer, or some other phosphor that is inherently faster, such as one of the rare earths. But note that *as the thickness of the active layer is increased the radiographic image becomes more blurred* (ie, *less sharp*) because an increase in average distance the emitted light has to travel to the film results in greater diffusion (spread) of the light rays (see Figure 15.8). Consequently, there is a practicable limit to the thickness of the active layer. Active layer thickness ranges from about 50 microns for detail (slow) screens, to 300 microns for fast calcium tungstate screens.

Theoretically, we should expect the size of the crystals to influence image sharpness because a larger crystal would produce a larger spot of light than a smaller crystal, but this turns out to be unimportant in actual practice. The crystals are extremely minute, averaging about 5 microns (0.005 mm) with a range of 4 microns (slow or "detail" screens) to 8 microns (faster calcium tungstate screens). This range of crystal size has a smaller effect on recorded detail than does active layer thickness.

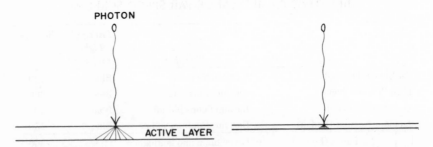

Figure 15.8. Effect of active layer thickness of an intensifying screen on image definition. Note that the light originating at points deep within the thinner active layer (right figure) spreads less before reaching the film, thereby producing a sharper image.

b. **Extrinsic Factors** include the conditions under which the screens are used, namely temperature and kV.

(1) *Temperature.* As room temperature rises, screen speed decreases and film speed increases. These two tendencies nearly cancel each other, so that no temperature correction is necessary for screen speed under ordinary conditions. However, at the high temperatures prevailing in the tropics, basic mAs values have to be increased about 40 percent at 50 C (120 F). On the other hand, in extreme cold such as may be encountered in industrial radiography, a decrease of about 25 percent in the basic mAs is required at − 10 C (15 F).

(2) *Kilovoltage.* The speed of rare earth screens does not remain constant over the useful kV range. Thus, speed is maximal at about 100 kV, gradually dropping to about 75 percent of maximum at 70 kV. These values are approximate and vary with the

type of rare earth phosphor. On the other hand, calcium tungstate screens such as High Plus show virtually no variation in speed with changes in kV.

4. **Screen Contact.** The film must be sandwiched uniformly between the two screens, with perfect contact throughout. Even the smallest conceivable space between the film and screen at any point will permit the light rays emerging from the screen at that point to spread over a wider area, producing a blurred image of that particular point (see Figure 15.9). You can easily ascertain the uniformity of contact of the screens with the film by placing a piece of hardware cloth with 1/8 inch mesh over the front of the cassette and making a film exposure — 40 kV, 10 mAs, and 100 cm (40 in.) focus-film distance, with a 3 mm Al filter. With satisfactory screen contact, the image of the wire mesh is sharp over the entire radiograph; but in areas of poor contact the image appears blurred and patchy (see Figure 15.10).

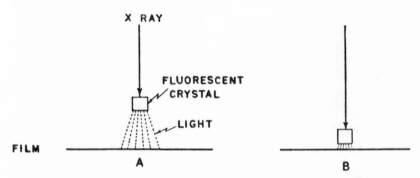

Figure 15.9. Poor screen contact causes a blurred image. In *A*, there is an appreciable space between the fluorescent crystal and the film (when screen contact is poor), so that a tiny but spreading bundle of light rays strikes the film, producing a blurred image instead of a fine point. In *B*, the crystal is in close contact with the film so that the image is about the same size as the crystal. (The crystal is magnified many times in the diagram.)

Screen contact is usually, though not universally, good in smaller cassettes. However, larger cassettes, especially 30 × 35 cm (11 × 14 in.) and 35 × 43 cm (14 × 17 in.) often exhibit poor contact even when new. Therefore, a layer of contact felt, fiberglass, or foam rubber should be cemented (preferably by an expert) as a cushion between the screen and the cassette. When the cassette is closed, the padding tends to equalize the pressure applied to the screens, squeezing them tightly against the film.

An improved light-weight cassette (Eastman Kodak) of high-impact plastic can be dropped without damage. But even more important, the front is deliberately warped inward to assure excellent film-screen contact.

A special vacuum cassette (Amplatz) achieves the ultimate in film-screen contact. After a special cassette has been loaded with film, a vacuum is induced by means of a suction pump. This causes the film and screens to be squeezed tightly together, resulting in noticeable improvement in recorded detail especially in angiography with or without magnification.

The vacuum principle is also being used with a plastic envelope and single, ultrafine detail screen in *mammography* to bring about a substantial reduction in radiation exposure to the breast.

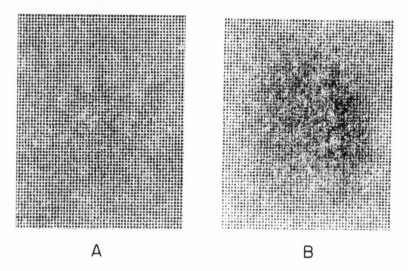

A   B

Figure 15.10. Tests for screen contact. In *A*, with excellent screen contact, the image of the wire screen is uniform. In *B*, with poor contact at the center, the image of the wire is blurred, producing a typical blotchy, dark area in the radiograph.

An improved lightweight cassette (Eastman Kodak) of high-impact plastic can be dropped without damage. But even more important, the front is deliberately warped inward to assure excellent film-screen contact.

It is essential that all new cassettes and, periodically, old ones as well, be checked for contact as described above. Whenever a radiograph appears sharper in one area than in another (for example, edges sharper than the center), poor screen contact should be suspected and the cassette tested without delay.

The **causes of poor screen contact** include (1) warped cassette front, (2) cracked or twisted cassette frame, (3) loose hinges or spring latches, and (4) local elevation of a screen by a foreign body underneath. Rough handling and dropping of cassettes are mainly responsible for damage leading to poor screen contact. Another important cause is the placement of a cassette without a tunnel under a patient in bed often resulting in a warped cassette.

5. **Recorded Detail with Screens.** In previous sections we described the relationship of intensifying screens to radiographic image sharpness. These data may be summarized to good advantage under a single heading. In general, *recorded detail is never so sharp with screens as with direct radiographic exposure of x-ray film in a cardboard holder,* provided the patient can be adequately immobilized. In actual practice, image sharpness with screens becomes worse as the thickness of the active layer increases. As noted before, a thicker active layer causes greater diffusion of light and blurring of the image. But remember that as the active layer thickness is decreased to improve recorded detail, as in detail screens, the screen becomes slower. Another fact to bear in mind is that regardless of the type of screen, recorded detail suffers when film-screen contact is poor. In nongrid radiography of small parts, detail screens give much better recorded detail and less mottle than medium speed or fast screens.

Another cause of impaired recorded detail with intensifying screens, related to diffusion of the image, is a condition known as *crossover* or *punch-through.* This is shown in Figure 15.11. Note that crossover occurs only with the double-emulsion films and two screens prevailing in general radiography. Light from one screen expands in the form of a cone as it passes successively through this screen, the nearer film emulsion, the film base, and the farther film emulsion where a slightly enlarged, less sharp image is formed. Recorded detail is thereby worsened. However, special dyes incorporated in the emulsion minimize crossover.

C = CROSSOVER RADIATION

Figure 15.11. Crossover or punch-through of light from one screen to the other in the form of an expanding small cone of light. This causes a blurring effect in the corresponding emulsion of the film, resulting in impaired recorded detail.

6. **Care of Screens.** Intensifying screens should be mounted with rubber cement or special adhesive tape, never with water-soluble paste. The screens ordinarily come in pairs, one screen being thicker than the other. The thin screen is mounted inside the front of the cassette, whereas the thicker screen is mounted inside the lid.

Screens should be kept scrupulously clean, since dust and other foreign materials absorb light from the screen and cast a white shadow on the film. Screens may be washed with cotton and bland soap, rinsed with cotton *moistened* with water (never dripping wet), and then dried with cotton. The screens are further dried by standing the half-opened cassette on its side for about one-half hour in a dust-free room. Special screen cleaners should be used only as recommended by the manufacturer.

Care must be taken not to nick, scratch, or chip the screens as, for example, by carelessly digging the film out of the cassette with the fingernail, or by scratching the screen with a corner of the film.

In loading the cassette, one carefully slips the film into the cassette with the lid elevated about 5 cm (2 in.). Doing this gently helps avoid static marks. To remove the film after exposure, one carefully raises a corner of the film, being certain that the fingernails do not slip across the surface of the screen.

The cassette must always be kept closed, except while being loaded or unloaded, to prevent accidental damage to the screen surface and help keep out dust. Scratch marks and dust block the light from the screen, leaving a *white spot* on the finished radiograph.

Fluoroscopic Screens

In principle, a fluoroscopic screen resembles an intensifying screen, but there are certain practical differences. *Zinc cadmium sulfide* is still the best phosphor for fluoroscopic screens, emitting green light to which the eyes are most sensitive at the low intensity of the fluorescent light. Crystal size is 30 to 40 microns (0.03 to 0.04 mm). The screen is backed by lead glass to protect the fluoroscopist.

Fluoroscopic screen phosphors display two kinds of luminescence, as described earlier:

1. *Fluorescence*—the emission of light promptly, while the screens are being exposed to x rays.

2. *Phosphorescence*—the persistent emission of light after the x rays have been turned off. Also known as *afterglow* or *lag,* it is relatively strong in fluoroscopic screens, but weak in intensifying screens.

QUESTIONS

1. Show by cross-section diagram the structure of x-ray film.
2. What is meant by safety film? Nonscreen film?
3. State two differences between screen and nonscreen film. What is mammography film?
4. Describe the structure of an intensifying screen. How does it differ from a fluoroscopic screen?
5. Define the intensifying factor or speed of an intensifying screen. State the speed *numbers* of slow, medium, and fast screens.

6. What are three differences in the composition of a slow screen and a fast screen? How do they differ in their effect on radiographic sharpness?
7. How does an intensifying screen intensify the x-ray image?
8. Why is an x-ray film coated on both sides with sensitive emulsion?
9. How do rare earth screens differ from ordinary intensifying screens?
10. Explain screen lag. Luminescence. Phosphorescence. Fluorescence.
11. How does active layer thickness affect image sharpness? Explain. What other factors cause impairment of image sharpness by screens? Explain.
12. Discuss the four intrinsic factors affecting screen speed.
13. How do temperature and kilovoltage influence screen speed?
14. In general, is recorded detail better with direct exposure radiography or with intensifying screen radiography? Why?
15. What is meant by the conversion efficiency of an intensifying screen? Screen efficiency?
16. Discuss rare earth phosphors on the basis of emitted color and conversion efficiency, as contrasted with calcium tungstate.
17. Discuss crossover or punch-through related to film-screen systems.
18. Why should we avoid scratching or otherwise marring a screen surface?
19. What is the effect of poor screen contact on radiographic sharpness? Why?
20. Describe a test for film-screen contact.

CHAPTER *16*   *THE DARKROOM*

T HE IMPORTANCE of the darkroom in radiography cannot be exaggerated. Radiography unquestionably begins and ends in the darkroom, where the films are loaded into suitable light-proof holders in preparation for exposure, and where they are returned for processing into a finished radiograph. In general, a darkroom is a place where the necessary handling and processing of film can be carried out safely and efficiently, without the hazard of producing *film fog* by accidental exposure to light or x rays.

The term "darkroom" overstates the case, since complete blackout is unnecessary. In fact, as will be shown later, a great deal of safe illumination can be provided to facilitate darkroom procedures. Although the term "processing room" is more accurate, it is not widely used. We shall therefore continue to refer to it as the "darkroom," bearing in mind that it is dark only insofar as *it must exclude all outside light and provide "safe" artificial light.*

Although this chapter will deal only with the darkroom designed for the *manual processing of films,* the basic principles apply also to darkrooms for automatic processing, to be discussed on pages 330–334.

Location of the Darkroom

Because of its overriding importance, the location of the darkroom should be determined during the planning stage of the Radiology Department. Convenient placement of the darkroom with relation to the radiographic rooms should save time and eliminate unnecessary steps. Walls adjacent to the radiographic rooms should be shielded with the correct thickness of lead all the way to the ceiling; 1.6 mm (1/16 in.) lead usually suffices. Stored radium and other radioactive materials should be located as remotely as possible from the darkroom because even as little as 5 mR total exposure from x or gamma rays causes detectable fog. As a general rule, protection of films approximates that of personnel.

Windows should be avoided because they are extremely difficult to render lightproof. Furthermore, they serve no useful purpose, since much more satisfactory methods of ventilation and lighting are available.

Finally, the darkroom should be readily accessible to plumbing and electrical service.

Building Essentials

Walls between the darkroom and adjoining x-ray rooms should contain enough lead thickness, or its equivalent in other building materials, for adequate protection of the films. This is especially important because efficiency demands that the darkroom be close to the radiographic rooms (see above).

In a busy department, the efficiency of work flow can be improved by having **passboxes** built into the walls at appropriate locations. Typical passboxes have two light-tight and x-ray proof doors that are so interlocked that both cannot be opened at the same time. The cassettes, after radiographic exposure, are placed in the passbox through the outside door, and then removed through the inside door by the darkroom technician. The most suitable location for the passbox is obviously near the film-loading bench although this is not always possible.

Darkroom walls should be covered with chemical-resistant materials, particularly near the processing tanks. Such materials include special paint, varnish, or lacquer. Ceramic tile or plastic wall covering provides a more durable finish.

Floor covering should consist of chemical-resistant and stainproof material such as asphalt tile. Porcelain or clay tile may be used, but a nonskid abrasive should be incorporated to minimize the danger of slipping. Ordinary linoleum and concrete are unsuitable because they are readily attacked by the processing solutions.

Entrance

Access should be conveniently located with relation to the dark-room equipment. The simplest type of entrance is a single door which must be made absolutely light-tight by weatherstripping. Such an entrance generally prevails in offices and hospitals, but it should have an inside lock to prevent opening while films are being processed.

Another type of protective entrance is a small hall with two electrically interlocked doors, so designed that one door cannot be opened until the other is completely closed, thereby preventing entrance of light (see Figure 16.1). A separate door should be provided for emergency use and for moving equipment into and out of the darkroom.

Figure 16.1. Darkroom floor plan with interlocked doors. If door *A* is opened, an electrical relay prevents anyone from opening door *B*, and vice versa. *C* is an emergency door, which is usually kept closed.

A more elaborate type of entrance is the ***maze,*** shown in Figure 16.2. Note that one must execute a complete turn in going through the three doorways. Serving as a light trap, the maze requires no doors, especially if the walls are painted black. Because of the high cost of the required floor area, mazes are rarely used today.

For most installations, the preferred modern type of entrance is the revolving door, shown in Figure 16.3. Several sizes are available. For example, one measures about 3 feet in diameter and, built into the wall, it extends about 15 in. into each adjoining room so that it occupies relatively little floor area. At the same time, it offers convenient, lightproof access to the darkroom. Models with three-way and four-way doors are also available.

Figure 16.2. Darkroom with maze or labyrinth entrance.

Figure 16.3. Diagram (top view) of a two-way revolving darkroom door. The outer cylindrical chamber, built into the wall, has two openings, one into the darkroom and the other into the lightroom. The inner chamber has one door which, suspended at its top by a central bearing, can easily be rotated by means of a handrail until its opening coincides with either of the openings in the outer chamber. The entire unit is completely lightproof and takes up very little space.

Size

Darkroom size will vary, of course, with the size of the department, but it must be large enough to house conveniently all the necessary benches for loading and unloading films, a film storage bin, cupboards, processing tanks, refrigeration system, and dryer. On the other hand, the darkroom should not be too large, since the excessive distances between various units of equipment result in wasted time and steps. Placement of the loading bench across the room from the tanks minimizes accidental splashing of water and solutions on the films, benches, cassettes, or other equipment that may come in contact with the films. However, this is not a problem in the darkroom with an automatic processor.

Ventilation

Essential to efficient work and to the technologist's health are the adequate removal of stale humid air and the supply of fresh air. Air conditioning is definitely the preferred method of ventilating the darkroom. However, in a small office or department in areas where climate permits, an exhaust fan may provide adequate air circulation. The system should be absolutely light proof and should include a means of filtering out dust at the point of entry of the fresh air.

Lighting

A properly designed darkroom should have three types of illumination: safelight, general, and radiographic.

1. **Safelight.** We must have a source of light which will not fog films and still provide adequate illumination under processing conditions. *Safelight lamps* serve this purpose; they must have filters of the proper color, such as the Wratten Series 6B® filter for ordinary blue-violet sensitive film, but a special filter such as the Kodak GS-1 must be used with green-sensitive Ortho-G film. The *working distance* from the safelight should be no less than 1 meter (3 ft), and bulb wattage should correspond to that specified on the lamp housing. If a brighter bulb is used, light transmitted even

through the correct filter may cause film fog. Safelights are designed for either indirect ceiling illumination or for direct lighting.

The safety of darkroom lighting may be tested as follows: subject a film in a cassette to a very small x-ray exposure, just enough to cause slight graying; screen film is more sensitive to fogging by light after initial exposure to the fluorescence of intensifying screens. Then remove the film from the cassette in the darkroom, cover one-half the film with black paper, and leave it exposed under conditions simulating as closely as possible those normally existing when a film is being loaded and unloaded. Process the film as usual. If the uncovered portion appears darker than the covered, you may conclude that the darkroom lighting is unsafe, and must then make every effort to eliminate the source of light responsible for the fogging. This may result from a cracked or an incorrect filter, a light leak in the safelight housing, or a leak around the entrance door to the darkroom.

Note that the darkroom walls do not have to be painted black. A light color enhances safelight illumination without increasing the risk of film fogging.

2. **General Illumination.** A source of overhead lighting is needed for general purposes such as cleaning, changing solutions, and carrying out other procedures that do not require safelight illumination.

3. **Radiographic Illumination.** A fluorescent illuminator for viewing wet radiographs should be mounted over the washing compartment to avoid contamination of processing solutions. In more elaborate darkrooms for manual processing the wash tank is installed partly through the wall into the light area to permit viewing the wet radiographs outside the darkroom, thereby minimizing traffic in the darkroom. With automated processing, a fluorescent illuminator helps only when the entire processor is located within the darkroom.

Apparatus and Equipment

Ready-mixed processing chemicals are available as liquid solutions and made up to the proper volume by the addition of water according to the instructions printed on the label. Two stirring paddles are needed, one for the developer and one for the fixer. A thermometer is used to determine the temperature of the developing solution and to check the temperature of water used to prepare the solutions. All apparatus coming in contact with the processing solutions must consist of materials such as plastic, hard rubber, enamelware, or stainless steel of the proper composition, to avoid corrosion and resulting contamination of the solutions.

Comprising the **major equipment** are the manual processing tanks. The simplest type consists of a three-compartment tank, one end-compartment being used for developing and the opposite one for fixing. The middle compartment serves both to rinse and wash the films and should be supplied with running water. Thermostatic temperature control produces optimal results.

Stainless steel of the proper alloy composition is the best material for processing tanks because not only does it resist corrosion but it also permits rapid equalization of the temperature of the processing solutions with that of the water in the middle compartment (stainless steel is an excellent conductor of heat in contrast to rubber or stone). Insulation of the outside walls of the tank prevents condensation of moisture and helps maintain the proper temperature within the compartments.

A more satisfactory arrangement is that shown in Figure 16.4, consisting of a large, insulated, stainless steel, double-compartment master tank. Two stainless steel insert tanks are placed in one of the compartments, the first insert being the developing tank and the other, the fixing tank. Water between the inserts in this compartment serves both to rinse the films and to control the temperature of the solutions. A fixing tank should have about twice the volume of a developing tank since the time required for fixing films is approximately twice that for development. The other main compartment serves as the washing tank and should be about twice the size of the fixing tank, since washing requires about twice as long as fixation.

Inserts should be measured when first installed to determine their correct volume. If the level of the solution is to be 2.5 cm (1 in.) from the top, then

$$\text{volume in liters} = \frac{(\text{height}_{cm} - 2.5) \times \text{length}_{cm} \times \text{breadth}_{cm}}{1000}$$

Figure 16.4. A convenient array of tanks for manual processing. The developing and fixing tanks are separate units placed in the master tank on the left. Note the relative sizes of the tanks.

or

$$\text{volume in gallons} = \frac{(\underset{in.}{\text{height}} - 1) \times \underset{in.}{\text{length}} \times \underset{in.}{\text{breadth}}}{231}$$

The wash tank should be deep enough for the water to pass completely over the tops of the hangers for thorough washing.

A conveniently located water inlet facilitates washing the tanks and making up the solutions. Thermostatically controlled warm water and refrigerated water are essential and should be circulated around the processing tank inserts to maintain optimal temperature.

Various types of *drying devices* help speed up the drying of films. Driers are available as enamel or stainless steel cabinets provided with a heating element and blower fan. Venting to the outside minimizes heat and humidity in the darkroom.

A *lightproof storage bin* for unexposed film should be placed under the loading bench. Vertical partitions subdivide the bin to accommodate film boxes of different sizes. Counterweighting the drawer of the bin makes it close automatically when released. A warning light must be posted on the front of the bin to prevent its being opened in white light. *Film hangers* of proper size and in sufficient number should be available to hold the films during processing, but these are unnecessary with automatic processing.

QUESTIONS AND PROBLEMS

1. Where is the best location for the darkroom? How should the walls be shielded?
2. Discuss the various kinds of darkroom entrances, including the advantages and disadvantages of each.
3. Describe interlocking doors. Passboxes.
4. What materials are preferred in the construction of processing tanks? Name the best material for tanks and dryers.
5. Describe a darkroom safelight lamp. What precautions are necessary to assure that the safelight is really safe?
6. How do you test a darkroom for safe illumination?
7. Which colors should be used in painting the walls of the darkroom? Of the maze?
8. Make a diagram of a convenient arrangement of the processing tanks, and indicate their comparative sizes.
9. A developing tank measures 8 in. wide × 16 in. long × 19 in. high. How many gallons of developer does it hold when filled to a level one inch below the top? Convert the data to the metric system and compute the volume in liters. Approximately how many liters equal 1 gallon?
10. How can you prevent x rays from entering the darkroom, and why?
11. Describe briefly a film drier.
12. Why is running water essential in the darkroom? Why do we need warm and refrigerated water?

CHAPTER *17*   *CHEMISTRY OF*
RADIOGRAPHY AND
FILM PROCESSING

Introduction

T HE BASIC PRINCIPLES of radiographic image formation in sensitive emulsions have been established for many years, evolving
as they have from ordinary photography. However, as we shall see
later, certain changes were required to adapt conventional film
processing to automation, these changes being perhaps more *physical*
than chemical. Therefore, a thorough understanding of radiographic
image formation and photographic chemistry should precede the
study of both manual and automatic processing.

Radiographic Photography

Fundamental to an understanding of the production of an image
on an x-ray film, is the concept of the *latent image.* An ordinary
radiographic film emulsion contains silver halides in the form of
minute crystals that are invisible to the naked eye (1 to 1.5
microns). These halides consist mainly of silver bromide (AgBr)
but also include a small amount of silver iodide (AgI) to enhance
sensitivity. When struck by light or x rays, these crystals undergo
an electrochemical change, which increases their susceptibility to
the action of certain chemicals (developers). Such exposed silver
halide crystals make up the *latent image, defined as that invisible
image produced in the film emulsion by light or x rays, which is
changed to a visible or manifest image during development.*
Let us now examine in greater detail what happens when light
or x rays strike a silver bromide crystal. Figure 17.1 contains a
diagram of the *lattice* structure of a silver bromide crystal. In it, the

positive silver ions alternate with the negative bromide ions (and an occasional negative iodide ion), all being held together by ionic bonds (see page 50), although some silver ions drift freely through

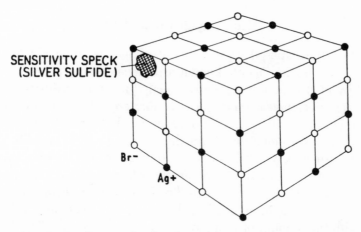

SENSITIVITY SPECK
(SILVER SULFIDE)

Br⁻

Ag⁺

Figure 17.1. Lattice diagram of a silver bromide (AgBr) crystal. The straight lines joining the Ag+ and Br− ions represent the electrovalence forces holding the ions together in the crystal. An occasional iodide ion (I−) may also be present in place of a Br− ion. The sensitivity speck (silver sulfide) renders the crystal highly sensitive to light and x rays.

the lattice. During the ripening phase of emulsion manufacture, *silver sulfide particles* serving as *sensitivity specks* or *development centers* appear on the surface of the crystals. Only those crystals having sensitivity specks can be affected by exposure to light or x rays. A photon entering such a sensitized crystal may interact with a bromine ion liberating a loosely bound (valence) electron and leaving a neutral bromine atom. As this valence electron drifts through the lattice, it may be trapped by a sensitivity speck to which it imparts a negative charge. A migrant positive silver ion, now attracted to the negatively charged speck, picks up the electron, and becomes neutralized to a silver atom. Another electron soon becomes trapped by the speck, and another silver ion drifts to it and is neutralized. This process, initiated by the photons entering the crystal, may be repeated many times in an extremely small interval of time. The number of susceptible crystals so affected depends on the number of photons falling on a given area of the film. Crystals in which the sensitivity specks have acquired silver atoms during exposure remain invisible and constitute a *latent image center.*

Radiographic Chemistry

When the exposed crystal (latent image) is subjected to the action of reducing agents known as *developers,* the process initiated by photon action is greatly speeded up; *the sensitivity speck acts as a development center for the entire crystal.* In fact, development intensifies the latent image about 10^8 times. The speck rapidly picks up electrons from the reducing agents and attracts more silver ions which become neutralized to silver atoms, growing into thread-like particles of *metallic silver.* Thus, the *dark areas in a radiograph consist of metallic silver in a very fine state of subdivision,* the amount of silver deposited in a given area increasing with the amount of radiation received by that area. The basic concepts of photographic chemistry are shown in Figure 17.2.

During development the bromine (and iodine) ions diffuse out of the developed crystals and into the solution. This, in addition to the gradual exhaustion of the reducing agents, eventually causes deterioration of the developer to the point where it must be discarded.

What happens to the portions of the film emulsion that are not affected by light or x-ray photons? Since the silver halides (AgBr and AgI) in these areas have not been altered, they are relatively unaffected by the developer. However, they must be removed in order to render the unexposed film areas *transparent,* and also to prevent *fogging* by subsequent exposure to light. The unexposed and undeveloped silver halides are eliminated from the emulsion by immersion in a *fixing agent,* ammonium thiosulfate, a process known as *fixation.* As a result, the areas from which the silver halides have been removed become clear, while the black areas remain black since metallic silver is not dissolved by the fixing agent in the ordinary course of processing. However, prolonged immersion in the fixing solution will cause bleaching of the image; this may be appreciable even in twenty-four hours.

A. EXPOSURE

Figure 17.2. Scheme of the basic theory of photographic chemistry. In *A*, radiant energy in the form of light or x rays converts a silver bromide (or silver iodide) crystal containing a sensitivity speck (silver sulfide) into a *latent image center*. In *B*, the developer reacts with the altered crystal and reduces it to metallic silver, which constitutes the *manifest image*.

The amount of blackening of a particular area of a radiograph depends on the amount of radiation it has received. This is the radiation that has passed through the various thicknesses, types, and densities of tissue interposed between the tube and the film and is called **remnant** or **exit radiation.** It comprises the **aerial image** (image in space) which, in cross section, consists of more or less closely spaced photons that will be displayed on the image receptor (film, intensifying screen, fluorescent screen) (see Figure 17.3).

Let us consider, for example, the simple case in which a radiograph of the hand is made by direct exposure to x rays (ie, without intensifying screens). The light areas represent the bones; because of their high calcium content, the bones absorb a large fraction of the incident x rays so that very few x-ray photons pass through them to the silver halide crystals in the film emulsion underlying them. Therefore, the reducing action of the developer on these crystals produces almost no darkening. The soft tissues, on the contrary, absorb only a relatively small fraction of the incident x rays and therefore the areas of film emulsion beneath the soft tissues receive a relatively large amount of remnant or exit radiation.

As a result, more silver halide crystals are affected in these regions and the developer causes considerably greater blackening. Notice that the finished radiograph is really a negative, corresponding to a negative in ordinary photography. It is actually the recorded aerial image of the tissues of different thicknesses and densities, which vary in their attenuation of x rays (mainly by photoelectric absorption). As was shown earlier (see pages 292–297), the radiographic effect of the aerial image is greatly enhanced by intensifying screens.

Figure 17.3. Formation of the aerial image. The x-ray beam, on passing through the body, undergoes absorption and scattering which depend on the kV and on the atomic number and density of any particular tissue. The beam emerging on the opposite side of the body contains information in terms of the number of photons per unit cross-sectional area of the beam; this comprises the *remnant* or *exit radiation*, which forms the *aerial image* or *image in space*. The resulting image on the film—the *radiographic image*—consists of the various densities corresponding to the aerial image.

MANUAL PROCESSING

We shall now turn to the practical aspects of *film processing*, which consist of (1) conversion of the latent image to a visible or manifest image and (2) the preservation of that image. This includes primarily development, rinsing, fixing, and washing. Each of these important steps will be described in detail for manual processing as an introduction to automated processing. Optional steps such as fixer neutralization and detergent rinse will also be included. Cleanliness of hands, utensils, and darkroom are of utmost importance in both manual and automated processing.

Development

The function of development is to convert the latent image to a visible image by means of a *developing solution* which contains four essential ingredients.

Developing Solution. Composition:

1. *Organic Reducing Agents*—usually include a mixture of *hydroquinone* and *metol* (or elon, a synonym for metol) for manual processing. The metol acts during the early stage of development, producing the basic gray image, whereas the hydroquinone acts more slowly, building up density and contrast to the desired level. Two such reducing agents in proper combination assure optimum development of the radiographic image. (A combination of hydroquinone and phenidone yields the high speed developer needed for automatic processing.)

2. *Preservative—sodium sulfite*—protects the organic reducing agents (hydroquinone and metol) from oxidation by the air, thereby prolonging the effective life of the developer. It also suppresses staining of the emulsion by decomposition products formed during development.

3. *Accelerator—sodium carbonate* or *sodium hydroxide*—swells the emulsion slightly, making it easier for the developing agents to enter the emulsion, and the products of the reaction to diffuse out. Furthermore, hydroquinone can act only in an alkaline medium. Thus, gel swell and alkalinization speed up development.

4. *Restrainer—potassium bromide*—preferentially holds back any

action of the developer on the unexposed silver bromide grains without preventing the action of the developer on the exposed grains. Thus, it inhibits fogging of the lighter areas without interfering significantly with the development of the radiographic image.

Practical Factors in Development. The two most important factors in development are (1) the *temperature* of the developing solution and (2) the total *time* of development. A correctly exposed film undergoes complete development with a particular combination of temperature and time; in fact, it is almost impossible to compensate for underexposure by prolonging development time.

The optimum temperature for development is 20 to 22 C (68 to 72 F). With cold developer, that is, below 16 C (60 F), the *action of hydroquinone ceases* and the resulting radiograph lacks contrast and density. However, even at 16 C (60 F) quality is not impaired if developing time is sufficiently long. Developer that is too warm, that is, above 24 C (75 F), may soften the emulsion and also produce chemical fog. At a given appropriate temperature there is a definite, correct developing time, best determined from the data furnished by the manufacturer of the films and solutions being used. However, various manufacturers recommend nearly the same developing times so that for practical purposes one may use the graph shown in Figure 17.4. This graph averages the data supplied by the two leading film companies (Eastman and DuPont), for *medium-speed screen film* and *rapid developer.* From this graph, we can readily determine the correct developing times at various temperatures, based on a normal time of 3 min at 20 C (68 F). At 17 C (62 F) the developing time is 4½ min and at 24 C (76 F) it is 2 min. Notice that an increase in temperature of the solution increases the speed of chemical action, so that developing time must be decreased according to the graph. Processing of films on the above basis is called *time-temperature development.*

With manual development radiographic exposure is based on *five-minute development at 20 C (68 F).* This produces radiographs of superior contrast with about 5 kV less exposure than is required for three-minute development.

When films are immersed in the developer they should be *agitated gently* at first and about once every minute thereafter to insure uniform development and prevent streaking. During

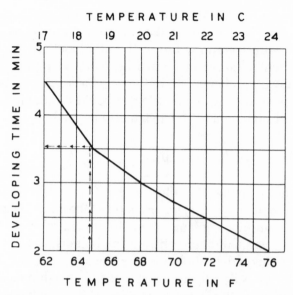

Figure 17.4. Time-temperature development chart. This is a composite based on the data furnished by the two leading American manufacturers for medium speed film and rapid developer.

development, bromides are freed from the emulsion and if not removed by agitation, tend to inhibit development wherever they cling to the film. This is most frequently manifested by light streaks below the letters of the identifying labels on the film. Agitation of the film removes these waste products and allows fresh solution always to be in contact with the film emulsion, thereby assuring uniform development.

Replenishment. With continued use of the developing solution its activity diminishes as the hydroquinone and metol are gradually exhausted during the reduction of exposed silver halides to metallic silver. Furthermore, the level of developer in the tank drops progressively because some is carried out with each film. Because of this gradual weakening and loss of volume of the developer, a special solution—*replenisher*—is added periodically to maintain constant activity and volume and assure uniform results. Replenisher composition differs from ordinary developer in having (1) no bromide, because this ion is released from the film emulsion and accumulates in the developer and (2) a higher concentration of hydroquinone, metol, and alkali, because these ingredients are exhausted with continued use of the developer. This method of replenishment requires that films be removed rapidly from the developer, without being allowed to drip back into the tank. With proper replenishment, the developer should be usable for two to three months before a fresh batch has to be made up.

Rinsing

After development, the film must be rinsed for about thirty seconds in running water to remove most of the adhering chemicals, thereby diminishing contamination of the next solution, the fixer. Rinsing can be made more efficient by immersing the films in a tank containing a dilute solution of acetic acid (about 1 percent), which neutralizes the alkali carried over from the developer. Otherwise, the alkali gradually neutralizes the acid in the fixing solution, decreasing its effectiveness as well as its useful life. *Without thorough rinsing, the fixer does not act evenly and the radiograph becomes streaked.* Rinsing is omitted in automatic processing.

Fixation

The purpose of this step is (1) to *remove the unexposed and undeveloped silver halides,* (2) to *preserve the film image,* and (3) to *harden the emulsion* so that it will not be easily damaged.

Fixing Solution. This consists of four essential ingredients:

1. *Fixing Agent—hypo* (*sodium thiosulfate* in powdered fixer; *ammonium thiosulfate* in liquid fixer)—*clears* the film by dissolving out the unexposed, undeveloped silver bromide and silver iodide, leaving the metallic silver in the exposed and developed areas of the film more readily discernible. Without fixation, the undeveloped silver halides would leave the radiograph nearly opaque. Moreover it would eventually turn black, completely hiding the radiographic image.

2. *Preservative—sodium sulfite*—protects the fixing agent from decomposition and helps clear the film.

3. **Hardener—chrome alum or potassium alum**—"tans" or hardens the gelatin in the emulsion, thereby protecting it against scratches.

4. **Acid—sulfuric acid or acetic acid**—serves two purposes: it neutralizes the alkali still remaining on the film, and provides an optimum medium for the fixer and hardener.

Fixing time depends on the age of the fixer and the number of films processed. A satisfactory fixer requires about one to four minutes to **clear** a film—that is, to remove all the unexposed silver halides—but it takes two or three times the clearing time to **harden** the emulsion. The solution should be discarded when it has become so exhausted that the fixing time is prolonged beyond ten minutes. When the films are immersed in the fixing bath, they should be **agitated** and **separated** to allow uniform action of the chemicals and prevent streaking. To avoid fog, white light should not be admitted until the films have been fixed for at least one minute. Prolonged fixation is to be condemned because the **hypo becomes so firmly bound to the emulsion that it cannot be removed in washing,** thereby causing eventual brown discoloration of the radiograph. Besides, prolonged fixation may cause **bleaching** of the image. The optimum temperature of the fixing bath is 18 to 24 C (65 to 75 F); at very low temperatures, chemical action is retarded, while at high temperatures the emulsion may be softened and easily damaged.

Replenishment requires the periodic addition of fresh fixer after an equal volume of older fixer has been discarded. Not only does this prolong the useful life of the fixing solution, but it also maintains its full strength. The level of solution in the tank remains constant (except for slight loss due to evaporation), because each film carries in about as much liquid as it carries out.

Washing

An important step in film processing is thorough washing to remove residual chemicals from the film emulsion. For example, hypo remaining in the emulsion will eventually change deposited black silver to brown silver sulfide, with gradual fading of the image. Ordinarily, if the volume of water flowing per hour is about eight times the capacity of the wash tank, washing is complete in 20 minutes at 20 C (68 F). This is the minimum washing time regardless of how fast the water changes. A slower flow rate makes for longer washing, but if excessive, this may soften the emulsion. Abnormally high temperature also softens the emulsion, whereas extremely cold water slows the washing process.

A *fixer neutralizer bath* significantly shortens washing time. After removal from the fixer, the films are rinsed briefly in the rinse tank and then immersed for two minutes in a tank containing a special solution which removes the fixer from the emulsion. Washing will then be complete (in running water) in five minutes.

Drying

Films can be dried by various methods. Although small numbers of films can be dried in wall-mounted racks, special film driers perform much more efficiently (see page 316).

A *wetting agent* such as household liquid detergent reduces washing time by about 50 percent. The washed films are immersed for two minutes in a tank containing one teaspoon of detergent per gallon of water, and then placed in the drier.

Darkroom Problems

It may be of some help to indicate the causes of the more common film defects.

1. **Fog.** There are many causes of film fogging, that is, a generalized darkening of the film.

a. *Exposure to Light.* This may occur when the darkroom is not light proof; the safelight contains too large a bulb; the safelight housing or filter is cracked; the safelight filter series is incorrect; or the exposure of the film to the safelight is prolonged, especially at short distances.

b. *Exposure to X Rays or Radionuclides.* Films should be shielded from these sources of radiation by distance and sufficient thickness of lead.

c. *Chemical Fog.* The many causes include overdevelopment or development at excessively high temperatures; oxidized, deterio-rated developer, which may also stain the film (oxidized developer is brown); prolonged or repeated inspection of films during develop-ment; and contamination from corroded tanks.

d. *Age Fog.* Either mottled or uniform fogging due to outdated films, or films stored under conditions of high temperature and excessive humidity.

2. **Stain.** Various types of discolorations may appear on films at different intervals after processing. These can generally be avoided by the use of reasonably fresh solutions and correct processing.

a. *Brown.* Oxidized developer.

b. *Variegated Color Pattern.* Inadequate rinsing.

c. *Grayish-yellow or Brown.* Excessive fixation, or use of exhausted fixer.

d. *Grayish-white Scum.* Incomplete washing.

3. **Marks and Defects.** There are several different kinds of characteristic markings which appear when films are not handled gently.

a. *Crinkle Marks* are curved black or white lines about 1 cm in length which result from bending the film acutely over the end of the finger.

b. *Static Marks* are lightning or tree-like black marks on the film, caused by static electricity due to friction between the film and other objects such as intensifying screens and loading bench. To avoid this, films should always be handled gently. In addition, the loading bench should be grounded in order to prevent the buildup of static electricity.

c. *Water Marks* are caused by water droplets on the film surface, which leave round dark spots of various sizes because of migration of silver particles.

d. *Cassette Marks* are caused by foreign matter such as dust, hair, fragments of paper, etc, or by screen defects, which leave a corresponding white mark on the radiograph.

e. *Air-bell Marks* result from formation of air bubbles in the developer. A bubble prevents developer from reaching the underly-ing film, and so leaves a small, clear circular spot on the radiograph.

f. *Streaking* is caused by a variety of technical errors and is one of the most troublesome types of film defects. It usually results from: (1) failure to agitate the films in the developer; (2) failure to rinse the films adequately; (3) failure to agitate the films when first immersed in the fixer; and (4) failure to stir the processing solutions thoroughly after replenishment.

AUTOMATED PROCESSING

A major improvement in radiography has been the perfection of automated processing of films. Successful marketing of automated processors has brought about a reduction in cost, thereby making such equipment available even to the department with a limited budget.

There are many outstanding advantages of automated processing. First, it **shortens total processing time to as little as one and one-half minutes,** in contrast to about one hour for the manual method. (Even with hypo neutralizer and wetting agent, manual processing can be reduced, at best, to about forty minutes.) Second, it **improves quality control** due to more accurate temperature regulation and more precise replenishment in the automated processor. Third, it increases the capacity of the Radiology Department or office by expediting work flow.

The manufacturers of the first automated processors were beset by four main problems: transport mechanism, processing chemicals, temperature control, and film characteristics. A discussion of these problems and their solution is essential to the understanding of the principles of automated processing, especially as they depart from manual processing.

1. **Transport Mechanism.** The basic mechanism of the auto-mated processor is a series of rollers which transport the films from the loader through the various sections — developing, fixing, washing, and drying. The speed of transport must be constant to assure correct sojourn of the films in each section. Spacing between the rollers must be accurate to an extremely small tolerance to avoid slipping or jamming of the films. Besides these operations, the transport system provides brisk **agitation** of the solutions over the film surfaces to assure uniform action of the developer. The squeez-ing action of the last few rollers in each section removes a large amount of solution from the films before they enter the next

Figure 17.5. Automated processing. In the upper part is shown a cutaway diagram of the processor (side view). In the lower part is shown a diagrammatic top view. (*Courtesy of Eastman Kodak Company.*)

section, thereby lessening contamination of the solutions. Finally, the terminal rollers in the wash section squeeze out most of the water and so hasten drying of the films. Figure 17.5 shows diagrammatically a typical automated processor; its apparent simplicity belies the difficulties encountered during its early development.

2. **Processing Chemicals.** Although the basic principles of photographic chemistry apply to both manual and automated processing, conventional solutions were found to cause insurmountable difficulties in the first automated experimental models. Roller spacing was so critical that the swelling of the emulsion in the developer, and its subsequent shrinkage in the fixer, caused the films either to jam between the rollers or to wrap around them. Further complications arose when an attempt was made to speed up processing through the use of stronger solutions.

Figure 17.6 shows a variation of about eleven units of *gel swell* of the emulsion during manual processing. This renders conventional solutions completely unsuited to automated processing; in fact, it turns out that the problem is largely *physical.*

To adapt solutions to automation with its decreased processing time, certain changes had to be made. These may be summarized as follows:

a. *Filters in Water Supply Line* to remove small-particle impurities. There is a separate porous filter for the hot and cold water supply. The filters must be replaced at regular intervals, depending on the purity of the water. Should the cold water filter become clogged and the hot water continue to enter the processor, the solutions would become overheated, resulting in overdeveloped, dark radiographs. Furthermore, the emulsion could soften, causing slippage or wraparound of the films as they proceed through the rollers. On the other hand, should the hot water line become clogged, the thermostat would cycle on and off more frequently to maintain processing temperature, increasing the likelihood of thermostat failure. Some processors operate on only a cold water supply requiring a single filter; in these units the thermostat and heater are designed to temper (warm) the incoming water without the need of a separate hot water supply.

b. *Increased Concentration of Solutions* to shorten greatly the processing times in the various sections. Hydroquinone and pheni-done are the developing agents, and cycon is added as an antioxidant (retards oxidation). A fresh developer bath consists of replenisher, properly mixed, to which has been added a **starter solution** to prevent excess alkalinity. Thereafter, a pump automatically feeds properly mixed replenisher solution from a storage tank into the development section. The fixer also has a higher concentration than in manual processing; here, too, a pump automatically feeds fixer replenisher solution from a storage tank into the fixer section.

Figure 17.6. Relative swelling of a film emulsion, in arbitrary units of gel swell, during various stages of *manual processing* at 68 F. Note the large variation in the degree of swelling of the emulsion. (*Courtesy of R. E. Humphries, GAF Corporation.*)

c. **Increased Processing Temperatures** to help speed up processing; for example, 35 C (95 F) in developer and fixer, 31 C (88 F) in wash, and 57 C (135 F) in dryer are typical of ninety-second processors. Drying time is reduced to 20 seconds. To combat chemical fog at these high temperatures, antifogging agents such as aldehydes are added to the developer.

d. **Hardening of Emulsion** to prevent softening by the solutions, as well as sticking to the rollers. For this purpose, special hardening agents such as glutaraldehyde or sodium metaborate are included in both the developer and fixer.

e. *Control of Emulsion Thickness* to keep it as constant as possible throughout processing, to permit the use of constant spacing between the rollers. Compounds such as sulfates are added to the developer to minimize swelling of the emulsion.

f. *Precise Replenishment* of the developer and fixer to maintain the proper alkalinity of the developer, acidity of the fixer, and the chemical strength of both solutions. Replenishment must be adjusted to a constant rate for each film processed, the fixer being replenished at twice the rate of the developer.

3. **Temperature Control.** As just noted, *high temperatures* prevail in automatic processing. This has resulted in marked shortening of processing time, but now extremely accurate temperature control has to be maintained in each section of the processor. This is accomplished by a pump, which circulates water at the proper temperature around the developer and fixer sections; the water finally enters the wash section. Incoming water temperature is usually lower than that of the processing solutions so that it can be heated to the correct temperature under thermostatic control. Temperature is even more critical than in manual processing because the technologist can no longer adjust development or fixing time for differences in temperature. Moreover, the very short developing time at high temperature makes the films much more susceptible to serious under- or overdevelopment when these factors differ even slightly from the normal.

4. **Film Characteristics.** The manufacture of films requires even more precise control than before to maintain constant thickness of the base and emulsion. Curling tendency must be eliminated to prevent wrapping around rollers or misdirection to the wrong rollers, causing jamming of the films. The emulsion characteristics must conform to the new types of processing solutions. Finally, stickiness of the emulsion has to be minimized to prevent adherence to the rollers and wrap-around.

The various modifications just described have made automatic processing so dependable that it has become practicable even in the private office and small hospital. Figure 17.7 shows how constant the thickness of the emulsion remains. The overall variation in gel swell from start to finish in automatic processing is about four units, but after the initial relatively slight swelling of the emulsion in the developer, the thickness remains virtually constant well into the drying phase.

TIME IN MIN.

Figure 17.7. Relative swelling of a film emulsion, in arbitrary units of gel swell, during various phases of *automatic processing* at 81 F. Note the small variation in the degree of emulsion swelling; this is due to special additives in the solutions. (*Courtesy of R. E. Humphries, GAF.*)

Table 17.1 contrasts the important steps in manual and automatic processing. It bears out the assertion at the beginning of this section that automation has removed one of the main bottlenecks in the Radiology Department.

The question naturally arises as to the frequency of breakdown of automatic processing equipment. Experience has shown that the greatest cause of breakdown is *failure to keep the rollers scrupulously clean,* as recommended by the manufacturer. Another cause is improper rate of automatic replenishment which should be carefully checked at regular intervals.

Sensitometry is coming into wider use to check the correctness of developer replenishment. It is long overdue as a method of quality control. Sensitometric testing of the developer should be done periodically, in addition to the usual test for replenishment, to assure

TABLE 17.1
COMPARISON OF MANUAL AND AUTOMATIC PROCESSING

	Manual	Automated°
		1½-minute
Developing Temperature	20 C (68 F)	35 C (95 F)
Fixing Temperature	20 C (68 F)	35 C (95 F)
Washing Temperature	20 C (68 F)	35 C (95 F)
Drying Temperature	43 C (110 F)	57 C (135 F)
Developing Time	3–5 min	25 sec
Fixing Time	2–10	21
Washing Time	15–30	9
Drying Time	15–20	20
Surface Change	Manual Agitation	Transport Rollers
Replenishment	Manual	Automatic

°Data vary with type of equipment, films, and chemicals.

uniformity of development during the useful life of the solution.

Several brands of high speed processors are available with ninety-second total processing time. Occupying an extremely small space, these units can accommodate about 300 films of assorted sizes per hour. To assure optimum film speed, contrast, and latitude, proper film and chemical combinations must be used.

As a rule, two smaller units are preferable to one larger unit of the same total capacity because (1) in the event of equipment failure, the second unit is still available; and (2) there is less waiting time in loading two processors during peak hours.

Several brands of automated processors are available and selection should be made carefully because they vary in performance. One should especially *avoid* those requiring more than ninety seconds because they lack important features and also demand an annoying increase in processing time. Furthermore, one should have ready access to competent repair service.

QUESTIONS

1. Define latent image. How is it produced?
2. Of what do the black areas on a roentgenogram consist? What factors determine the various densities in a radiograph?

3. What is the purpose and theory of development? Fixation?
4. List the ingredients of a manual developing solution and describe the function of each one.
5. List the ingredients of a manual fixing solution and describe the function of each one.
6. What is meant by time-temperature development?
7. Discuss replenishment of developer and fixer in manual and automated systems.
8. What is included in the term "film processing"?
9. Name five causes of film fogging and state how they can be avoided.
10. Describe four causes of streaking of radiographs.
11. Why should overfixing be avoided?
12. Describe the important differences in the composition of processing solutions in automated and manual systems.
13. What problems would arise if manual processing solutions were used in an automatic processor?
14. List the important advantages of automated processing over manual processing.
15. State and explain briefly the three functions of the transport system.
16. Why are automated processors operated at high temperature? How critical is the developer temperature in automated processing in comparison with manual processing?
17. How can one decrease the frequency of automated processor breakdown?
18. Why are filters used in the water supply of automated processors? What is the result of clogging of these filters?

CHAPTER *18* RADIOGRAPHIC QUALITY

Medical radiography seeks to provide the maximum diagnostic information about a particular anatomic area by recording the radiographic image, usually on film. Its success depends on the production of radiographs of superb quality. A radiograph of poor quality may cause serious error in diagnosis through inadequate recording of information.

What do we mean by radiographic quality? This refers to the visible sharpness of images of structural details such as bone trabeculae and small pulmonary vessels. We use the expression *recorded detail* to denote radiographic quality. Other terms include definition, sharpness, detail, and visibility of detail, but an all-inclusive term like recorded detail is preferred so as to avoid confusion.

Recorded detail refers to the distinctness of radiographic image margins. When such margins are blurred (ie, fuzzy), recorded detail is poor. The sharpness of image margins can be measured objectively as acutance—the abruptness of the boundary between a detail and its surroundings. Another concept is resolution, which measures the ability of an image receptor (screen-film, fluoroscopic screen, image intensifier, etc) to produce separate images of closely spaced small objects. Although acutance and resolution are related, they are affected differently by such factors as contrast and density.

Five principal factors influence recorded detail: blur, density, contrast, distortion, and noise. These will now be considered separately and as they relate to one another.

338

BLUR

There are four causes of image blurring or unsharpness. One is geometric in origin, depending primarily on the measurable size of the focal spot. The other three have to do with motion of the object, the nature of the image receptor (eg, film-screen system), and the shape of the object being radiographed.

Geometric or Focal Spot Blur

The arrangement in space relating the x-ray source (focal spot), anatomic part, and film, controls the degree of geometrically produced blurring. We shall simply call this *geometric* or *focal spot blur.* The terms penumbra and edge gradient may be used as synonyms for geometric blur, but are no longer preferred in radiography.

In practice, geometric blur depends on three factors: (1) effective focal spot size, (2) focus-film distance (FFD), and (3) object-film distance (OFD). (It should be mentioned that official publications use the term source-image receptor distance (SID) rather than focus-film distance, but the latter is at present much more widely used and is more familiar to radiographers.) All these factors influence geometrically recorded detail (ie, image sharpness), which improves as geometric blur is reduced.

1. **Size of Effective Focus.** According to elementary geometry, the effective or apparent size of the focal spot has a profound influence on recorded detail. Figure 18.1 shows an anatomic object situated between an x-ray tube and a film. If the focal spot were assumed to be a point (having no dimension), all x rays passing the edge of the object would produce a point-for-point sharp image of the object margin on the film. But in practice the focal spot has a finite width, usually ranging from 0.3 to 2.0 mm. Therefore, as shown in Figure 18.2, x rays originate over innumerable points on the focal spot, spread as they pass the edge of the object, and proceed toward the film. This produces a blurred margin, the width of the blur being proportional to the effective focal spot size (compare Figure 18.2A with Figure 18.2B). In other words, to obtain minimal blur we should use the smallest practicable focal

spot. Since we have already indicated that blur impairs recorded detail, we may conclude that *tubes with smaller focal spots provide better recorded detail, with resulting improved image quality.*

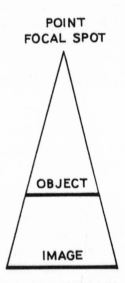

Figure 18.1. Image production by a hypothetical (imaginary) *point* focal spot. All the rays passing the edge of the object would produce a point-for-point sharp image of the object margin. The result would be nearly perfect geometrically recorded detail (no blur or penumbra).

2. **Focus-film Distance (FFD).** The degree of blur (ie, blur width) also depends on the distance between the focal spot and the film. As the FFD is increased while the object-film distance (OFD) remains unchanged, the x rays arising from innumerable points on the focal spot undergo relatively less spread after passing the edge of the object, on their way toward the film. As shown in Figure 18.3A, at a shorter FFD, the image margin is blurred more than in Figure 18.3B where the FFD is longer. Therefore, blurring decreases and recorded detail improves with increasing focus-film distance.

3. **Object-film Distance (OFD).** The third geometric factor in blurring is the object-film distance (OFD). If the focal spot size and the focus-film distance remain constant, a decrease in the OFD decreases blur and improves recorded detail. This

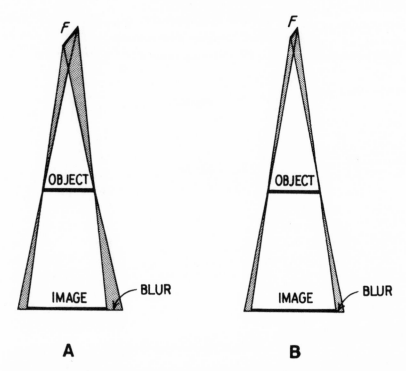

A   **B**

Figure 18.2. Influence of focal spot size on recorded detail. In *A*, the larger effective focal spot produces more blurring (wider penumbra) than the smaller effective focal spot in *B*. Focal spot blurring is caused by x rays, which are emitted from the entire focal spot area, converging toward the edge of the object and then diverging toward the edge of the image at the film or other image receptor. Thus, *a smaller focal spot produces better geometrically recorded detail.*

is readily seen by comparison of Figures 18.4A and 18.4B.

The above geometric factors in image blurring (penumbra) may be conveniently summarized by a simple equation derived from Figure 18.3 where F is the *effective* focal spot width, a is the focus-object distance, b is the object-film distance, and B is geometric blur. By the rules governing similar triangles,

$$B/F = b/a$$

so

$$B = Fb/a$$

$$\text{geometric blur} = \frac{\text{effective focus size X object-film distance}}{\text{focus-object distance}} \quad (1)$$

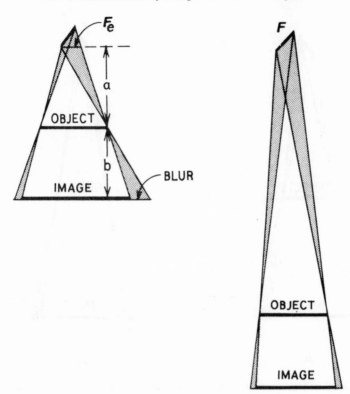

Figure 18.3. Influence of focus-film distance on recorded detail. The object-film distance is the same in A and B, but the *focus-film distance* is longer in B than in A. Note that there is less blurring of the image in B. Thus, *increasing the focus-film distance improves geometrically recorded detail.*

As will be shown later (see pages 373 to 374), recorded detail is closely related to *magnification,* which increases with an increase in object-film distance, and with a decrease in focus-object distance (see Figure 18.4). In fact, geometric blur is directly proportional to *percentage magnification* (*not* magnification factor), all other factors being constant.

In summary, then, recorded detail (image sharpness) is enhanced by any factor that decreases geometric blur or penumbra, namely, (1) small tube focus, (2) long focus-film distance (*FFD*), and (3) short object-film distance (*OFD*). Accordingly, you should place

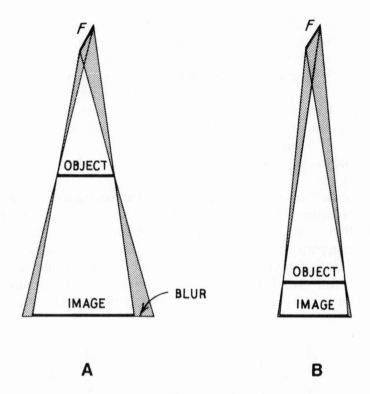

A   **B**

Figure 18.4. Influence of object-film distance on recorded detail. The focus-film distance is the same in *A* and *B*, but the *object-film distance* is shorter in *B* than in *A*. Note that blurring of the image is less in *B* than in *A*. Thus, *decreasing the object-film (ie, part-film) distance improves geometrically recorded detail.*

the part to be radiographed as close to the film as possible and use an appropriately long focus-film distance, with the smallest applicable focal spot.

Focal Spot Evaluation

As we have seen, the size of the focal spot strongly influences recorded detail. Unfortunately, there is no simple method of evaluating the focal spot, nor is there universal agreement, even among physicists, as to how it should be done. At the present time there are three general ways of designating focal spot characteristics:

1. **Nominal Size.** As quoted by the manufacturer, this is based on *computation* or *measurement* at very low mA (pinhole camera). However, the nominal size often understates the *effective* or *projected size* of the focal spot by a significant margin. Based on the ±50 percent tolerance customarily allowed in manufacture, a 0.3 mm focal spot may be as large as 0.45 mm, a 0.6 mm focal spot 0.9 mm, and a 1.0 mm focal spot 1.5 mm.

We shall now turn to the methods of practical evaluation of focal spot size.

2. **Pinhole Camera.** The *projected (effective) focal spot* dimensions can be measured by a *pinhole camera* as described in detail in *ICRU Report No. 10f.* A pinhole camera consists of a tiny hole drilled in a plate made of a gold-platinum alloy. For example, hole diameter is 0.03 mm for focal spots smaller than 1 mm, and 0.075 mm for focal spots 1 to 2.5 mm. These very small holes minimize blur (penumbra), making for more accurate measurement of the

Figure 18.5. Principle of the pinhole camera for measurement of focal spot size. In *A* the pinhole is located midway between the tube focus and the film, so the image *i* of the focal spot has the same size as the effective or apparent focal spot F_{eff}. In *B*, with the pinhole located twice as far from the film as from the focus, the image *2i* is twice the size of the focal spot. Thus, proper correction must be made for the position of the pinhole in measuring focal spot size. In addition, the vertical axis of the pinhole must be perfectly aligned with the central ray.

Figure 18.6. Effect of milliamperage (mA) on focal spot size. Note that x-ray emission is most intense along the edges of the focal spot—the so-called *edge* or *band effect*. Also, the size of the focal spot increases significantly with mA, a condition known as *blooming*. (*Adapted from Bernstein, Bergeron, and Klein, courtesy of Radiology.*)

focal spot image. At the same time, the small pinhole requires very long exposures, so that care must be taken not to damage the target of the x-ray tube. It is extremely important that a pinhole camera conform to rigid specifications and be purchased from a reputable dealer.

In actual use, the pinhole is placed between the focal spot and a fine grain x-ray film, perfectly aligned with the central ray, perpendicular to it and parallel to the film. Figure 18.5 shows the arrangement. For focal spots up to 2.5 mm the pinhole-film distance is twice the focus-pinhole distance to give a magnification factor of two. Measurement of the pinhole image is made with a calibrated lens and corrected for magnification.

As shown in Figure 18.6, the x rays emitted by the focal spot have a nonuniform intensity distribution (ID), being concentrated along two edge bands. In fact, such an ID makes the focal spot behave as though it consisted of two narrow focal spots, the effect being to impair image resolution when compared with an ID that has a central peak of intensity. Doi and Rossman have shown that with a computerized simulated system in small vessel angiography, focal spot size may be more important than ID.

Also note that focal spot size increases with increasing mA, a condition known as **blooming** (but decreases with increasing kV). Since the focal spot is smaller when hot than when cold, blooming does not depend on temperature; rather it results from space charge effects associated with higher mA. It is important to know that in angiography, for example, the projected focal spot size increases about 50 percent in going from 200 to 1000 mA. Because focal spots are measured at the factory at mA values much below those prevailing in radiography, their sizes are significantly understated. Thus, the pinhole camera permits the evaluation of focal spots as to size, shape, and intensity distribution under actual operating conditions in the Radiology Department.

3. **Resolution Test Patterns.** Inasmuch as the pinhole camera does not show directly the resolution capability of a focal spot, another method has had to be devised—the **star pattern resolution object.** Resolution designates the smallest distance between two objects such that they appear as two separate images. Figure 18.7A shows a star pattern object. It provides a continuous change in spacing between thin radiopaque lines (usually lead), the limit of resolution being indicated by the blending of the line images. The theory underlying the use of resolution test objects is too complex to be considered here. However, it should be noted that there may be a ringed zone of apparently good resolution within the blurred zone, but this represents spurious resolution.

Another type of resolution test object consists of a series of grouped **parallel opaque lines** that differ in thickness and spacing (see Figure 18.7B). With this test object, resolution is related to the thinnest and most closely spaced line pairs resolved by the particular focal spot and is expressed as the maximum number of line pairs per mm. A line pair consists of a line and one adjacent space.

In summary, then, focal spot measurement is necessary to assure satisfactory recorded detail, since the true effective focal spot size may be appreciably larger than the nominal size. However, such measurements require experienced personnel using precision instruments. The two most widely used devices are the standard pinhole camera and some type of resolution test object; the former measures the physical size of the projected (effective) focal spot

A   B

Figure 18.7. Examples of resolution test patterns. *A*. Star type, useful in measuring focal spot resolution. *B*. Parallel line type for measuring resolution of intensifying screens. (*Courtesy of Nuclear Associates, Inc.*).

(also, shape and intensity distribution), whereas the latter measures its resolution capability. It behooves the purchaser of an x-ray tube to demand a suitably narrow tolerance range, especially for fractional focal spots such as 0.3 mm, and for angiography and magnification radiography. But in any case, measurement should be verified by one or both of the described methods.

Motion Blur

Motion of the part being radiographed may be regarded as the greatest enemy of recorded detail because it produces a blurred image and cannot be completely avoided. Motion can be minimized in three ways: (1) by careful immobilization of the part with sand bags or compression band, (2) by suspension of respiration when examining parts other than the limbs, and (3) by using exposures that are as short as possible, generally with intensifying screens of adequate speed, provided quantum mottle is not excessive (see pages 349–350). Although screens contribute blur, this detrimental effect is usually more than compensated for by the reduction of motion blur.

Screen Blur

Recorded detail is better in radiography with cardboard holders than with intensifying screens, provided *immobilization is adequate.* However, when fast exposures are needed to minimize the effects of uncontrolled motion, screens must be used; under these circumstances, the gain in sharpness with screens and short exposures usually more than compensates for the blur that would result from the increased effect of motion accompanying the use of cardboard holders or detail (slow) screens with long exposures. In general, screen blur is greater than that caused by a 1 mm focal spot. On the other hand, extremely short exposures using high speed screens with very low mAs can impair recorded detail as a result of excessive quantum mottle (see pages 349–350). Insofar as *film-screen combination* is concerned, better recorded detail results from a fast film and medium speed screen combination than from the reverse. This is explained by the following data on calcium tungstate screens:

Screen blur is generally of the order of about six times inherent film blur.

Blur with medium-speed *screens* is about one-half that with high speed screens.

Blur with high and medium speed *films* is virtually negligible in radiography.

Why is recorded detail impaired by intensifying screens even when the patient is adequately immobilized? We may summarize the reasons as follows:

1. **Crystal Size.** Recall from Chapter 15 that intensifying screens produce a radiographic image because of *fluorescence of crystals* in the active layer. Since each crystal, despite its very small size, produces a spot of light of similar size on the film, image lines are broader than when they are formed directly by x-ray photons. Image blur increases with increasing crystal size, but this is of relatively minor importance in practice because crystals do not vary widely among various types of screens.

2. **Active Layer Thickness.** The diffusion (spreading) of light in the active layer due to its measurable thickness increases image blur (see pages 300–302).

3. **Film-screen Contact.** Cassettes are provided with spring-metal clamps to secure close contact between the film and screens. Even very slight separation between them allows the light from any point in the screen to spread on its way to the film, thereby contributing to blur with impaired recorded detail (see pages 303–305).

Because of these factors, slow screen-film systems (detail screens) should be used in the radiography of small parts (hands, feet, wrists), especially in infants and small children, to obtain adequate recorded detail. However, in the radiography of parts measuring 8 to 10 cm thick, medium or high speed screens should be used routinely; and above 10 cm, a grid also.

4. **Mottle.** In examining, with a magnifying glass, a radiograph that has been exposed by means of *intensifying screens,* you will find that it has a mottled or grainy appearance. Only a small part of this is contributed by radiographic mottle, which comprises the granular structure of the screens and the clumps of silver in the radiographic image.

More important is *quantum mottle,* produced by the nonuniform intensity over the cross section of an x-ray beam as it leaves the tube port. Recall that the beam consists of photons or quanta having a random distribution in space. Thus, in a film that has been exposed to such a beam, different areas have actually received different numbers of photons.

With *slow image receptors* such as slow screen-film combinations, or direct exposure film, a large number of photons are needed for a particular degree of film density (darkening). Under these conditions the photons striking the image receptor are closely crowded, the variation in the number of photons from area to area is small, and the image is relatively uniform. On the other hand, with *fast image receptors* such as high-speed screen-film combinations, a smaller number of photons can provide the same overall density, but now there is a larger variation in the number of photons from area to area (statistical fluctuation) and the image appears mottled. This is a simplified version of quantum mottle.

Quantum mottle increases with high contrast films because density differences are exaggerated. But increased diffusion of light in intensifying screens, such as those with thicker active layers, increases image blurring and at the same time makes quantum mottle less apparent. Quantum mottle is one type of *noise,* which impairs recorded detail (see pages 360, 380, and 387).

Aside from the image receptors themselves, there is another factor in the production of quantum mottle. This is the *kV.* As kV is increased, each x-ray photon gives rise to more light photons, so the screen intensifying factor increases. Thus, fewer information-carrying x-ray photons are ultimately required for a given degree of film darkening with a particular film-screen combination. This explains why high kV increases quantum mottle, especially with very low mA.

In summary, then, quantum mottle increases with fast image recording systems and with high energy photons. In any given instance, the decision has to be made as to whether high speed or minimal mottle is more important.

Object Blur

Most anatomic structures, which we here refer to as objects, have rounded borders. These introduce a blur factor, demonstrated in Figure 18.8. Note that in *A* the object has a shape conforming to that of the x-ray beam, so all the rays pass through the full thickness of tissue. As a result, the radiographic image presents a sharp boundary or *density gradient* as seen from the density trace at the bottom of the figure. In *B,* the rays pass through progressively thinner portions of the object toward its periphery so that image density fades off gradually at the border. In *C,* the round object also gives rise to an image with fading density at its boundary. Thus, in both *B* and *C* the image border has a long density gradient with increased blurring, its degree depending on the distance over which the density falls off. The effect of object blur is greater than is often appreciated, and it may even exceed geometric blur.

DENSITY

The amount of darkening of an x-ray film, or of a certain area on the film, is called *radiographic density.* It should be recalled that any region of the film emulsion exposed to light from intensifying

Figure 18.8. Object blur caused by object shape. In *A* the shape of the object conforms to that of the beam, so the density fall off sharply at the edge of the image which therefore has an abrupt or sharp border. In *B* a progressively smaller thickness of the object intercepts the beam toward the edge, so the density falls off gradually at the image boundary, which is therefore less sharp than in *A*. In *C* a rounded object also produces a less sharp image than in *A*. (*Adapted from Seemann, H. E.: Physical and Photographic Principles of Medical Radiography; by permission of John Wiley & Sons, Inc.*)

screens, or directly to x rays, becomes susceptible to the action of the developer. The silver halides that have been so affected are changed by the developing agent into tiny particles of ***metallic silver*** which appear black because of their finely divided state. The greater the total amount of radiation that reaches the film, the greater will be the final degree of blackening. Areas receiving only a small amount of radiation undergo little or no subsequent action by the developer, such underexposed areas appearing gray or translucent in the finished radiograph. Thus, in the final analysis, ***radiographic density*** (ie, degree of blackening or opacity) ***depends on the amount of radiation reaching a particular area of the film and the resulting mass of metallic silver deposited per unit area during development.*** Standardization of development should produce optimal film density for a correctly exposed film.

Density is measured by an instrument known as a ***densitometer,*** which indicates the relationship between the intensity of light falling upon one side of a given area of a radiograph (as from an illuminator) and the intensity of the light passing through (transmitted). This relationship is given by the following equation:

$$\text{density} = \log \frac{\text{incident light intensity}}{\text{transmitted light intensity}} \qquad (2)$$

The equation can best be explained by numerical examples. If the incident light intensity is ten times the transmitted intensity, then the density is $\log 10 = 1$; if the incident light intensity is one hundred times the transmitted intensity, then the density is $\log 100 = 2$; etc. One need not be conversant with logarithms to use a densitometer, since it is calibrated to read density directly. With this method, clear film base has a density of 0.06 to 0.2, depending largely on the amount and shade of blue dye present. A diagnostic radiograph usually has densities varying from about 0.4 in the lightest areas to 3.0 in the darkest. Obviously, excellent radiographic quality requires optimal density for any particular anatomic structure; the correct exposure is supposed to be incorporated in the technic chart.

Density is an extremely important factor in radiographic quality because it carries **information.** Without density there is no image and therefore no recorded detail. However, density must be optimal because, in excess, it may actually conceal information, just as too much light in ordinary photography may destroy detail.

Five factors govern the radiation exposure and resulting density of a radiograph: (1) kilovoltage, (2) milliamperage, (3) time, (4) distance, and (5) thickness and nature of part being radiographed.

1. **Kilovoltage.** An increase in kV applied to the x-ray tube increases both the exposure rate and the percentage of higher energy (short wave length) photons. These more penetrating photons are not so readily absorbed by the structures being radiographed, and therefore a larger fraction of the primary radiation eventually reaches the intensifying screens. Thus, an increase in kV increases the exposure rate at the film and the resulting radiographic density. In general, ***an increase of 15 percent in kV approximately doubles the exposure.*** For example, we can double the exposure at 40 kV by adding 6 kV, and at 70 kV by adding 10 kV. Note that although radiographic density increases as exposure increases, this relationship is not strictly proportional.

Under ordinary conditions, with grids having a ratio of 8 or less, it is unwise to exceed 85 kV because this produces an excess of **scattered radiation,** which fogs the radiograph and impairs contrast.

On the other hand, the efficiency of x-ray equipment improves at higher kV because of the considerably smaller heating load on the anode (see page 231) and the greater certainty of penetration. It has been found that *high voltage radiography* at 100 to 130 kV and a high ratio grid (12 or 16) offer advantages over conventional radiography, including greater latitude and a smaller dose to the patient.

2. **Milliamperage.** For practical purposes, x-ray output (R/min) is proportional to the mA. Hence, doubling the mA doubles the radiographic exposure rate; tripling the mA triples the exposure rate. Tube current (mA) is governed by the number of electrons passing from cathode to anode *per second.* As the flow of electrons per second is increased, more x rays per second are produced at the target. Note that the *mA determines only the exposure rate; it has nothing to do with the penetrating power of the beam.*

3. **Time.** An increase in exposure *time* causes a proportional increase in the number of x-ray photons reaching the intensifying screens, and therefore a proportional increase in the total *exposure* of the film. Thus, doubling the time doubles the total exposure, and tripling the time triples the total exposure. A longer exposure time allows the radiation of a given exposure rate to act longer, thereby eventually affecting more silver halide crystals in the film emulsion and increasing the *density* of the radiograph. In actual practice the mA and exposure time are usually multiplied and called *milliampere-seconds* = *mAs;* this represents the amount of electron charge transferred from the cathode to the anode of an x-ray tube during the exposure. For example, if the technic is set up for 100 mA and $1/10$ sec, then multiplying $100 \times 1/10 = 10$ mAs. If a shorter exposure is needed, as in radiographing a small child, and the density is to remain unchanged, the mA can be increased to 400 and the time reduced to $1/40$ sec; $400 \times 1/40 = 10$ mAs. In other words, the old mA times the old time in seconds equals the new mA times the new time in seconds, as expressed in the following equation:

$$mA_1 s_1 = mA_2 s_2 \tag{3}$$

This relationship, known as the *reciprocity law,* holds reasonably well throughout the diagnostic x-ray region, provided the x-ray generating equipment has been **properly designed** and **calibrated.** You should cultivate the habit of thinking in terms of mAs because it greatly facilitates the modification of established technics, thereby increasing the flexibility of the technic chart.

4. **Distance.** The effect of distance on exposure rate is not so simple as some of the other factors, but it is easily understood by keeping in mind the following elementary geometric rules:

a. X-ray photons actually originate from innumerable points on the focal spot of the x-ray tube, spreading in all directions from their points of origin.

b. In considering the effect of distance on exposure rate, we shall assume that the focal spot acts as a point source from which x rays spread in the form of a cone after leaving the circular port of the tube housing. We normally modify the beam by a collimator (beam-limiting device), which gives it a rectangular or square cross section.

Since the x-ray photons diverge (spread) *the width of the beam increases as the distance from the target increases.* This means that the same amount of radiation is distributed over a larger area the farther this area is from the tube focus. Obviously, the same radiation spread over a larger area must spread itself "thinner." If, at a certain distance from the tube focus, the beam were to cover completely a film of a certain size, then at a greater distance it would cover a larger film. However, the radiographic density of the latter would be less in a given exposure time because each square centimeter of this film would have received less radiation than each square centimeter of the first film. We may therefore conclude that *radiographic exposure rate decreases as the focus-film distance increases.*

We can determine by simple geometry *how much* the exposure rate decreases as the focus-film distance increases. In Figure 18.9 the slanting lines represent the edges of a beam emerging from the focus at the target, *T,* and restricted by a square collimator. Two planes, *ABCD* and *EFGH,* are chosen perpendicular to the direction of the central ray of the beam (represented by the dotted line). Both planes are assumed to be squares. Plane *EFGH* is located twice as far from the target as plane *ABCD.* Therefore each side of the lower plane, such as *HE,* is twice as long as a side of the upper plane, such as *DA,* because triangles *FHE* and *FDA* are similar and their corresponding sides are proportional. To simply the discussion, let X equal a side of the upper plane. Then $2X$ must equal a side of the lower plane. The area of the upper plane will then be $X \times X = X^2$, and the area of the lower plane will be $2X \times 2X = 4X^2$. Thus, the lower surface, *EFGH* has four times the area of the upper surface, *ABCD.*

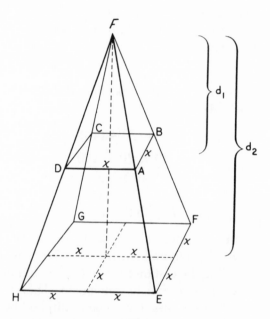

Figure 18.9. Inverse square law of radiation. The lower plane surface (*EFGH*) is selected at twice the distance from the point source of radiation (tube focus) than is the upper plane (*ABCD*). Each side of the lower plane ($x + x$) is twice as long as each side of the upper plane (x). It is evident from the diagram that the lower surface area is four times as large as the upper surface area, which means that at twice the distance from the target the x-ray beam covers four times the area and therefore the brightness of illumination must be only one-fourth as great.

It is evident that *when the distance is doubled, the same radiation is spread over an area four times as great.* Therefore, the brightness or illumination must be 1/4 as great. The *inverse square law of radiation* applies to both x rays and light, and may be stated as follows: *the intensity or exposure rate of radiation at a given dis-*

tance from a point source is inversely proportional to the square of the distance. For example, if the exposure rate of an x-ray beam at 20 in. from the focus is 100 R/min, what will it be at 40 in.? Let us set up the inverse square law in equation form:

$$I/i = d^2/D^2 \tag{4}$$

where

I is the exposure rate at 40 in. = ?
i is the exposure rate at 20 in. = 100 R/min
d = 20 in.
D = 40 in.

Note again the inverse square proportion. Substituting the above values in equation (4):

$$I/100 = (20)^2/(40)^2$$

$$I = \frac{\cancel{20} \times \cancel{20} \times 100}{\underset{2}{\cancel{40}} \times \underset{2}{\cancel{40}}}$$

$$I = 25 \text{ R/min}$$

Thus, at twice the distance the exposure rate is one-fourth the initial value (25 as compared with 100). This means that in radiography, doubling the distance while the kV and mAs are held constant reduces the exposure to one-fourth. Therefore, to keep the exposure constant the mAs has to be multiplied by four.

Let us take another example. If the exposure rate of radiation at 60 in. is 10 R/min, what will the exposure rate be at 20 in.? Again using equation (4), let i represent the unknown exposure rate at point d located 20 in. from the focus. Then, using the data given in the above problem,

$$10/i = (20)^2/(60)^2$$

$$1/i = \frac{\cancel{20} \times \cancel{20}}{10 \times \underset{3}{\cancel{60}} \times \underset{3}{\cancel{60}}}$$

$$1/i = 1/90$$

$$i = 90 \text{ R/min}$$

In other words, the distance has been reduced to $20 \div 60 = \frac{1}{3}$ and the exposure rate has increased by $90 \div 10 = 9$ times.

There is a ***much simpler method*** of applying this law. Rearranging equation (4),

$$ID^2 = id^2 \tag{5}$$

This means that for a given set of factors (kV, mA, filter, etc) the exposure rate at a particular point in the beam, times the square of the distance of the point from the focal spot, is a ***constant.*** Thus, in equation (5), id^2 is a constant. In the problem on page 356, it is stated that $i = 100$ R/min at distance d, 20 in. Therefore,

$$id^2 = 100 \times 20 \times 20$$

The problem is now solved by substituting this constant and the ***new*** distance, 40 in., in equation (5).

$$I \times 40 \times 40 = 100 \times 20 \times 20$$

$$I = \frac{100 \times \overset{1}{\cancel{20}} \times \overset{1}{\cancel{20}}}{\underset{2}{\cancel{40}} \times \underset{2}{\cancel{40}}}$$

$$I = 25 \text{ R/min}$$

In actual practice, a therapy machine must be calibrated for each treatment distance because of deviation from the inverse square law due to the large focus. However, the law is sufficiently accurate for approximation in diagnostic radiology and in protection problems.

In radiography we use a ***direct square law*** when changing focus-film distances because we are ***compensating*** for the reduced or increased exposure as the distance is increased or decreased, respectively. Assuming that the kV remains constant, we may obtain the mAs required to compensate for a change in distance by using the following equation:

$$\textit{new mAs/old mAs} = \textit{(new distance)}^2/\textit{(old distance)}^2 \tag{6}$$

For example, if the factors 100 mAs, 100 kV, and 40-in. (100 cm) distance produce a radiograph having the proper density, what will be the mAs needed to maintain the same radiographic density at a focus-film distance of 60 in. (150 cm)?

new mAs/100 mAs $= (60)^2/(40)^2$

new mAs $= 100 \times 3600/1600 = 225$ mAs

5. **Radiographic Object.** The human body consists of tissues and organs that differ in thickness and density with resulting difference in radiolucency—the ability to transmit x rays. Thicker and denser anatomic parts, whether normal or pathological, attenuate (ie, absorb or scatter) x rays to a greater degree, leaving less exit or remnant radiation to reach the film. Ranging from the greatest to the least density or radiopacity are: (1) dental enamel, (2) bone, (3) tissues of "water density" such as muscle, glands, and solid nonfatty organs, (4) fat, and (5) gas. Pathologic processes such as pneumonia increase the density of lung tissue. On the other hand, destructive bone diseases reduce the density of bone. Exposure factors—kV and mAs at a particular distance—are optimally selected for the thickness and density of the part being radiographed.

CONTRAST

A radiograph consists of light and dark areas; that is, it shows variations in density. The range of density variation among the light and dark areas is called *radiographic contrast.* While density represents the amount of silver deposited in a given area, contrast represents the relative distribution of silver in various areas of a radiograph. To be perceptible to the average human eye, the difference in density of adjacent areas must be at least 2 percent. *Optimum contrast enhances recorded detail.*

There are three kinds of contrast. *Radiographic contrast*—the overall contrast of a radiograph—depends on *subject contrast* and *film contrast.* These will be discussed separately and interrelated. However, the unqualified term contrast usually means radiographic contrast.

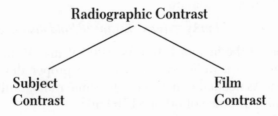

Radiographic Contrast

Subject Contrast   **Film Contrast**

Radiographic Contrast

We usually designate radiographic contrast as *long scale* (low) or *short scale* (high). This concept may be explained as follows: suppose a radiograph were cut into small squares representing each of the different densities present, from the lightest to the darkest, and these squares were then arranged in order of increasing density. If there should be many such squares with very little difference in the density of successive squares, then the original radiograph must have had *long scale* or *low contrast.* On the other hand, if there should be relatively few squares with a large difference in density between successive ones, then the original radiograph must have been of *short scale* or *high contrast.* In other words, a long scale or low contrast radiograph has a long range of tonal gradation from white, through many shades of gray, to black; whereas a short scale or high contrast radiograph has a short range between white and black (see Figure 18.10).

Contrast improves recorded detail and is optimal when it produces sufficient difference in density among the various details to make them distinctly visible in all areas of the radiograph. This is usually achieved by *medium scale contrast.* Excessively short scale contrast tends to impair detail; an example is the so-called "chalky" radiograph which may lead to error in interpretation, especially in the detection of fine fracture lines. However, short scale contrast is desirable under special circumstances such as angiography.

Subject Contrast

As indicated earlier, *subject contrast* is one of the factors in radiographic contrast, the other being film contrast. Before defining subject contrast, we must first introduce appropriate basic concepts.

An x-ray beam undergoes *attenuation* or loss of photons while passing through a patient, because of absorption, scatter, and inverse square law. But attenuation is not uniform throughout the cross section of the *exit beam,* that is, the beam leaving the patient. If we could somehow "see" the exit beam in cross section from the standpoint of the film, we would observe a variation in the number

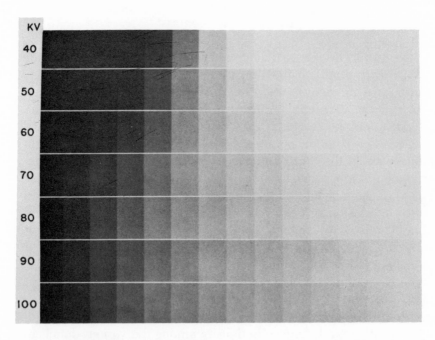

Figure 18.10. Effect of kilovoltage on contrast, using an aluminum stepped wedge. The short range (high) contrast with 40 kV, as compared with long range (low) contrast with 100 kV, is obvious.

of photons per cm^2 at different locations in the beam. This results from unequal degrees of attenuation of x rays by various tissues. It is the spatial distribution of photons in the cross section of the exit beam that constitutes the *aerial image* (see Figure 17.3), which will eventually be recorded on the film (or some other image receptor) as the *radiographic image.* This distinction must be kept in mind.

Thus, *subject contrast may be defined as the contrast in the aerial image.* It is actually the ratio of the number of photons in two or more equal small zones of the aerial image.

Note that the aerial image contains information derived from the patient. But in addition to the wanted information, the aerial image becomes contaminated with *noise,* this being *unwanted* radiation that impairs the quality of the information and ultimately degrades the quality of the resulting radiograph. Such noise factors, which include scattered radiation, quantum mottle, and fogging, obscure recorded detail.

We shall now explore the factors that affect subject contrast, namely, radiation quality, radiographic object, scattered radiation, and fogging.

1. **Radiation Quality**—determines penetrating ability (transmission) of an x-ray beam. This is the inverse of attenuation. We found in Chapter 12 that an increase in the kV across the x-ray tube increases the penetrating ability of the resulting x-ray beam. A beam of high penetrating ability goes through tissues of various densities more uniformly than does a beam of low penetrating ability. For example, in radiography of a leg, the bony structures absorb a much greater fraction of the primary x rays than do the soft tissues. As the kV and consequent penetrating ability of the primary photons increase, the difference in the absorption of the radiation, as between bone and soft tissues, becomes smaller. Consequently, the transmission of x rays through bone is more nearly like that through soft tissue and there is less difference in radiographic density between them; in other words, there is a reduction in subject contrast. Figure 18.10 shows the effect of various kilovoltages on contrast. You can see that an *increase in kV produces longer scale or lower contrast* in the radiograph of an aluminum stepped wedge (a bar made up of a series of increasing thicknesses of aluminum).

An additional factor at higher kV is the loss of contrast resulting from the increase in the fraction of scattered radiation, but this is largely removed by the use of high ratio grids.

2. **Radiographic Object**—thickness and nature of object being radiographed. As already described on page 358, the human body consists of tissues that differ in transparency or *radiolucency* to x rays—the greater the attenuation coefficient (ability to absorb and scatter x rays) of a given type of tissues, the less its radiolucency and the smaller the amount of transmitted or exit radiation reaching the film. Ranging from the greatest to the least radiopacity are (1) tooth enamel, (2) bone, (3) tissues of "water" density such as muscle, glands, solid nonfatty organs, (4) fat, and (5) gas. For example, a radiograph of the abdomen has a light zone in the center representing the vertebral column which attenuates more

radiation than an equal mass of soft tissue. Various soft tissues are represented as shades of gray, depending on differential attenuation. The fat around the kidneys, along the psoas muscles, and in the abdominal wall, appears as dark gray or nearly black lines.

The differential attenuation of x-ray photons produces subject contrast in the aerial image, ultimately contributing radiographic contrast, which improves recorded detail. A number of organs and anatomic regions do not have sufficient inherent contrast for plain radiography. In such cases adequate contrast enhancement becomes possible by the use of *contrast media.* For example, dense media such as barium sulfate in the gastrointestinal tract, and iodinated compounds in the gall bladder, kidneys, vascular system, and bronchial tree. Note that the photoelectric effect produces a sharp peak in absorption of x-ray photons, approximately equivalent to a 65-kV beam, because the binding energy of the K-shell electrons of iodine is 32 keV. Optimal contrast would therefore be obtained at about 65 kV. However, we find in practice that adequate contrast between iodine and soft tissue occurs with x-ray beams generated at 65 to 80 kV. Sometimes a less dense medium can be used, such as air in the ventricles of the brain. At this point you should review the physical reasons for the difference in attenuation of x rays by various tissues, discussed on pages 189–190.

3. **Scattered Radiation** — a noise factor, obscuring information, or detail, in the radiographic image. Scattered radiation impairs contrast by a fogging effect mainly on the **lighter areas** of the radiograph, and may be controlled by means of stationary or moving grids and by limiting the size of the x-ray beam with a collimator, cone, or aperture diaphragm (see Chapter 19).

4. **Fogging** from any cause contributes to noise, imparting an overall gray appearance to the radiograph with reduction in contrast.

Film Contrast

As we have already pointed out, film contrast and subject contrast make up radiographic contrast. However, in considering film contrast we must include the type of image receptor (in this instance, film), its use with or without screens, and the processing system. It is therefore more appropriate to speak of the *film imaging system,* a designation which includes film and processing, with or without screens.

Films themselves vary in their *inherent contrast,* depending on their emulsion characteristics. Thus, films are specifically designed for long, medium, or short scale contrast.

The *development process* also affects film contrast. For example, a developer containing sodium hydroxide as an accelerator produces greater contrast than one containing sodium carbonate. Within the normal range of time-temperature development, contrast is not appreciably influenced by the temperature. However, at excessively high temperature or unduly prolonged developing time chemical fog may occur, reducing contrast. Gentle agitation during development improves contrast. More important, a decrease in radiographic exposure with appropriate increase in developing time, within reasonable limits, enhances contrast. For optimum contrast, strict adherence to the correct time-temperature curve is essential. With automated processing, optimum contrast is readily achieved by precise control of time and temperature.

Finally, you should recall that *intensifying screens* convert 98 percent or more of the radiologic image to light. In other words, the aerial image is changed almost completely to a light image which is then recorded by the film. This conversion process enhances contrast because screen-type film has more inherent contrast for the light emitted by screens than for x rays directly. In general, contrast increases and latitude decreases with faster film-screen systems.

There is no simple definition of *film* contrast. It can be understood only by studying the so-called *characteristic* or *sensitometric* curve of a particular film recording system, shown in Figure 18.11. This type of curve was first used in photography by Hurter and Driffield and is often referred to as an H & D curve. Film manufacturers use such curves to monitor film quality and consistency. H & D curves show the density response of film to various exposures under experimental conditions. Radiographic density is then plotted as a function of exposure (actually, density versus log relative exposure). Referring to Figure 18.11, we note that at a value of 0.5 on the horizontal axis the beginning of the curve already lies above this axis because of *inherent* or *base film density of 0.2.* As the exposure is increased, film density at first increases gradually with an upward curve in the *toe portion*, then more steeply along a *straight line*, and finally along a *shoulder portion.* The slope of the straight line joining the point on the curve near the toe corresponding to base density $0.2 + 0.25 = 0.45$, and the point on the curve near the shoulder corresponding to base density $0.2 + 2.0 = 2.2$, has been defined arbitrarily as the *average gradient* (see dashed line in Figure 18.11). The average gradient includes the useful exposure-density range of a film and varies with the type of film. *Those films with greater average gradients show greater contrast for a given subject contrast.* A film with an average gradient greater than 1 will heighten subject contrast.

The characteristic curve also shows that at low densities (toe portion) and at high densities (shoulder portion) contrast is poor. Maximum contrast occurs in the straight portion. An average radio-graph displays poor contrast in both the lightest (toe) and darkest (shoulder) regions. Furthermore, underexposure exists in the toe region, and overexposure in the shoulder region. It is precisely in these regions where recorded detail is poor.

Most radiographic *technic charts* are based on the different densities of various parts of the body, and on different thicknesses of the same part of the body in different individuals. The thicker or denser the part, the greater is the required exposure in terms of kV, mA, and time. Some technic charts keep the mAs constant for a given region of the body and vary the kV according to part thickness. Others show *optimum kilovoltage* for a given part and vary the mAs. If high kV equipment is available, we can use 100 to 140 kV with grids having a ratio of 12 or 16. High voltage radiography produces radiographs with good definition, wide latitude, and moderate contrast, provided suitable filters and grids are employed; besides, patient exposure is reduced with high kilolvoltage exposure.

Soft Tissue Radiography — Mammography

In soft tissue radiography, of which mammography is a specialty, we are dealing with essentially two types of structures—those of *water density* (eg, muscle, glands, fibrous tissue, blood vessels) and

Figure 18.11. Characteristic (H & D) curve of a typical screen-type x-ray film. *G,* the slope (steepness) of the straight portion of the curve, represents the region of maximum film contrast. *G'* is the slope at one extremely short segment of the toe portion; note that here the slope varies along the curve and is less than that of the straight portion so that contrast is low. In the shoulder portion contrast is also low. Furthermore, the toe portion is a region of underexposure, and the shoulder a region of overexposure. The dashed line represents the *average gradient* (average slope) and encompasses that portion of the curve corresponding to the useful exposure-density range of the film in question.

fat. With conventional exposure factors, these tissues exhibit poor subject contrast. However, by selection of suitable exposure factors we can enhance radiographic contrast between fat and any tissue of water density. But there is no way to distinguish radiographically the various tissues of water density unless they happen to be surrounded by fat, short of using contrast agents. This important principle applies directly in mammography in that lesions such as tumors (water density) can be separated radiographically from the surrounding fat which is often present in sufficient amount to act as a natural contrast agent, especially in older or obese women. Furthermore, since about one third of breast cancers contain microcalcifications (0.05 mm or less) that require viewing with a hand lens, superb recorded detail is essential.

Film Mammography. Since conventional radiography, especially with ordinary films, does not provide the high soft-tissue contrast and excellent recorded detail needed in mammography, we must use special exposure factors and films: (1) low kV, (2) minimum filtration of the beam, (3) small focal spot, and (4) industrial-type fine grain film or special single-emulsion film with a single screen. As we found earlier, the lower the kV the greater the radiographic contrast, a relationship that is particularly important in soft tissue radiography. Thus, Egan's original mammographic technic called for a nominal 20 to 30 kV and 1200 to 1800 mAs, with appropriate calibration of each x-ray machine. However, these exposure factors impose such a heavy load on the ordinary x-ray tube that its useful life is shortened. Special tungsten target tubes are available to permit operation at the high mAs levels needed with low kV.

All added filtration must be removed in order to use the lowest energy radiation for contrast enhancement. Inherent filtration (ie, tube port and oil) should not exceed 1 mm Al. General radiographic equipment is usually unsuitable for mammography not only because it may not operate below 40 kV, but also because of the excessive filtration by the plastic cover of the collimator and the inherent filtration of the tube.

The smallest available tube focus should be used, certainly never more than 1 mm. Unduly heavy loading of the tube prevents the use of an ordinary x-ray tube with a fractional focus.

Extremely slow, fine grain film without screens contributes not only to contrast enhancement, but also superb definition. Modern mammographic film is a modified industrial-type film that can be processed in an automated processor. Unfortunately, this mammographic system, with industrial film alone, delivers excessive radiation doses to the breast. For this reason, the image receptor has been replaced by a single emulsion film with a single screen, housed in a vacuum-type film holder. This *low-dose system* provides excellent contrast and recorded detail while delivering a much smaller dose to the breast. Although graininess exceeds that with nonscreen technic, it is not detrimental to diagnostic accuracy.

In 1966 a new type of radiographic tube was invented in France by J. R. Bens and J.-C. Delarue. Knowing that optimum contrast is achieved in soft tissue radiography with x rays ranging in wavelength from 0.6 to 0.9 Å, or average energy of about 17.5 kV, they designed an x-ray tube with a *molybdenum (Mo) target.* They selected Mo because at about 30 kV it emits characteristic radiation with energies of 17.14 and 19.5 kV (average 19 kV). Note that the energy of this radiation matches fairly closely the optimum for soft tissue radiography (in fact, it is slightly higher than the optimum 17.5 kV, and this is desirable). Furthermore, they introduced a 0.03 mm *Mo primary filter* into the beam to remove much of the radiation with energy above and below the desired range, thereby producing a *nearly monoenergetic beam.* Using the *same* metal—Mo—for *both* the target and the filter utilizes the principle of the *spectral window;* that is, a filter readily transmits the characteristic radiation produced initially by the same element, while absorbing much of the general radiation (continuous spectrum). Note that a tungsten target emits only a continuous spectrum (ie, no characteristic radiation) at 30 kV; although it is nearly monoenergetic, it is of such low intensity that a large mAs must be used.

Several special mammographic tubes are available, equipped with molybdenum anodes. One has a rotating molybdenum anode with superimposed 0.6 and 1.2 mm focal spots. Inherent filtration is high enough to reduce the danger of skin "burn" if a molybdenum filter is accidentally omitted but low enough to transmit the low energy radiation (Machlett Dynamax "M64").

Another type of mammographic tube also has a rotating anode, but it is an alloy of molybdenum and tungsten to provide low energy radiation for film mammography as well as higher energy radiation for xeromammography as described below (General Electric Company.)

A third type of mammographic tube has a water-cooled, grounded, stationary anode with a molybdenum target having a 0.7 mm focal spot (CGR Medical Corporation). Off-focus radiation, which would impair recorded detail, is minimized by a hood (see Figure 18.12). This tube has a beryllium window to transmit low energy radiation and a built-in molybdenum filter to obtain nearly monoenergetic radiation as described above.

Figure 18.12. Stationary anode tube with a hooded molybdenum target, which helps minimize off-focus radiation by trapping scattered and secondary radiation. (*Courtesy of CGR Medical Corporation.*)

Molybdenum targets are generally regarded as being superior to tungsten targets for film mammography because of the improved recorded detail. However, tungsten targets are preferred for xeromammography, although many experts use the special mammographic units with molybdenum targets in xeromammography.

Before leaving this subject you should turn to pages 470–472 for a discussion of xeroradiography. Because of certain inherent advantages, not the least of which is the better detail visibility, xeromammography is posing a serious challenge to film mammography.

DISTORTION

A radiographic image does not faithfully represent the anatomic part, but differs from it in varying degrees of size and shape. Such *misrepresentation of the true size and shape of an object is called distortion.* The amount of distortion depends on several factors, to be discussed in this section. While distortion generally has a degrading effect on radiographic quality, we cannot completely eliminate it because the image lies in a single plane and is two dimensional, whereas the object, being solid, is three dimensional. In fact, we often use distortion deliberately to bring out a structure that would otherwise be hidden, for example, in oblique radiography of the gall bladder to separate it from the vertebral column.

The two kinds of distortion—*size* and **shape**—will now be described.

1. **Size Distortion—Magnification.** X rays emerge from the tube focus in all directions, but the tube port delimits them to form a beam that is circular in cross section. As the beam advances it broadens, becoming cone shaped. Finally as it passes through the collimator, the x-ray beam acquires a rectangular cross section.

Geometric rules prevail in the realm of x-ray image formation just as they do in photography with light. We can easily show that when an object is held between a source of light and a white surface, the size of the shadow enlarges as the object is moved nearer the light, and shrinks as it is moved closer to the white surface. This is due to the ***divergence of image-forming light rays in*** the beam. In Figure 18.13 the divergent beam of light ***magnifies*** the shadow more in *A* than in *B*; that is, the shorter the distance between the object and the source of light the greater the magnification. ***The law of image magnification states that the width of the image is to the width of the object as the distance of the image from the light source is to the distance of the object from the light source.***

$$\frac{\text{image width}}{\text{object width}} = \frac{\text{image distance}}{\text{object distance}} \tag{6}$$

Precisely the same law applies to radiographic image formation. For example, in cardiac radiography the standard procedure is to use a 2-meter (6-ft) focus-film distance to minimize size distortion or magnification of the heart, so that measurement of the transverse cardiac diameter on the radiograph gives virtually the true diameter. On the other hand, contrary to what is often taught, the cardiothoracic ratio, or the ratio of the transverse cardiac diameter to the transverse thoracic diameter, undergoes no significant change as

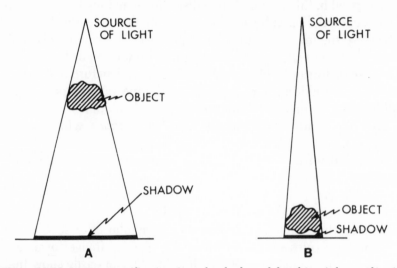

A   **B**

Figure 18.13. Image magnification. In *A* the shadow of the object is larger than in *B*, because in *A*, the object is nearer the source of light. The same principle applies to the formation of x-ray images.

the focus-film distance is varied between 100 cm (40 in.) and 1.8 m (72 in.), if the patient's position remains constant. This results from the fact that as the focus-film distance (FFD) is changed, these two diameters change at virtually equal rates, as shown in Figure 18.14.

Thus, magnification is unavoidable in radiography because of the geometric nature of image formation. As a rule, *magnification or size distortion can be decreased either by reducing the object-film distance (OFD) or by increasing the focus-film distance (FFD)*.

Radiographic magnification is easily derived from the geometric relationship of similar triangles (see pages 18–20). For example, suppose that an object measures 15 in. (37.5 cm) in diameter and lies 10 in. (25 cm) above the level of the film. If the focus-film distance is 40 in. (100 cm), what is the magnification of the radiographic image? We must first determine the width of the image by constructing a diagram as shown in Figure 18.15 and applying proportion (6):

$$\frac{\text{image width}}{\text{object width}} = \frac{\text{focus-film distance}}{\text{focus-object distance}}$$

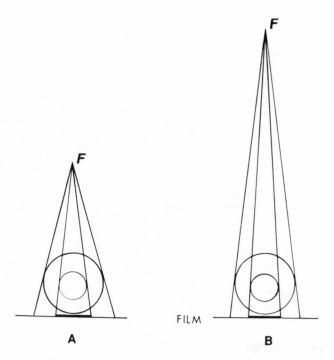

Figure 18.14. Effect of focus-film distance on magnification. In *A*, with a shorter focus-film distance, magnification is greater than in *B*. However, in this example, the *ratio* of the diameter of the *image* of the inner circle to that of the outer circle is essentially the same in both *A* and *B*.

$$\frac{\text{image width}}{15} = \frac{40}{30}$$

$$\text{image width} = \frac{40 \times 15}{30} = 20 \text{ in.}$$

The *linear magnification of the image,* or the enlargement of its width relative to that of the object, may now be expressed in one of two ways:

a. *Magnification Factor.* This is defined as the ratio of image width to object width:

$$\text{magnification factor} = \frac{\text{image width}}{\text{object width}} \qquad (7)$$

Figure 18.15. Magnification of the image in radiography. Image width/object width = 40/30. $x/15 = 40/30$. $\therefore x = 20$ in.

In the above example,

$$\text{magnification factor} = \frac{20}{15} = 1^{1/3}$$

b. *Percentage Magnification.* We define this as the difference between image width and object width, relative to object width, expressed in percent.

$$\% \text{ magnification} = \frac{\text{image width} - \text{object width}}{\text{object width}} \times 100 \quad (8)$$

In the above example,

$$\text{percentage magnification} = \frac{20 - 15}{15} \times 100$$

$$= {}^{1/3} \times 100$$

$$= 33^{1/3}\%$$

The same geometric law of image formation gives the *diameter of the object* being radiographed when the image diameter, the focus-film distance, and the object-film distance are known — draw a diagram as in Figure 18.15, insert the known values, and find the object diameter from the proportion (equation 6). This underlies most methods of finding the pelvic measurements of the mother with relation to the size of the fetal skull, a procedure known as *cephalopelvimetry.*

2. **Shape Distortion.** This is caused by misalignment of the central ray, the anatomic part, and the film. In Figure 18.16, an oval piece of lead placed in the x-ray beam nonparallel to the film, casts a circular shadow. A rectangular piece of lead can be placed in a beam so that it casts a square shadow. With these objects placed perpendicular to the central ray and parallel to the film, the images will, of course, show no appreciable shape distortion and appear oval and rectangular, respectively. Under certain conditions, deliberate distortion may bring out parts of the body that are obscured by overlying structures; for example, in radiography of the gall bladder the patient is often rotated to displace the gall bladder shadow away from the vertebral column.

We can summarize the data on distortion as follows: *there are two types of distortion—size distortion and shape distortion. Size distortion* is magnification caused by progressive divergence (spread) of the image-forming x rays in the beam: the shorter the object-film distance and the longer the focus-object distance, the less the degree of size distortion.

Shape distortion results from improper alignment of the central ray, object, and film. It is, of course, possible to have shape and size distortion occurring together if the causative factors of both conditions are present.

Since distortion (both size and shape) and recorded detail are influenced by the same factors — focus-film distance and object-film distance — the greater the distortion of the radiographic image the poorer the recorded detail (see Figures 18.4 and 18.16). You can readily demonstrate this principle by observing the shadow cast by an object such as a pencil on a white surface. As the pencil is moved toward the light (away from the white surface), the shadow not only becomes larger (magnification distortion) but also becomes more blurred (poorer recorded detail). As the pencil is

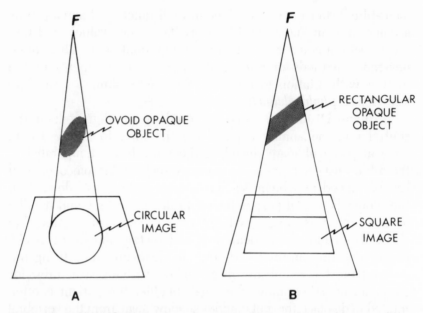

Figure 18.16. Shape distortion. In *A* the projected image of an oval opaque object is circular because the object is not parallel to the film. In *B* the image of a rectangular opaque object is almost square.

moved nearer the white surface, the shadow becomes smaller and sharper.

Direct Magnification or Enlargement Radiography (Macroradiography)

We have already learned that as we move an object away from the film, toward the x-ray tube, image magnification increases if the focus-film distance remains unchanged (see Figure 18.15). At the same time, blurring increases and recorded detail worsens (see Figure 18.4). If we could preserve recorded detail while achieving magnification, we should have a satisfactory method of *direct magnification radiography,* also known as *macroradiography.*

The introduction of tubes with *fractional focal spots,* that is, *microfocus tubes,* confirmed the feasibility of producing directly enlarged radiographic images. Although the 0.3 mm focal spot initially seemed to give reasonably good results insofar as image quality was concerned, subsequent work indicated that even smaller focal spots were needed to *minimize geometric blur and enhance recorded detail* during magnification to produce images with truly superb resolution. In fact, with two-diameter magnification a focal spot larger than an anatomic object (eg, tiny blood vessel) will generate blur wide enough to wipe out the image of the detail as shown in Figure 18.17. This explains why a focal spot no larger than 0.3 mm should be used in macroradiography.

Tubes have been designed with focal spots as small as 0.1 mm and, in fact, some experts believe that really high quality radiographic enlargement cannot be achieved with focal spots larger than 0.2 mm (Rao and Clark). However, their use in radiography is still severely restricted by the very limited heat loading capacities of these tubes.

In practice, two times linear (four times area) magnification is most often used. This requires placing the *anatomic part or object midway between the tube focus and the film* (see Figure 18.18).

Figure 18.17. When the object is smaller than the effective focal spot, blur *B* dominates the image, so the true image or umbra disappears. This explains why, in two-diameter macroradiography, vessels smaller than the focal spot disappear in an angiogram and also emphasizes the importance of using the smallest practicable focal spot when utmost recorded detail is sought.

There we see that the magnification factor depends on the following relation:

$$\text{magnification factor} = \frac{\text{focus-film distance}}{\text{focus-object distance}} \qquad (9)$$

or

$$m = \frac{FFD}{FOD} \qquad (10)$$

Since, in Figure 18.19, FOD is equal to ½FFD, substituting the value ½FFD for FOD,

$$m = \frac{FFD}{\text{½}FFD} = 2$$

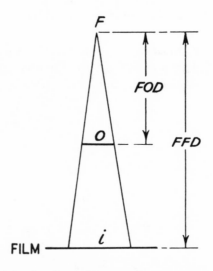

Figure 18.18. Principle of radiographic magnification. *Image size/object size = focus-film distance/focus-object distance;* or, magnification factor *m* = *i/o* = *FFD/FOD.*

At the same time, Figure 18.19 shows that the geometric blur *B* (penumbra) at two times magnification equals the effective focal spot size.

It should be noted that the discussion thus far has dealt with *transverse magnification;* that is, the magnification of an object lying in a plane parallel to the film. On the other hand, the concept of **longitudinal magnification** (Doi and Rossman, 1975) refers to magnification of an object lying in a plane perpendicular to the film, relative to the size of its image in conventional radiography. Important for us is the fact that longitudinal magnification increases the resolution of vertically oriented objects by increasing their separation in the magnified image. Thus, two objects lying above each other would show greater image separation (resolution) during magnification than they would in ordinary radiography (see Figure 18.20).

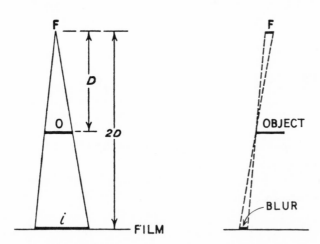

Figure 18.19. In the diagram on the left, the object is located midway between the tube focus and the film. Therefore, the magnification factor $m = 2$, because $m = 2D/D = 2$. In the diagram on the right, blur B equals the effective focal spot size when m = 2. o = object. i = image.

It is obvious that an appreciable **air gap** must exist between the object and the image receptor (film-screen system) in magnification radiography (see pages 374–376). For example, focus-film distance is normally 40 in. (100 cm), so that with a magnification factor of two, an air gap of 20 in. (50 cm) will be present between the object and the film (neglecting the thickness of the object itself). In fact, a 20 in. (50 cm) air gap provides cleanup of scattered radiation as well as a 15 ratio grid. Therefore, we can omit the grid in magnification radiography. At the same time, close beam limitation and precise alignment to the anatomic area

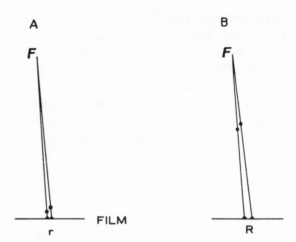

Figure 18.20. In *A*, transverse magnification is less than in *B*. At the same time, longitudinal magnification, or the resolution of two points lying at different distances above the film, is greater in *B*. (*R* in *B* is larger than r in *A*.)

of interest are essential to high quality magnification radiography, just as in ordinary radiography.

Bear in mind that bringing the anatomic part closer to the tube increases the exposure at the level of the part. This is governed by the inverse square law; for example, with a magnification factor of two, the focus-object distance is decreased by one-half relative to the usual focus-film distance in ordinary radiography. Reduction of the distance by one-half increases exposure four times = (magnification factor)^2 = 2^2. However, this applies only to the center of the object; the tube side of the patient will receive an even greater increase in exposure. But the increased dosage is partly offset by dosage reduction through elimination of the radiographic grid in the presence of the air gap.

Insofar as **screen** and ***film blur*** are concerned, the latter is not significant. Much more important is screen blur resulting from diffusion of light in the active layer. Fortunately the ***intensifying screen becomes more efficient when the same information in the enlarged image is spread over a larger area,*** thereby enhancing recorded detail beyond that in conventional radiography.

Although the above discussion of macroradiography would seem to indicate that the last word has been written on the subject, you should know that experts differ as to its value in routine radiography. For example, convincing data by Rao and Clark favor the use of detail screens or nonscreen technic in the radiography of *small* parts that can be well immobilized, the image being viewed with the aid of an excellent convex hand lens. This gives a degree of resolution approaching that in macroradiography. At any rate, there is general consensus that tubes with focal spots larger than 0.3 mm should not be used in magnification radiography. Full advantage of the fractional focus tubes prevails only in close collimation to the area of interest, close apposition of the beam-limiting device to the tube aperture, and accurate centering of the beam.

A critical examination of macroradiography (Rao, Clark, and Gayler) with a 0.25 mm focal spot, taking into account the factors of screen blur, motion of the object, and scattered radiation, led the authors to the following conclusions:

1. In *cerebral angiography* where scatter is moderate and motion relatively small, the best recorded detail is obtained with high speed screens and a magnification factor of two. This results from increased screen efficiency, that is, decreased screen blur in macroradiography as explained above.

2. In *abdominal angiography* where scatter and motion effects are both large, the best recorded detail is obtained with ultra-speed screens and a magnification factor of three, provided close collimation is used. The very fast screens and the large air gap allow for a significant reduction in exposure time and good cleanup of scattered radiation. The large magnification factor improves screen efficiency.

As noted above, with stationary objects, excellent recorded detail occurs with nonscreen or detail screen exposures for small parts, using focal spots 0.3 mm or smaller and optical magnification with a hand lens.

In general, we can say that the advantages of magnification radiography, where applicable, depend on three factors:

1. *Sharpness factor*—the magnified image is spread over a larger area of the intensifying screens and therefore exhibits better

recorded detail than the corresponding nonmagnified image.

2. *Noise factor*—while the image is magnified, screen mottle is not. Thus, recorded detail improves (greater resolution) but the noise factor (screen mottle) remains unchanged, so we say that the **signal-to-noise ratio is increased.**

3. *Visual factor*—visual recognition of images improves with magnification.

We may therefore conclude that the advantages of radiographic magnification in certain kinds of examinations outweigh the disadvantages, such as the limited heat-loading capacity of microfocus tubes, the slightly increased geometric blur, and the limited field size. Macroradiography will therefore continue to play an important part, especially in such procedures as angiography. In fact, the perfection of tubes with focal spots as small as 0.1 mm having an adequate tube rating and the introduction of faster screens should result in even wider application of direct magnification radiography in the future.

MODULATION TRANSFER FUNCTION

The term **modulation transfer function (MTF)** often appears in textbooks and literature dealing with radiographic quality. The technologist should therefore be aware of its significance, at least in a general way. This has prompted a short, simplified treatment of the subject.

As noted earlier, the recording of a radiologic image by any type of image receptor (radiography, image intensification, TV, etc) entails the transfer of information from the object to the image. In the process there is inevitably some loss of information, such as recorded detail. The MTF represents a mathematical method of expressing the efficiency of any imaging system, that is, the part of the information put into the system, which becomes recognizable as the image. In a practical sense, then, **MTF may be regarded as a measure of imaging system quality.**

It should be pointed out that we can obtain MTFs for the individual components of an imaging system; for example, in radiography we can derive the MTF separately for the focal spot, geometry, film-screen system, motion of the object, etc. Multiplication of the individual MTFs gives the total MTF of the system:

$$MTF_{total} = MTF_1 \times MTF_2 \times MTF_3 \times \ldots \ldots \times MTF_n$$

How is MTF obtained? It turns out that while this involves a complex mathematical procedure, we can still gain sufficient practical knowledge about it without necessarily understanding all of the involved mathematics. Basically, MTF is derived from what is known as *line spread function (LSF)*. If we were to expose *directly* (without screens) a film to an extremely narrow beam of x rays collimated by a slit about 10 microns wide, we would obtain a sharp line image. However, a film-screen combination exposed to the same beam would record a line having blurred edges due to diffusion of light in the active layer of the screen. The LSF represents the width of this line as measured by a microdensitometer, with relative density plotted as a function of distance from the center of the line (see Figure 18.21).

By a complex mathematical process known as Fourier analysis, LSF may be converted to MTF which is then plotted (as in Figure 18.22). Here MTF on the vertical axis receives a maximum value of one, since the ratio of the amount of information recorded in the image to the amount put into the system can never exceed unity, and is usually much less. In the examples shown in the figures, we are considering two different film-screen systems. You can see from Figures 18.21 and 18.22 that the superior film-screen system insofar as image quality (sharpness, resolution, and contrast is concerned, has a narrower LSF, and an MTF that is higher at larger "spatial frequencies" (sine functions analogous to the number of line pairs resolved per mm). The MTF for other components of the imaging system can be obtained by mathematical transformation of the appropriate LSF.

At present, MTF is the best available means of evaluating the quality performance of an imaging system, derived from the MTFs of its constituent parts. As time goes on, we anticipate a growing use of this concept in the specification of radiographic equipment and image receptors, both as a whole and with regard to their individual components.

Figure 18.21. Hypothetical example of line spread function for high speed (upper curve) and medium or par speed (lower curve) screens. The image of the slit with high speed screens is wider, giving poorer resolution, than with par speed screens. *Adapted from K. Rossman, courtesy of Radiology.*

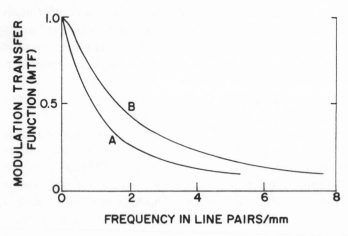

Figure 18.22. Hypothetical modulation transfer function (*MTF*) for high speed (*A*) and medium or par speed (*B*) screens. Par speed screens have a larger *MTF* for a particular value of resolution (spatial frequency in terms of line pairs/mm) and are able to resolve more line pairs/mm than high speed screens (*MTF* curve *B* extends to higher values of resolution).

QUESTIONS AND PROBLEMS

1. Define radiographic quality. How does it relate to recorded detail?
2. What is meant by sharpness; blur; acutance; resolving power; image receptor? How are they related?
3. List the five factors that affect recorded detail.
4. What are the three factors in geometric blur? Explain each one.
5. State the equation that relates the factors in geometric blur.
6. Describe briefly the two main methods of evaluating focal spot size.
7. Define focal spot blooming. What exposure factor influences the degree of blooming?
8. How important is motion of the part being radiographed insofar as recorded detail is concerned? How can motion be controlled?
9. Discuss the factors of crystal size, active layer thickness, film-screen contact, and mottle as they affect blur.
10. How does object shape influence blur?
11. Define radiographic density. Explain the five factors that determine it.
12. State the inverse square law in your own words, and the two forms of the applicable equation. How is it modified in radiographic practice?
13. At a point 50 cm from the tube focus the exposure rate of an x-ray beam is 20 R per min. What will the exposure rate be at 25 cm? 100 cm?
14. A certain technic calls for 50 mA and 0.1 sec at 65 kV. If we have an uncooperative patient and wish to reduce motion by using an exposure time of 1/60 sec, what will the new mA value be?
15. What is meant by the penetrating ability of an x-ray beam? How can the penetrating ability of a beam be changed?
16. A certain technic calls for an exposure of 70 kV and 180 mAs at a distance of 60 in. (150 cm). If we wish to decrease the distance to 20 in. (50 cm), what new mAs value will be required to maintain the same radiographic density?

17. How do intensifying screens affect density? contrast? recorded detail?
18. List the main materials in the human body in decreasing order of their radiographic density.
19. Define radiographic contrast. On what two kinds of contrast does it depend?
20. What is the function of radiographic contrast? Can there be too much contrast?
21. How are the following terms related: low contrast; high contrast; long scale contrast; short scale contrast?
22. Define subject contrast. How is it related to the aerial image? remnant (exit) radiation?
23. What is film contrast? Draw and explain the characteristic curve of a film. Discuss average slope (average gradient).
24. Name the factors that influence subject contrast.
25. Discuss the advantages of a molybdenum anode in mammography. With which type of image receptor should it be used?
26. Describe the xerographic process. What advantages dose it offer in mammography?
27. How do xerographic images differ from film images?
28. Define distortion. Name and explain the two kinds.
29. What effect does distortion have on recorded detail?
30. How can size and shape distortion be minimized?
31. An anatomic part is located 4 in. (10 cm) above the image receptor (film-screen system). The focus-film distance is 40 in. (100 cm), and the diameter of the anatomic part is 9 in. (23 cm). Find the size of the image, percent magnification, and magnification factor.
32. What is quantum mottle? State its importance in radiography. Under what conditions is it accentuated?
33. Discuss the principle of direct magnification radiography (macroradiography). How do we compensate for the increased blurring inherent in this system?
34. How does magnification radiography affect patient exposure?
35. Why can the radiographic grid be eliminated in magnification radiography? Is this always desirable?

37. On what is modulation transfer function based? What does it measure?

CHAPTER 19 *DEVICES FOR IMPROVING RADIOGRAPHIC QUALITY*

I N THE PRECEDING chapter we described the important factors affecting radiographic quality. We shall now show how the quality of a radiograph can be improved by the use of various special devices. Recall that recorded detail is the ultimate criterion of radiographic quality.

As already noted, the rotating anode tube with its small focus provides excellent recorded detail. Furthermore, this tube has made possible the use of high mA with very short exposures, thereby minimizing motion, the greatest enemy of recorded detail. Thus, while the inherent construction of modern equipment should provide radiographs of superb quality, certain auxiliary devices are needed to reduce *scattered radiation,* which lowers contrast and impairs radiographic quality by obscuring recorded detail.

Scattered Radiation

You should recall from Chapter 12 that the primary x-ray beam leaving the tube focus is polyenergetic in that it contains photons of various energies. The primary beam consists of *brems radiation* resulting from the conversion of the energy of the electrons as they are stopped by the target, and *characteristic radiation* emitted by the target metal due to excitation of its atoms. As the primary beam passes through the patient, some of the radiation is absorbed, while the rest is scattered in many directions. In the diagnostic range of 30 to 140 kV the scattered radiation generated in the body consists mainly of scattered photons produced by Compton interaction, but also includes characteristic radiation resulting from photoelectric interaction. Recall that the energy of the Compton (scattered) photons increases with increasing kV. Characteristic photons have extremely low energy and are absorbed locally in the tissues, but ***many of the Compton (scattered) photons have enough energy to pass through the body and approach the film from many directions*** (see below).

This multidirectional scattered radiation is a ***noise factor*** which seriously impairs radiographic quality by its fogging effect, diffusing x rays over the surface of the film and thereby ***lessening contrast*** (see Figure 19.1). You can see that the larger the percentage of scattered radiation relative to the primary radiation, the greater will be the loss of contrast of a detail such as *P*. In a radiograph of good quality, less than one-fourth the density should result from scattered radiation.

Figure 19.1. Deleterious effect of multidirectional scattered radiation on radiographic quality. This causes *loss of radiographic contrast* of a detail such as *P*. *F* is the focal spot.

The ratio of scattered radiation to primary radiation is not uniform over the surface of the radiograph. In fact, with relatively opaque objects, the ratio increases toward the image border, so that scattered radiation tends to ***degrade edge contrast*** (Jaffe and Webster).

Of the total radiation reaching the film, the *ratio of scattered radiation relative to primary radiation increases with the following factors:*

a. An *increase in the area of the radiation field and the thickness of the part* traversed by the beam. As the beam increases in cross section it irradiates a larger volume of tissue and generates more scattered radiation.

b. An *increase in tube potential.* As the kV is increased, there is an increase in the probability of Compton interactions *relative to* photoelectric interactions (see page 188); recall that the Compton interaction produces scattered radiation. Furthermore, at higher kV the 45° scattered photons, because of their greater energy and penetrating ability, are more likely to reach the film. In general, the energy of the scattered photons is only slightly less than that of the primary photons, as shown in Table 19.1. Finally, an increase in the applied kV causes more and more of the radiation to scatter in a forward direction, that is, at an angle of 45° or less with relation to the direction of the primary beam. Thus, increasing kV increases not only the energy of the scattered photons but also the number directed toward the film, so that a larger fraction of the scattered radiation can reach the film and reduce contrast.

c. An *increase in the density of the tissues* traversed by the primary beam; for example, as between air and soft tissue. In nongrid exposures of the chest and abdomen, the following are approximate relative values of the scattered and primary radiation reaching the film:

chest   50% scattered   50% primary
abdomen   90% scattered   10% primary

REMOVAL OF SCATTERED RADIATION BY A GRID

Since scattered radiation cannot be entirely eliminated because of the very nature of x rays and their interaction with matter, we can only attempt to remove as much of it as possible once it has been produced, so as to improve radiographic contrast. This is especially important in the radiography of large anatomic areas

Table 19.1
RELATIONSHIP BETWEEN PRIMARY PHOTON ENERGY
AND ENERGY OF PHOTONS SCATTERED AT 45°

Primary Photon	*45° Scattered Photon*
keV	*keV*
40	39
60	58
80	76
100	94
120	112

such as the abdominal viscera, because of the greater amount of scattering by such large volumes of tissue. Most effective in removing scattered radiation are the *stationary grid* and the *moving grid.* Although the latter is by far the more frequently used of the two, the stationary grid will be discussed first because of its historical priority and relative simplicity.

Stationary Grid

In 1913 Gustav Bucky introduced the *stationary radiographic grid,* a device placed between the patient and the cassette for the purpose of reducing the amount of scattered radiation reaching the film and so *improving radiographic contrast.* As shown in Figure 19.2, Bucky's original grid was of the *cross hatch type,* consisting of wide strips of lead arranged in two parallel series, which are mutually perpendicular. Despite the coarseness of the early grids, with their 2 cm × 2 cm spacing, they removed a significant amount of scattered radiation, as shown by the frontal skull radiograph at the Smithsonian Institution.

A *modern stationary grid* has a very different appearance (see Figure 19.3). It consists of extremely thin, closely spaced lead strips measuring about 0.05 mm in width. They are separated by radiolucent material, usually plastic or aluminum, measuring about 0.33 mm wide. *Aluminum* is preferred for improved durability of the grid, and to absorb scattered radiation from the lead strips. The entire array of lead strips and spacers is bonded firmly together and sliced into flat plates measuring

Figure 19.2. Photographic reproduction of Bucky's original radiographic grid. Note the cross-hatch pattern and the very coarse spacing. Yet, this grid achieved significant cleanup of scattered radiation, although a pattern of the lead strips appeared on the radiograph. (*Photograph [No. 47022] furnished by courtesy of Smithsonian Institution.*)

less than 5 mm thick (eg, for grid ratio 12, thickness is 12 × 0.33 = 4 mm).

Figure 19.4 shows an enlarged diagram of a grid. Only those x-ray photons passing directly through the narrow aluminum spacers will reach the film-screen system. Since the scattered photons proceed at various angles, most of them will strike the lead strips and undergo absorption without reaching the film. Such a grid may absorb as much as 90 percent of the scattered radiation and entail a notable improvement in contrast and recorded detail.

The stationary grid has one main disadvantage—as the lead strips absorb radiation, they cast shadows on the radiograph as thin white lines; but at the usual radiographic viewing distance, and especially with high quality grids, these lines are almost invisible. Besides, their presence is more than compensated for by the improved quality of the radiographic image. Because of the

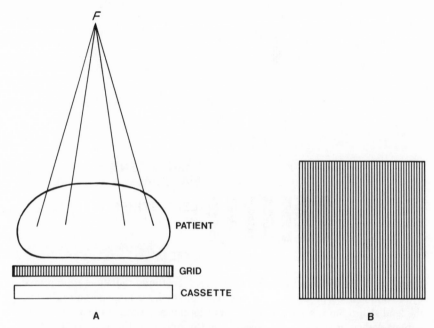

Figure 19.3. Stationary parallel or nonfocused grid, seen in cross section in *A* and top view in *B*. *F* is focal spot of x-ray tube.

interposition of the grid in the x-ray beam, an appreciable part of *both primary and scattered radiation is absorbed,* and therefore the exposure must be increased according to the type of grid being used.

Efficiency of Radiographic Grids

Certain criteria have been established to designate the quality or efficiency of radiographic grids; that is, *their ability to remove scattered radiation,* or *"cleanup."* These apply to both stationary and moving grids (to be described later), and include *physical* and *functional* aspects.

Physical Factors in Grid Efficiency. The two physical factors mainly responsible for grid efficiency are *grid ratio* and *grid frequency.*

Figure 19.4. Principle of the radiographic grid. Scattered radiation, represented by the dotted lines, proceeds in various directions and is in large part absorbed by the lead strips. Since scattered radiation is not image forming but contributes to patient dosage, it should be removed by a grid insofar as this is possible. Those primary rays that pass through the radiolucent aluminum spacers between the lead strips reach the image receptor (eg, film-screen system). The lead strips are actually very thin.

1. **Grid Ratio** is defined as **the ratio of the height of the lead strips to the distance between the strips,** as expressed in the following equation:

$$r = \frac{h}{D} \tag{1}$$

where r is the grid ratio, h is the height of the lead strips, and D is the width of the spaces between the strips. These factors appear diagrammatically in Figure 19.5. As an example, if the lead strips are 2 mm high and the space separating them is 0.4 mm, the grid ratio is $2/0.4 = 5$.

Notice in Figure 19.5 that grids A and B have the same ratio, despite the difference in their heights. Grid D has the same height as B, but D's ratio is greater because its lead strips are closer. Further comparison of the grids in Figure 19.5 reveals that the paths of the most divergent scattered photons in grids A and B

Figure 19.5. Effect of grid ratio on maximum angle of obliquity of a scattered ray that can get through the grid. In A and B, it is obvious that the ratio may be the same in grids of different thickness, and 7° is the maximum angle that a ray can make with the vertical and still pass between the lead strips. In D, with the grid ratio twice that in A, the maximum obliquity of a transmitted ray, 3° 35′ is half as large as that in A. Note the smaller frequency of grid B relative to grid A despite their identical grid ratio.

make the same angle with the lead strip, whereas they make half that angle in grid D. Thus, the higher the grid ratio, the "straighter" the rays have to be to get through the grid interspaces. It is like a line of cars passing through a tunnel; any car that strays too far off the road will hit the side of the tunnel. All other factors being equal, the higher the grid ratio, the better will be the "cleanup" of scattered radiation and the resulting radiographic contrast, with improved recorded detail.

2. *Grid Frequency,* defined as the number of lead strips per cm or per inch, has an important bearing on grid efficiency. Available grids range in frequency from 20 to 40 lines per cm (50 to 100 lines per in.). In general, the greater the grid frequency, the thinner the lead strips have to be, and the greater will be the

likelihood of scattered photons passing *laterally* through the strips, especially at high kV. With grids of equal ratio, the one having fewer and thicker strips per cm possesses superior quality but at the same time the visibility of the grid lines becomes more objectionable (except in moving grids). Conversely, *as the grid frequency increases, the grid ratio must also be increased to maintain the same efficiency.*

Closely related to grid ratio and frequency is the *lead content* in terms of mass per unit area—g/cm²—of grid surface. For grids of equal ratio, the one with thicker strips (lower frequency) will be more efficient in removing scattered radiation and improving contrast, by virtue of its greater lead content. But, at the same time, it must be kept in mind that it will also remove more primary radiation and so require a larger exposure for the same film density. In general, lead content serves as an indicator of performance if the grid has an adequate ratio and frequency.

Functional Factors in Grid Efficiency. Knowing that a grid has a particular ratio and frequency (as well as lead content), how can we judge its ability to minimize scattered radiation? In other words, is there a quantitative measure of grid efficiency based on its actual function? Fortunately, there are several criteria of grid performance, the best ones being *selectivity* and *contrast improving ability,* as defined by the ICRU in *Handbook 89.*

1. *Selectivity.* Since the grid lies in the path of the x-ray beam, its lead strips absorb a fraction of *both* primary and scattered radiation. The absorption of primary radiation by a grid is known as *grid cutoff.* Obviously, a grid should transmit as large a fraction of the primary radiation as possible, to keep the exposure of the patient small. At the same time, it should absorb a maximum of scattered radiation to provide the best possible improvement in radiographic contrast. As specified by the ICRU, if Greek letter Σ (sigma) represents selectivity, T_p the fraction of *primary* radiation transmitted through the grid, and T_s the fraction of *scattered* radiation transmitted through the grid, then

$$\Sigma = \frac{T_p}{T_s} \tag{2}$$

Thus, the larger the ratio of the transmitted fraction of the primary radiation, to the transmitted fraction of the scattered radiation reaching the film, the greater will be the selectivity of the grid. At the same time, it must be remembered that the larger the fraction of the **total radiation** (primary plus scattered) that is transmitted and reaches the film, the less will be the exposure required for a given radiographic density.

2. *Contrast Improvement Factor.* The ultimate criterion of the efficiency of a grid is its actual performance in improving radiographic contrast, as explained earlier in this chapter. The contrast improvement factor, K, is defined as the ratio of the radiographic contrast with grid divided by the contrast without grid:

$$K = \frac{\text{radiographic contrast with grid}}{\text{radiographic contrast without grid}} \tag{3}$$

Unfortunately, this factor is so dependent on kV, field size, and thickness of part that it cannot be specified for a given grid under all conditions. (The ICRU has given special recommendations for measuring K in a 20-cm thick water phantom at 100 kV.)

We must emphasize that selectivity and contrast improvement factor have certain limitations because they are measured in a water phantom, which is inherently different from the human body. In making these measurements, certain conditions of standardization have to be laid down, and these may or may not hold during practical radiography. However, selectivity and contrast improvement serve as useful criteria for the intercomparison of grids.

TYPES OF RADIOGRAPHIC GRIDS

Stationary Grids. These come in various sizes. When the grid is larger than the cassette, a wooden frame must be placed around the cassette to avoid bending the grid. Because of their light weight, stationary grids facilitate portable radiography, and radiography with a horizontal beam.

A special *crossed grid* is available, consisting of two sets of grid lines arranged perpendicular to each other. They are not often used in general radiography but may be advantageous in special procedures such as cerebral angiography with biplane equipment. A more versatile arrangement is the superimposition of two lower-ratio grids, one of which is turned 90° relative to the other; the grid ratio of such a combination of crossed grids equals the sum of the individual grid ratios. For example, crossing grids with ratios of 5 and 8 give a cross-grid combination with a ratio of 13, although centering of the x-ray beam need not be any more perfect than with an 8-ratio grid (Cullinan). On the other hand, the grids can be used separately when a lower grid ratio suffices. Crossed grids do not lend themselves to angled beams because of excessive cutoff.

Grids are used with intensifying screen cassettes because of the relatively heavy exposures that would otherwise be required. Because the grid is very thin and does not appreciably increase the object-film distance, it causes little or no distortion of the radiographic image. The *grid cassette,* whose front has a built-in grid, is much more convenient to use than an ordinary cassette with a separate grid.

1. *Parallel or Nonfocused Grid.* Most stationary grids are parallel or nonfocused—the lead strips are all oriented parallel to one another. When such a grid is used at excessively short focus-film distances, the more slanting rays toward the periphery of the beam strike the sides of the more peripheral lead strips. This causes progressively greater absorption of primary radiation toward the edges of the grid, with corresponding underexposure of the radiograph toward its sides relative to its center. What has just been described is an example of *peripheral cutoff,* caused by *distance decentering* of the grid. To minimize this problem, parallel grids should be used at a distance of 48 in. (125 cm) or more with films larger than 8 in. × 10 in., because the rays are practically parallel at distances beyond 48 in.

If the beam is not perpendicular to the grid, with a tilt across the long axis of the lead strips, progressively more radiation is absorbed by the grid in the direction of the beam as shown in Figure 19.7. This is another example of *peripheral cutoff,* but it is now asymmetrical in that the side of the radiograph toward which the beam was angled is underexposed. Tilting of the beam across the lead strips as just described may be called *angulation decentering.* However, with the beam tilted parallel to the long axis of the

Figure 19.6. The effect of *distance decentering* of a *parallel* grid that was caused by excessively short focus-film distances (less than 48 in. or 125 cm). Because of the divergence of the rays in the beam, the more slanting rays toward the edges of the beam will undergo greater absorption by the grid than will the central rays. Therefore, the lateral portions of the radiograph will be progressively more underexposed relative to its center. This is *symmetrical grid cutoff*.

strips, density will not vary across the radiograph, except for the heel effect (see pages 421–422).

Figure 19.7. The effect of *angulation decentering* of a *parallel* grid, which was caused by angulation of the beam across the long axis of the lead strips. In this case, the radiograph will be underexposed on the side toward which the beam is directed. This is *asymmetrical peripheral cutoff*. Angulation decentering is also called *off-level decentering*.

2. *Focused Grid.* This type of grid consists of lead strips that are tilted more and more toward the edges of the grid as shown in

Figure 19.8. Focused grid. The lead strips are inclined so that their extensions, indicated by the broken lines, meet along a specified imaginary line, *C*, above the grid, called the *convergence line* (seen end-on). The vertical distance from the center of the grid surface to the convergence line is called the *focusing distance*, f_0. See also Figure 19.9.

Figure 19.8. If one extends the planes of these tilted strips upward, the imaginary planes intersect along a line called the **convergence line,** which is parallel to the surface of the grid. Naturally, when seen end-on as in the figure, the convergence line appears to be a point. The vertical distance between the convergence line *C* and the center of the grid is called the **focusing distance** f_0 of the grid. This term should not be confused with the focus-film distance.

Moving Grid

To eliminate the grid lines produced in a radiograph by a stationary grid, Dr. Hollis Potter, in 1920, conceived the idea of **moving the grid** between the patient and the film during x-ray exposure, in a direction perpendicular to the lead strips. The moving grid has come to be called, loosely, a Potter-Bucky diaphragm, but the ICRU recommends instead the term **moving grid,** reserving the name Potter-Bucky for the mechanism that activates the grid. However, the term Bucky for the grid and mechanism together has become so standardized in diagnostic radiology that it would seem futile to try to discard it.

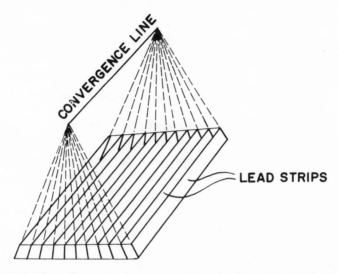

Figure 19.9. Three-dimensional representation of a focused grid, showing the inclined lead strips whose imaginary extensions upward intersect along the *convergence line.*

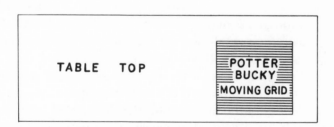

Figure 19.10. Top view of a radiographic table equipped with a Potter-Bucky diaphragm. Note that the lead strips are parallel to the long axis of the table.

The direction of grid travel is important. As just mentioned, a grid must move in a direction perpendicular to the long dimension of the lead strips. Thus, in Figure 19.8 the grid would move from left to right, or from right to left. Obviously, if it were to move "into" or "out of" this page, the images of the lead strips would be visible (no blurring) and the effect would resemble that of a stationary grid. The relation of the moving grid to the radiographic table is shown in Figure 19.10.

The moving grid is of the focused type, but the lead strips are thicker than those in a stationary grid because its motion during the exposure blurs out the lead shadows ("grid lines") on the radiograph.

Precautions in the Use of Focused Grids

Care must be taken to use *focused* grids properly to take advantage of their maximum efficiency; that is, to achieve the least absorption of primary radiation and the greatest absorption of scattered radiation in the lead strips. In the following sections we shall deal with the factors governing **grid cutoff**, which may be defined as the increased absorption of primary radiation in the lead strips resulting from an incorrect focus-film distance, or improper alignment or centering of the beam to the grid.

1. *Focus-film distance (FFD).* A grid with a ratio of 8 or less tolerates, without appreciable loss of efficiency, a range of FFD equal to the focusing distance ±25 percent. Thus, with a focusing distance of 40 in. (100 cm), FFDs of 30 to 50 in. (about 75 to 125 cm) give satisfactory results with an 8-ratio grid. Below or above these limits, *peripheral cutoff* becomes significant as shown in Figure 19.11. With a grid ratio of 12, and even more so with a grid ratio of 16, tolerance is extremely small, so the FFD must more nearly coincide with the focusing distance to minimize peripheral cutoff.

2. *Angulation of the Beam.* With a *focused* grid, angulation of the beam across the long dimension of the lead strips causes uniform decrease in density of the radiograph. (Recall that with nonfocused or parallel grids, such angulation causes asymmetrical peripheral cutoff.) This resembles the decentering of the beam relative to the center of the grid, as will be shown below. The tube, however, may be angled in a direction parallel to the strips without causing grid cutoff, provided the vertical FFD remains within the correct limits of grid focusing distance. In practice, a moving grid is located under the table with the lead strips oriented parallel to the long axis of the table, as shown in Figure 19.10. Consequently, the tube may be angled in the direction of the long axis of the table without entailing grid cutoff.

3. *Centering of the Tube.* The tube must be centered to the center of the grid to avoid off-axis decentering. With the tube

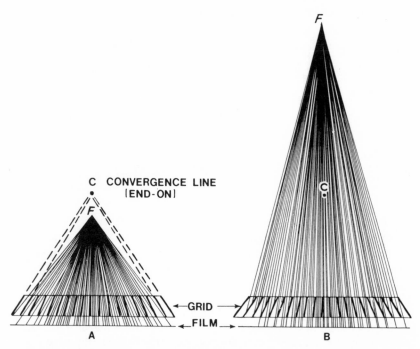

Figure 19.11. The effect on focus-film distance on the efficiency of a focused grid. In *A*, the focus-film distance is less than the grid focusing distance minus 25 percent, and more and more rays are absorbed by the lead strips near the edge of the film. In *B*, the focus-film distance is more than the grid focusing distance plus 25 percent, and again there is relatively greater absorption of the beam at the edges of the film. In either case, the periphery of the radiograph will show reduced density — *grid cutoff.*

decentered, that is, off-centered across the long axis of the lead strips, *the effect on radiographic density depends on the FFD relative to the grid focusing distance.* If the FFD is *equal to* the grid focusing distance, but the tube is decentered across the lead strips, there will be uniform reduction in the density of the radiograph, that is, uniform cutoff, as in Figure 19.12A. This can be readily proved by elementary geometry. If the tube focus is at an appreciable distance *above* the convergence line, and is at the same time decentered, the area of the film directly beneath the focus will be lighter than the remainder of the film. If the tube focus is *below* the convergence line and decentered, then the area of the film directly below the focus will be darker than the rest of the film.

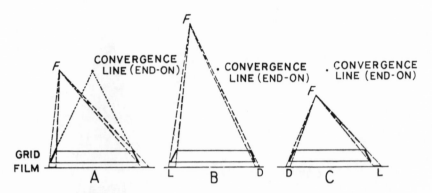

Figure 19.12. Effects of focus-film distance and lateral decentering on efficiency of a focused grid.

In *A*, the tube focus is decentered but level with the grid convergence line. The projections of the lead strips on the film are equal in size, but are broader than they would be if the tube were not off-center. Therefore, the radiographic density is uniformly decreased over the entire radiograph.

In *B*, the tube focus is decentered but is *above* the level of the grid convergence line. The projections of the lead strips lying more directly under the tube are broader than those of the corresponding lead strips on the opposite side (*L* is broader than *D*). Therefore the radiograph will show less density on the side toward which the tube is shifted.

In *C*, the tube focus is decentered but at a level below the grid convergence line. The result is opposite that in *B*. *L* = lighter. *D* = darker.

These relationships are illustrated in Figure 19.12.

4. *Tube Side versus Film Side.* The focused grid has a "tube side" and a "film side." In all the above figures, the grid is shown correctly with the tube side toward the tube target. If the grid is inserted reversed, as in Figure 19.13, the tilted strips near the edges of the grid will absorb progressively more radiation, causing severe peripheral cutoff. However, with parallel grids either side may face the tube or film.

PRACTICAL APPLICATION OF RADIOGRAPHIC GRIDS

The absorption of both primary and scattered radiation by a grid requires an increase in exposure beyond nongrid technic. Moving grids with a ratio of 12 are most often used in conventional radiog-

Figure 19.13. The focused grid is inverted, with the "tube side" away from the tube focus. Therefore, the outer regions of the radiograph will show decreased density or *peripheral grid cutoff*.

raphy at or below 100 kV; here the Bucky or grid factor ranges from about four at 70 kV, to about 5 at 100 kV (Liebel-Flarsheim Company). The Bucky or grid factor is defined as follows:

mAs with grid = grid factor × mAs without grid

for equal density at a particular kV. Table 19.2 summarizes the grid factors over a practical kV range. One may, instead, prefer to

TABLE 19.2
GRID OR BUCKY mAs FACTORS AT TYPICAL kV VALUES
FOR VARIOUS GRID RATIOS*

Grid Ratio	70 kV	95 kV	120 kV
No Grid	1	1	1
5	3	3	3
8	3.5	3.75	4
12	4	4.25	5
16	4.5	5	6
5 crossed	4.5	5	5.5
8 crossed	5	6	7

*Experimental data from Liebel-Flarsheim Company. In practice, these may have to be increased by 25 to 30 percent for grids with ratios of 12 or more.

TABLE 19.3
APPROXIMATE CHANGE IN kV (IN THE USUAL kV RANGE) RELATIVE
TO NONGRID TECHNIC FOR VARIOUS GRID RATIOS

Grid ratio	kV increase
5	+ 8
8	+15
12	+20–25
16	+20–25

°Adapted from J. E. Cullinan: *Illustrated Guide to X-ray Technics*, Philadelphia, Lippincott, 1980. (*By permission of the publisher.*)

compensate for the grid by changing kV instead of mAs. Table 19.3, adapted from Cullinan, gives the approximate change in kV relative to nongrid technic for various grid ratios. In any case, because of uncertainties in the percentage of radiation absorbed by any particular grid, the quoted grid factors should be confirmed by trial exposures with a phantom. Since grids must be used in the radiography of parts measuring 11 cm or more in thickness, intensifying screens are required to reduce the patient's exposure and minimize the effect of motion.

At this point we should state the relative merits of grids with ratios of 12 and 16 in *general medium-kV radiography.* A grid with a *ratio of 12 is preferred* for the following reasons:

1. Its efficiency in cleaning up scattered radiation (contrast improvement) is not much less than that of a grid with ratio 16 in routine general radiography below 100 kV.

2. Centering is less critical, allowing a larger permissible margin of error.

3. Less exposure of the patient is required for a particular film exposure.

4. Lead strips can be thicker (more lead content), thereby absorbing more efficiently the higher energy scattered radiation.

Above 100 kV a 16-ratio grid must be used to obtain radiographs of optimum quality. Table 19.4 compares the practical characteristics of various types of grids. In general, positioning latitude—permissible error in centering, angulation, and distance—is worse with parallel than with focused grids of like ratio at focus-film distances under 40 in. (100 cm).

TABLE 19.4
CHARACTERISTICS OF VARIOUS TYPES
OF GRIDS, STATIONARY AND MOVING

Ratio	Type	Recommended kV	Positioning Latitude	Cleanup
16	linear	above 100 kV	very poor	
				superlative
6	crisscross	above 100 kV	good	
12	linear	up to 100 kV	poor	
				excellent
5	crisscross	up to 100 kV	excellent	
8	linear	up to 90 kV	fair	good
6				
	linear	up to 80 kV	excellent	moderate
5				

Specification of Grids. In 1963 the ICRU, in *Handbook 89*, recommended that manufacturers include certain data to specify the important characteristics of focused grids:

1. **Grid ratio**—the height of the lead strips divided by the distance between successive pairs.
2. **Grid frequency**—the number of lead strips (lines) per in. or per cm; for example, 100 lines/in.
3. **Focusing distance**—the distance between the convergence line and the grid surface.
4. **Focus-grid distance limits**—the maximum percent variation in the tube focus-to-grid surface distance within which no excess grid cutoff (ie, absorption of primary radiation) occurs. This is usually equal to the focusing distance ±25 percent.
5. **Contrast improvement factor**—under standard conditions.

Although the first four items are to be included in grid labeling, the fifth is also included in grid specification.

Patient Dosage with Grids. Various combinations of kV and grid ratio affect the radiation exposure of the patient. Table 19.5 compares these factors obtained at the University of Rochester School of Medicine, in the radiography of the lumbar spine in the lateral projection. All the radiographs were diagnostically equivalent. Evidently, in radiography at 70 kV, the radiation exposure of the patient doubles as the grid ratio increases from 8 to 16.

Therefore, **grids with a ratio of 16 should not be used in conventional radiography**— below about 90 kV. On the other hand, **above 100 kV** a 16 ratio grid produces far better cleanup of scattered radiation than lower ratio grids without a significant increase in patient exposure. For general radiography **up to 100 kV** a 12 ratio grid serves as a satisfactory compromise both from the standpoint of grid efficiency and patient exposure.

TABLE 19.5

EFFECT OF GRID RATIO AND CORRESPONDING kV AND mAs
ON ENTRANCE SURFACE EXPOSURE OF PATIENT
IN LATERAL PROJECTION OF LUMBAR SPINE.
ALL RADIOGRAPHS OF COMPARABLE DIAGNOSTIC QUALITY*

Grid Ratio	kV	mAs	Entrance Exposure	Entrance Exposure as % of Maximum
			R	%
16	70	1,000	18.9	100
8	70	500	9.5	50
16	100	160	5.9	31
8	100	120	4.5	25

*University of Rochester School of Medicine, Department of Radiology.

Potter-Bucky Mechanisms. As mentioned before, the Potter-Bucky grid moves during the x-ray exposure. In the obsolete **single-stroke** type, one first "cocked the Bucky"; that is, pulled it to one side of the table by a lever, putting a spring under tension. When the grid was released (either by a string or by an electromagnetic tripping device), the spring pulled it across the table, its motion being smoothly cushioned by a piston acting against oil in a cylinder.

The **reciprocating** Potter-Bucky mechanism has no separate timer, since it oscillates continuously during the exposure. It is moved rapidly forward (0.3 sec) by a solenoid, while tension is placed on a spring, and returns slowly (1.7 sec) by action of this spring against oil in a chamber as in the single-stroke Bucky. Minimum exposure is 1/20 sec.

The **recipromatic** Potter-Bucky is activated entirely by an electric motor, the speed of both strokes being identical; exposure times may be as short as 1/60 sec.

The **oscillating** or **trill** Potter-Bucky mechanism is the most advanced type available today and is relatively simple. The grid is supported on four blade springs near its corners (see Figure 19.14). Just before the start of an exposure, the grid is pulled an appropriate distance across the table by a series of relays and then suddenly released. Thereupon, it oscillates or vibrates over a rapidly decreasing distance until after the end of the exposure. The trill Bucky allows very short exposures without grid lines because of the continually changing position of the grid with relation to the bursts of x-ray photons in the beam throughout the exposure.

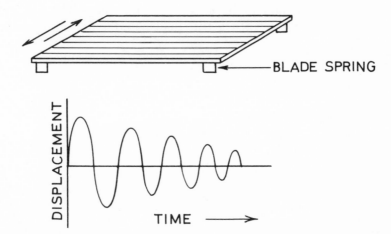

Figure 19.14. Oscillating "trill" mechanism for moving grids. The upper figure shows the grid mounted on four blade springs. A system of relays, synchronized with the exposure switch, starts the grid vibrating in the direction of the arrows just before the beginning of the exposure and stops the exposure just before the grid stops vibrating. The lower figure shows the "damped" (decreasing) oscillation or vibration of the grid. Very short exposures are possible with this type of moving grid mechanism, without the possibility of synchronism.

Moving grids have their greatest application in the radiography of thick parts, measuring 11 cm or more.

There are several causes of **grid lines** in a radiograph made with older types of moving grids. Since they have relatively thick lead strips, the appearance of these grid lines in the radiograph as alternating light and dark stripes—the so-called corduroy effect—is especially objectionable because it impairs recorded detail. The causes of grid lines with moving grids of various kinds include:

1. Synchronism. We found in Chapter 12 that an x-ray beam is not generated continuously, but rather in intermittent showers or bursts of photons corresponding to the peaks in the voltage applied to the tube. If the travel of the grid is such that a different lead strip always happens to be above a given point on the film at the same instant that a kV peak is reached, the images of different lead strips will be superimposed on the same point on the film, even though the grid is moving (see Figure 19.15). The net effect is the same as though the grid were stationary. This series of events cannot occur with a trill Bucky under normal operating conditions.

Figure 19.15. Grid synchronism. If the grid moves to the left at certain speeds, a different photon is intercepted by a different lead strip over the *same* point on the film. Hence, a shadow of the lead strip appears on the film just as though the grid were stationary.

2. Exposure starting before grid has reached full speed, or continuing after grid travel has slowed down or stopped. Correct relationship between grid travel and exposure time prevents the appearance of grid lines. An electric contactor starts the exposure only when grid travel has reached the correct speed, and stops the exposure before the grid stops moving. Grid lines appear whenever exposure occurs with the grid stationary.

3. Grid moving too slowly may produce either clearly visible

grid lines or density variations in the radiograph.

In recent years, stationary grids have been so perfected that the grid lines are virtually invisible at the usual viewing distance. Such ultrafine line grids may often be used in place of moving grids. Stationary grids are considerably less expensive because the Bucky mechanism is eliminated. Furthermore, there is less exposure of the patient with a stationary grid for the same radiographic density because no decentering occurs during the exposure. On the other hand, with a moving grid, as much as 3 cm of decentering occurs with reduction in density of almost 20 percent (Christensen, Curry, and Nunnally).

REMOVAL OF SCATTERED RADIATION BY AN AIR GAP

Although the radiographic grid is the most effective and widely used device for removing scattered radiation arising in the patient, one can do this nearly as well by increasing the object-film distance. The space between the patient and the image receptor (eg, film-screen system) is commonly referred to as an *air gap.* As noted in Figure 19.1, when an x-ray beam enters the body, some of the radiation is scattered in all directions. That which reaches the film, being non-image forming, causes loss of image contrast and impairs recorded detail. Increasing the thickness of the air gap allows more and more of the scattered photons to move laterally outside the film area (see Figure 19.16). This is especially true of photons that have been scattered at large angles (ie, more oblique to the central ray). In other words, less scattered radiation reaches the film as we increase the object-film distance. This is entirely a geometric effect; there is virtually no absorption of scattered radiation in the air gap. Because of the loss of scattered photons, air gap technic requires a compensatory increase in exposure factors to keep radiographic density unchanged, provided the focus-film distance remains constant.

Comparison of an air gap with a grid insofar as contrast improvement in a water phantom is concerned has been reported (Gould and Hale). The practical consequences of this study are that a 10-in. air gap gives about the same degree of cleanup as a 15-ratio

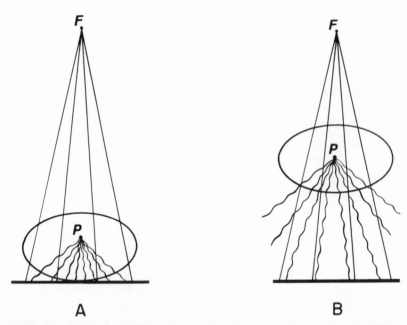

Figure 19.16. Effect of air gap thickness on reduction of the amount of scattered radiation that reaches a film or other image receptor. In *B*, the object is farther from the film, (nearer the tube) and more of the scattered radiation generated in the patient at a point, such as *P*, misses the film than is the case in *A* where the object is nearer the film.

grid for a thin patient measuring 10 cm, but the same grid is a little more efficient than the 10 in. air gap for a 20-cm patient.

The effectiveness of an air gap is not influenced by kV. In the radiographic range of 40 to 120 kV, scattering occurs almost equally in all directions.

Air gap technic has a place in chest radiography, magnification radiography, and in cerebral and renal angiography. Further improvement in recorded detail can be achieved, especially in cerebral and renal angiography, by the use of a low ratio grid in addition to the air gap.

In chest radiography, a 10-in. (25-cm) air gap effectively reduces the amount of scattered radiation. The accompanying image magnification must be compensated by an increase in focus-film distance from the customary 6 ft (2 m) to 10 ft (3.3 m). At the same time, this helps reduce the blurring associated with the increased object-film distance. However, an increase in focus-film distance from 6 ft to 10 ft requires a much larger exposure by a factor of $10^2/6^2 = 100/36 = 2.7$ times (according to inverse square law). Air gap technic in chest radiography therefore calls for 110 to 120 kV.

Magnification technic (see pages 374–378) can aid in the detection of suspected hairline fractures. An air gap is inherent in this procedure. The increase in patient exposure that would occur with the part midway between the tube and image receptor is partly offset by elimination of the radiographic grid. Similar conditions prevail in cerebral and renal magnification angiography. In each instance, the loss of recorded detail associated with the increased object film-distance (air gap) must be compensated by use of a fractional focal spot.

REDUCTION OF SCATTERED RADIATION BY LIMITATION OF THE PRIMARY BEAM

By modifying the primary x-ray beam (ie, the beam coming from the focal spot), we can decrease the fraction of the photons that are scattered in the body. This depends on two well-known facts. First, *an increase in kV increases the fraction of radiation undergoing scatter.* Therefore, the kV for a given anatomic part should be just enough to penetrate it. Excessively high kV should be avoided, unless a grid with higher grid ratio is used. Under ordinary conditions, with a 12-ratio grid, 100 kV should not be exceeded. Above this level, one should use a 16-ratio grid.

Second, *the fraction of radiation scattered increases as the volume of irradiated tissue increases.* Therefore, the larger the area and the thicker the part being radiographed, the greater will be the amount of scattered radiation and resulting impairment of radiographic quality through loss of contrast. The practical lesson to be learned from this is the need of limiting the cross-sectional area of the beam to encompass the smallest area that will include the selected anatomic region. We do this by placing various *beam-limiting devices* in the path of the x-ray beam as close to the tube port as the housing permits.

Beam limitation is most effective when the field is less than 6 in.

(15 cm) in diameter, especially in nongrid radiography. However, with larger areas such as the abdomen, the proper **grid** excels as a means of reducing scattered radiation; beam limitation further improves radiographic contrast when large areas are to be covered, but this is most effective if the collar of the beam-limiting device reaches and surrounds the tube port to remove as much off-focus radiation as possible. Such off-focus radiation arises when unfocused electrons strike parts of the anode other than the target area itself and may amount to as much as 25 percent of the on-target radiation (Ter-Pogossian).

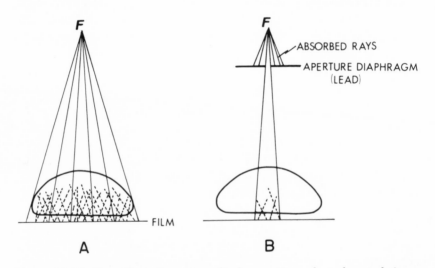

Figure 19.17. The effect of aperture diaphragm *C* on the volume of tissue irradiated and the resulting scattered radiation. In *A* there is no restriction of the x-ray beam; a large volume of tissue is irradiated, with resulting abundance of scattered radiation. In *B* the aperture diaphragm narrows the beam, a small volume of tissue is irradiated, and there is less scattered radiation.

About 50 to 90 percent of the density of a radiograph may result from scattered radiation, so that restriction of the primary beam requires an increase in exposure to compensate for the loss of density. The increase in exposure must be found by trial or in published tables. In setting up a technic chart, we must state the dimensions of the beam (or film size) for each technic. Any further increase or decrease in beam area may entail a compensatory decrease or increase in exposure, respectively.

1. *Aperture Diaphragms.* Figure 19.17 shows how an aperture diaphragm decreases scattered radiation, thereby enhancing contrast. The aperture diaphragm would be very efficient if the x rays originated at a true point source. However, since the tube focal spot has a finite (measurable) area, x rays originate from it at innumerable points and proceed in all directions. Some of these x-ray photons, in addition to those comprising off-focus radiation, "undercut" the edge of the diaphragm opening and pass outside the desired confines of the beam, showing up on the radiograph as a gradually fading rather than a sharp border. Thus, a diaphragm fails to provide adequate beam limitation (see Figure 19.18), although it may be better than nothing under unusual circumstances.

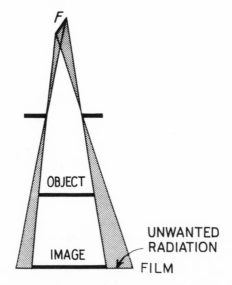

Figure 19.18. Inefficiency of an aperture diaphragm as a beam-limiting device or collimator. Since, in practice, a focal spot has a finite (measurable) size, the edge of the beam is not sharply defined—unwanted radiation "undercuts" the edges of the diaphragm, traverses the patient, and reaches the film.

2. *Cones.* A radiographic cone is a metal tube that flares outward, away from the tube aperture (see Figure 19.19), and is supposed to limit the beam. However, a cone deserves the same criticism as

an aperture diaphragm in that it fails to provide adequate beam limitation, as shown in Figure 19.19A. A cone limits a beam by virtue of its upper opening only, which actually acts as an aperture diaphragm. A modification of the cone, the extension cylinder, has openings of equal size at both ends, so the lower opening acts as an aperture diaphragm. Because of the longer distance of the lower aperture from the focal spot, beam limitation is better than that with a cone (see Figure 19.19B).

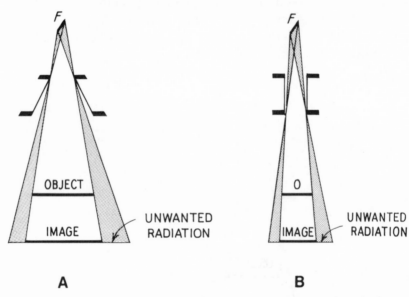

A   **B**

Figure 19.19. Comparison of the effectiveness of a flared cone and a cylinder on beam limitation. In *A*, the upper aperture limits the beam, similar to an aperture diaphragm. In *B*, the lower aperture of a cylinder limits the beam. The width of the interval between the inner and outer rays at the film represents radiation outside the desired beam. Thus, the cylinder in *B* provides better beam limitation than the flared cone in *A*.

Another serious shortcoming of the flared cone is the excessive area of the circular field required to cover a rectangular film of any given size (see Figure 19.20). This is objectionable because not only does it lead to the production of more scattered radiation, but it also exposes the patient to radiation outside the area of interest.

A partial solution might be to have cones with rectangular openings to cover each film size at various focus-film distances, but this would be impracticable. The variable aperture device does this much more efficiently, as described in the next section.

Figure 19.20. The x-ray beam cuts the corners of the film when limited by an aperture diaphragm or cone, but the dashed circle indicates the excessive volume of irradiated tissue.

3. *Variable Aperture Beam-limiting Devices.* These — also known as *collimators* — combine the best features of the cone and aperture diaphragm. The term collimator, although generally used, is inaccurate because, strictly speaking, it is a device that is supposed to line up rays so as to make them parallel to one another. In radiographic usage, the collimator simply limits or shapes the beam to the desired area; the radiation continues to diverge after leaving the collimator. However, the term collimator has become so ingrained in radiology and is so much simpler than the term variable aperture beam-limiting device that we shall continue to use it. It should be mentioned that some are using the term **BLD** (for beam-limiting device) to designate a collimator.

A typical collimator comprises a box-like apparatus (see Figure 19.21) equipped with two or more sets of adjustable diaphragms, stacked one above the other, which can be opened or closed to delimit accurately a beam of any desired rectangular configuration. In addition, the multiple diaphragms more effectively reduce the amount of radiation passing outside the edge of the beam, thereby giving it a sharper margin as shown in Figure 19.21B, provided they are properly aligned. The best modern collimators have a collar extending to and surrounding the tube port for the purpose of further improving recorded detail by removing off-focus radiation. As stated above, circular beams shaped by aperture diaphragms or cones allow radiation to pass beyond the zone of interest (see Figure 19.20), increasing the fraction of scattered radiation and unnecessarily exposing the patient. Thus, they do not adequately limit the beam (see Figure 19.21A.

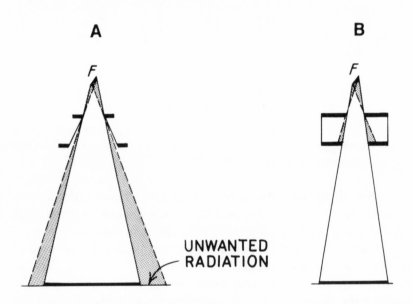

Figure 19.21. Effect of a well-designed collimator (variable aperture beam-limiting device) on beam restriction as compared with a cone. In *A*, a cone reduces beam area, but there is "undercutting" of the upper aperture by unwanted radiation. In *B*, a double-diaphragm collimator markedly improves beam restriction by absorbing unwanted radiation in the lower diaphragm. Further improvement occurs with more than two levels of variable diaphragms.

When used with an extension cone, the collimator should be narrowed to the smallest square that encloses the circular field to improve further the efficiency of beam limitation. However, not all collimators can accept an extension cone.

Collimators are equipped with an ***illuminated field and beam-centering device.*** They also have calibrated scales to allow aperture adjustment for films of various sizes at different focus-film distances.

According to federal regulations, collimators for all new equipment must be electrically interlocked with the clamps in the Bucky tray so that the apertures adjust automatically to the size of the cassette. Such a collimator is known as a ***positive beam-limiting device (PBLD)***. A manual override allows beam-shaping for special field sizes.

Film Coverage by Aperture Diaphragms and Cones. As just noted, collimators are calibrated, thus obviating the need of calculations. However, with aperture diaphragms and cones, we can compute film coverage by apertures of various sizes at desired focus-film distances. Since film sizes are still generally stated in inches, we shall use these units in our example. Computation of film coverage requires the following information:

1. Distance from focus to aperture.
2. Distance from focus to film.
3. Diameter of aperture.

The computation of film coverage by a beam limited by an aperture diaphragm is not difficult. In Figure 19.22, with an opening 1 in. in diameter and 4 in. from the focal spot, and a focus-film distance of 40 in., what will be the diameter of the beam at the surface of the film, disregarding geometric blur? Note that the x-ray beam continues to broaden after passing through the aperture. In longitudinal section, this forms a larger triangle with its apex at the tube focus and its base on the film, and a smaller triangle with its apex at the tube focus and its base at the aperture. These are similar triangles (see pages 18–19), so by the application of elementary geometry we obtain the proportion:

$$AB/AC = d/x$$

where AB = focus-to-aperture distance
AC = focus-film distance
d = diameter of aperture
x = diameter of beam at film plane

Substituting the numerical values in the proportion,

$$4/40 = 1/x$$

$$4x = 40 \text{ in.}$$

$$x = 10 \text{ in.}$$

Figure 19.22. Method of calculating film coverage with an aperture diaphragm. In this example, x/1 = 40/4. Therefore, 4x = 40 and x = 10 in.

An x-ray beam 10 in. in diameter is obviously too small to cover a 10 in. × 12 in. film but will cover adequately an 8 in. × 10 in. film. Since the diagonal of this film is 12.8 in., its corners will be clipped (see Figure 19.20).

The same principle applies to the *flared cone* whose **upper** opening limits the beam (see Figure 19.19A). Calculations must be made as though an aperture diaphragm were located at that level, the lower opening being ignored.

With a *cylinder* the **lower** aperture always limits the size of the beam (see Figure 19.23), and therefore the calculations are made as though an aperture diaphragm were present at the level of the lower opening. The following proportion may be used to find the film coverage diameter, that is, the diameter of the beam at the film:

$$\frac{\text{film coverage diameter}}{\text{cylinder diameter}} = \frac{\text{focus-film distance}}{\text{focus-to-lower aperture distance}}$$

where the "focus-to-lower aperture distance" is obtained simply by adding the distance between the focus and the top of the cylinder, to the length of the cylinder. Substituting the corresponding values from Figure 19.23 in the above equation,

Figure 19.23. The effect of a cylinder in limiting the size of an x-ray beam.

$$\frac{film\ coverage\ diameter}{4} = \frac{40}{3 + 10}$$

$$film\ coverage\ diameter = \frac{4 \times 40}{13} = \frac{160}{13} = 12.3\ in.$$

Thus, an 8×10 film will have about 1/4 in. cut off all four corners under these conditions, provided the beam has been centered exactly to the film. In general, bringing the cylinder closer to the patient improves beam limitation.

OTHER METHODS OF ENHANCING RADIOGRAPHIC QUALITY

Moving Slit Radiography

Introduced by Jaffe and Webster as a method of improving radiographic contrast, moving slit radiography extends the principle that a very narrow (slit-limited) x-ray beam engenders less scattered radiation than does a circular beam of the same area. A suggested prototype model (see Figure 19.24) consists of two lead sheets of appropriate thickness, in which have been cut a series of twelve parallel slits 3 mm in width spaced 2.5 cm apart. One lead sheet would be placed above, and the other below, the patient. Corresponding upper and lower slit pairs must be coaxially aligned in the beam. Movement of the assembly during exposure wipes out the images of the slits in the same manner as a moving grid. With this system, radiographic contrast should be enhanced by a factor of two to three relative to that with a grid. However, this would require a tenfold increase in x-ray output by the tube. The ultimate practicability of this device must await further development.

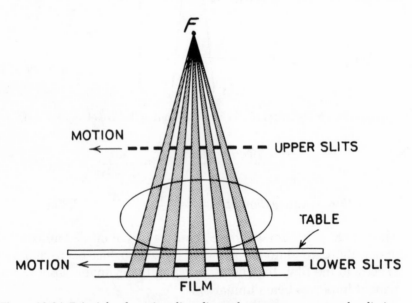

Figure 19.24. Principle of moving slit radiography to remove scattered radiation. The upper and lower lead plates, one above and the other below the patient, each has a series of twelve parallel slits. These are aligned coaxially with the beam as shown. The lead plates move together across the patient in the direction of the arrows. Movement of the lead wipes out the images of the slits on the radiograph in the same way as those of the lead strips in a moving grid system. Image contrast is said to be enhanced two or three times relative to that with a grid but requires about a tenfold increase in exposure.

The Anode Heel Effect—Anode Cutoff

As it leaves the focal spot, the primary beam displays as nonuniform distribution of radiation intensities (see Figure 19.25). The exposure rate at any point in the beam depends not only on the distance from the focus (inverse square law) but also on the *angle the rays make with the face of the target.* Figure 19.25 shows a 20° anode with the angular distribution of the relative exposure rates in an x-ray beam, based on the assumption that the exposure rate on the central axis of the beam (at a given distance) is 100 percent. Thus, if the beam falls on a 14 in. × 17 in. (35 cm × 43 cm) film placed lengthwise with relation to the long axis of the tube, at a focus-film distance of 40 in. (100 cm), the exposure rate at the end of the film below the cathode will be about 105 percent, and at the end of the film below the anode about 80 percent of the exposure rate at the center of the film. This discrepancy becomes less pronounced as the focus-film distance is increased and the size of the film is decreased. The variation in exposure rate according to the angle of emission of the radiation at the focal spot is called *anode cutoff,* or *anode heel effect.* The smallest exposure rate occurs at the anode end of the beam. This is useful in certain procedures; for example, in radiographing a region of the body, which has a wide range of thicknesses, we can take advantage of the heel effect by placing the thickest part toward the cathode end of the beam (where the exposure rate is greatest) and the thinnest part toward the anode (where the exposure rate is least). Accordingly, a more uniform radiographic density is recorded despite varying thicknesses of the object. For example, in radiography of the thoracic spine in the anteroposterior projection the patient should be placed with the head toward the anode and the feet toward the cathode. Figure 19.26 explains the physical basis of the heel effect. Note that it becomes more pronounced with a smaller anode angle.

Figure 19.25. Angular distribution of radiation intensities (exposure rates) in an x-ray beam. The exposure rate is maximal in the central portion of the beam, falling off more toward the anode side of the beam; this is *anode cutoff,* known also as the *heel effect.* Note that anode cutoff becomes less pronounced as the focus-film distance increases and as the film size decreases.

Figure 19.26. Explanation of anode cutoff (heel effect). X-ray photons such as *1* undergo greater attenuation than photons such as *3* because they pass through a larger thickness of anode "heel." This effect becomes more pronounced as the anode angle decreases.

COMPENSATION FILTERS

Various types of filters can be used in radiographing parts of the body that differ greatly in thickness or density so as to record them with more uniform density on a single film. Such compensation filters have traditionally been made of an aluminum or barium-plastic compound. For example, in radiography of the foot in the anteroposterior projection, an aluminum wedge can be placed with its thickest part under the toes so as to even out the image density of the toes and heel. However, this increases the part-film distance and impairs recorded detail. One solution has been to place a wedge filter in the filter slot of the tube housing, but this is impossible with modern equipment.

There is now a type of transparent filter material composed of clear plastic incorporating 30 percent lead by weight. It is the Clear-Pb™ compensation filter (Victoreen Nuclear Associates), which can be mounted on the face of the collimator by a specially designed magnetic system. These filters are thin and lightweight. The simplicity of this system will undoubtedly find wide application in general radiography in such examinations as combined mediastinal-pulmonary tomography, aortic arch angiography, and anteroposterior projections of the foot.

Some dedicated chest radiographic units provide for a *trough filter*—one that is thinner at the center than at the edges—to permit heavier exposure of the mediastinum than of the lungs (see Figure 19.27).

A simple method of compensation for differences in tissue opacity calls for the insertion of a sheet of black paper between one screen and the film in that part of the cassette which is to lie behind the more radiolucent tissues. Sufficiently heavy exposure can then be given to penetrate the denser structures without overexposing the less dense ones, provided the difference in opacity is not excessive. For example, in radiography of the chest when one lung has become partly opacified by disease, we can use a sheet of black paper to block the half of one screen behind the normal lung. We can then increase the exposure to penetrate the diseased lung without overexposing the normal lung, provided there is only a moderate density difference between them.

Figure 19.27. Principle of the trough filter. There is more attenuation of the beam as it passes through the lateral portions of the filter than in the center. Such a filter provides greater exposure of the mediastinal structures than of the aerated lungs, thereby compensating for inherent density differences.

SUMMARY OF RADIOGRAPHIC EXPOSURE

In Figure 19.28 a typical arrangement of x-ray equipment and patient in radiography is shown to summarize the important items in radiographic exposure.

QUESTIONS AND PROBLEMS

1. Discuss the three factors affecting the percentage of scattered radiation relative to primary radiation at the film surface.
2. Describe the principle and construction of a radiographic grid.
3. Explain the physical factors in grid efficiency, including grid ratio and grid frequency.
4. Discuss the functional characteristics of grid efficiency, including selectivity and contrast improvement factor.

Figure 19.28. Summary of radiographic exposure.

5. What is meant by the convergence line of a grid? The focusing distance of a grid?
6. Discuss four precautions in the use of a grid.
7. What is the preferred grid ratio in conventional radiography? In high voltage radiography?
8. Explain the decreased density at the edges of a radiograph, which may occur when a grid is used. What is it called?
9. Describe briefly the main types of Potter-Bucky mechanisms.
10. Name three causes of grid lines with a moving grid and state how each can be corrected.

11. Under what conditions may the x-ray beam be angled with respect to a radiographic stationary or moving grid?
12. Describe four causes of grid cutoff.
13. Define grid ratio. What is the relationship between grid ratio and grid efficiency?
14. Explain how air gap technic reduces the amount of scattered radiation reaching an image receptor?
15. How does the efficiency of a air gap compare with that of a grid in improving contrast (ie, "cleanup")?
16. Describe three examples in which air gap technic may be advantageous. How does one minimize blurring associated with an air gap, and what effect does it have on exposure?
17. How does an aperture diaphragm diminish scattered radiation?
18. An aperture diaphragm measuring 2 in. (5 cm) in diameter is located 5 in. (12.7 cm) below the tube focus. What will be the diameter of the beam at 40 in. (100 cm)?
19. Describe a typical radiographic collimator (variable beam-limiting device). Why is it the most desirable type of beam limiter?
20. A cylinder measuring 12 in. (30.5 cm) in length is used to limit an x-ray beam. The lower opening is 15 in. (38 cm) from the tube focus and measures 4 in. (10 cm) in diameter. What is the largest standard film that will be covered (except for the corners) at a focus-film distance of 40 in. (100 cm)?
21. Summarize the methods of minimizing scattered radiation in radiography.
22. Define and explain the cause of the anode heel effect. How is it influenced by the focus-film distance? By the anode angle? By the size of the film?
23. Draw a simple diagram summarizing radiography.
24. What is the purpose of a compensation filter? Discuss the available materials for compensation filters and give their relative advantages.
25. Describe the form, function, and application of a trough filter.

CHAPTER *20* SPECIAL EQUIPMENT

A NUMBER OF USEFUL modifications of radiographic equipment are available for special purposes. Of these we shall describe, in particular, image intensification, stereoscopic radiography, tomography, computed tomography, photofluorography, and xeroradiography.

Bright Fluoroscopy (Image Intensification)

Fluoroscopy, an essential procedure in diagnostic radiology, makes possible the visualization of organs in motion, positioning of the patient for spotfilming, instillation of opaque media into hollow organs, insertion of catheters into arteries, and a variety of other procedures. Unfortunately, *direct* or *dark* fluoroscopy with a zinc cadmium sulfide screen is an extremely inefficient process, both physically and visually. This results from the very low brightness level of the direct fluoroscopic image, about 1/30,000 that of a radiograph on a fluorescent illuminator, but also to the nature of human vision which we shall explore briefly in introducing the subject. Therefore, direct fluoroscopy has become virtually obsolete.

The human eye is a living camera. Light reflected from an object enters the eye and passes through the lens which focuses it on the *retina,* a membrane lining the inside surface of the back of the eye (see Figure 20.1). Within the retina there are two types of light-sensitive cells, the *cones* and the *rods.* Present in other areas, but concentrated in a small spot at the center of the retina—the *fovea centralis*—the cones respond to light at ordinary brightness levels, and not to the dim light from a zinc cadmium sulfide fluoroscopic screen.

The rods, microscopic rod-shaped cells distributed throughout the periphery of the retina, respond to light at the low *brightness*

levels prevailing in direct fluoroscopy, but they exhibit very poor visual acuity—the ability to discriminate small images. In fact, we know that the contrast (difference in brightness) of two adjacent images must approximate 50 percent to be perceived by rod vision, but cones can discriminate images with a contrast of about 2 percent in high level radiographic illumination. Since fluoroscopic image contrast averages one-fourth to one-half that in a radiograph, the visibility of details is poor on the dim fluoroscopic screen. Another factor in rod vision is the prolonged dark adaptation, 20 to 30 min, required for the rods to attain adequate sensitivity, which then has to be preserved during fluoroscopy in an almost completely darkened room. Fortunately, the rods are particularly sensitive to the green light emitted by the zinc cadmium sulfide screen.

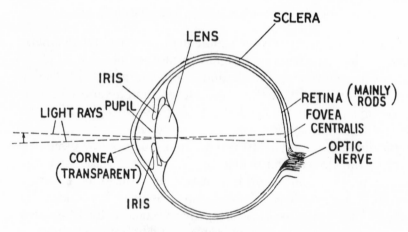

Figure 20.1. Diagram of midsagittal section of human eye.

In summary, then, direct fluoroscopy is an exceedingly inefficient process because of the low brightness level, the low contrast, the dependence on rod vision with its poor visual acuity, and the need of prolonged dark adaptation.

In 1942 Dr. W. E. Chamberlain, in a classic paper, predicted that if the brightness of the fluoroscopic image could be increased about 1,000 times, cone vision would be brought into play and visual acuity enhanced by a factor of ten (ie, 10 times greater) relative to rod vision. Besides, dark adaptation and a completely darkened room would become unnecessary.

After extensive research by various manufacturers, marked brightening of the fluoroscopic image was realized throught the development of the *x-ray image intensifier.* Its main component is the image tube, an electronic device that promptly converts, in several steps, an x-ray image pattern into a corresponding visible light pattern of significantly higher energy per square cm of viewing screen. Figure 20.2 shows the basic construction of a typical image intensifier. After passing through the patient, the x-ray beam enters the *highly evacuated glass envelope* of the image tube and produces a fluorescent image on the zinc cadmium sulfide *input screen,* which resembles an old style fluoroscopic screen except for its finer grain and the presence of silver as an activator. The light from this screen falls on the closely applied *photocathode,* liberating electrons in the form of an *electronic image* that duplicates the light image but consists of various densities of electrons instead of photons. Sharpness of the electronic image is enhanced by having the photocathode curved as shown in Figure 20.2. The electrons forming the image undergo acceleration toward the cathode by an applied high voltage—about 25 kV—and are focused, by a series of electrostatic "lenses," on the *output screen* which has the same phosphor as the input screen, but with an even smaller crystal size for optimal resolution. This phosphor layer has a thin coating of aluminum on the side toward the photocathode to permit the passage of electrons and at the same time prevent the flow of light back to the photocathode. Furthermore, the aluminum is grounded to prevent the accumulation of electrons.

In the output screen the electrons' energy is converted to a corresponding but inverted visible light pattern—an image whose brightness is about 4,000 to 7,000 times that on an ordinary fluoroscopic screen operating under similar conditions, a comparison designated as *brightness gain.* The image finally undergoes processing through an optical system for one or more of the following options: direct viewing with a mirror, closed circuit television, cine (motion picture) recording, videotape, or videodisc.

Brightness gain depends on two main properties of the image intensifier. In the first place, in an image tube with a 9-in. input

Figure 20.2. Image intensifier. X rays produce an image on the *input screen,* whose light liberates *electrons* from the *photocathode.* The concentration of the electrons is proportional to the light intensity at any given point on the photocathode, so they form an *electron image* in space. The electrons are then accelerated at 25 kV and electrostatically focused on the *output screen,* where the final intensified image is formed. This image may be viewed by a system of lenses and a mirror or by closed circuit TV; it may also be recorded on cine film, video tape, or video disc.

screen and a 1-in. output screen, the ratio of the output screen area to the input screen area is $(1/9)^2$ or $1/81$. Since the light photons have been "crowded" into an an area about $1/80$ as large, the brightness will increase eighty times simply through reduction in size or **minification** of the image; this is called **minification gain.** In the second place, the acceleration of the electrons results in a multiplication of photons at the output screen, a process known as *flux gain*—the ratio of the number of photons at the output screen to the number at the input screen for a given exposure. In general,

$$\text{brightness gain} = \text{minification gain} \times \text{flux gain} \qquad (1)$$

With a minification gain of 80 and a flux gain of 50,

$$brightness\,gain = 80 \times 50 = 4,000$$

which means that the brightness of the image at the output screen is 4,000 times that at the input screen.

Further increase in brightness can be achieved by application of higher accelerating voltage, but this is not unlimited. On passing through the optical lens and mirror system (see Figure 20.2), the final image will have regained about 80 to 90 percent of its original size without appreciable loss of brightness.

The ICRU has proposed a standard for specifying the intensifying ability of an x-ray image intensifier, based on strictly defined conditions. This is the ***conversion factor***, defined as the ***ratio of the brightness (ie, luminance) of the output screen to the x-ray exposure rate at the input screen.*** The conversion factor is a more precise concept than brightness gain and may eventually replace it.

The main advantage of the image intensifier lies in its brightness gain, with activation of cone vision (also called photopic vision) and improved visual acuity—ability to see fine detail. Besides, it has done away with the inconvenience of dark adaptation. However, contrast in the intensified image may be lessened by the "fogging" effect (noise factor) of some x-ray photons passing directly from the input screen to the output screen, bypassing intermediate conversion to light and electron images. Moreover, some light photons pass in the reverse direction, from the output screen to the input screen, eventually contributing to image fog and loss of contrast. Contrast can be significantly improved by a television system.

The introduction of cesium iodide (CsI) as the input screen phosphor has resulted in notable improvement in recorded detail by virtue of the increased image resolution and contrast. This depends on the fact that CsI crystals can be crowded much more closely and in a thinner layer than zinc cadmium sulfide crystals onto the input screen. CsI is also a more efficient absorber of x-ray photons, thereby improving recorded detail and contrast. As a result, CsI has become the preferred phosphor in image intensifiers.

Recorded detail is actually a little poorer with image intensification than with direct fluoroscopy because of slight loss of information at each stage of image formation (ie, x rays, light, electrons, light, final viewing system). Also, there is poorer focusing of electrons toward the outer portions of the output screen, especially with large image intensifiers. This causes not only some loss of recorded detail but also distortion of lines toward the edges of the screen ("pincushion effect").

In summary, the advantages of image intensification far outweigh the disadvantages and have led to the obsolescence of direct or dark fluoroscopy. Image-intensified fluoroscopy:

1. Increases brightness level and image contrast. Cone vision is brought into play by the higher brightness level, resulting in improved visual acuity.

2. Eliminates dark adaptation and an almost totally darkened fluoroscopic room.

3. Decreases radiation exposure rate to patient, although this is less than was first anticipated because a certain irreducible minimal brightness is needed at the input screen to reduce quantum mottle and provide good recorded detail in the final intensified image.

4. Can be used to localize certain structures such as the optic foramina for spot filming.

5. Can be used with a television system for more convenient viewing and for enhancement of contrast (see Figure 20.3). Note that the image intensifier by itself cannot increase the inherent contrast of the image presented to it on the input screen.

Figure 20.3. Two common auxiliary methods of recording the image in an image intensifier. A movie camera is used in the upper diagram, and closed circuit television in the lower diagram. (*Adapted from ICRU Handbook 89.*)

6. Can be used in cineradiography (see Figure 20.3) or in a video tape or video disc system.

The basic x-ray image intensifier has been so improved in its maneuverability, phosphor (cesium iodide), optical system, and adaptability to routine fluoroscopic procedures, that it has become an indispensable part of the equipment, not only in the hospital Radiology Department, but also in the private radiology office. The improvement in the auxiliary systems, such as television, cine, video tape, and video disc has immeasurably widened its field of usefulness.

STEREOSCOPIC RADIOGRAPHY

Stereoscopy means "seeing solid," that is, seeing in three dimensions. An ordinary photograph appears flat, lacking depth, because the camera has one "eye" and projects the image of an object on the film in only two dimensions. But when a pair of human eyes sees the same object, the brain perceives it as a three-dimensional solid body.

How is this brought about? Each eye sees the object from a slightly different angle, depending on the distance of the object, its size and shape, and the distance between the pupils of the eyes (see Figure 20.4). As a result, slightly different images are formed on the retinas of the respective eyes and are carried separately over the optic nerves to the brain. Here the two images are fused and perceived as one having three dimensions—height, width, and depth.

Stereoscopic vision also permits us to judge the relative distances of various objects. You can easily verify this by trying to touch something with one eye closed, and then with both eyes open. Still, it is possible for a one-eyed person to learn to judge distance fairly well, although stereoscopy is impossible.

We are not born with stereoscopic vision but develop it during infancy. Many years ago Dr. O. V. Batson showed that we differ in our ability to fuse stereoscopic images, and that in many instances this ability can be improved by corrective glasses, exercise, and practice.

Figure 20.4. Stereoscopic vision. Each eye sees a slightly different view of the solid object. These two images are blended in the brain to give the impression of one image having a solid appearance; that is, height, width, and depth.

Principle of Stereoradiography. We can produce a stereoscopic image radiographically by applying the principle of stereoscopic vision. First, we make *two separate exposures of the same object from different points of view;* the x-ray tube takes the place of the eyes, exposing two films from slightly different positions (see Figure 20.5). The part being examined is immobilized while the tube is shifted to obtain the two stereoradiographs. Second, we must *view properly* the pair of stereoradiographs if we are to achieve stereoscopic or depth perception.

Tube Shift in Stereoradiography. The question arises, "How far must the tube be shifted between exposures to obtain a satisfactory pair of stereoradiographs?" The interpupillary distance, that is, the distance between the pupils of the eyes, averages 2.5 in. (6 cm), whereas the average viewing distance is 25 in. (64 cm). These two distances are in the ratio of $2.5/25 = 1/10$, and the same ratio governs the relationship between tube shift and focus-film distance:

$$\frac{\text{tube shift}}{\text{focus-film distance}} = \frac{1}{10} \tag{2}$$

According to this equation, stereoradiography at a focus-film distance of 40 in. requires a tube shift of 4 in.; for a focus-film distance of 72 in., the tube shift is about 7 in. We may conclude that the *tube shift is theoretically one-tenth the focus-film distance when the viewing distance is 25 in.* (64 cm). While, in most instances, this ratio lays down the conditions for excellent stereoradiographs,

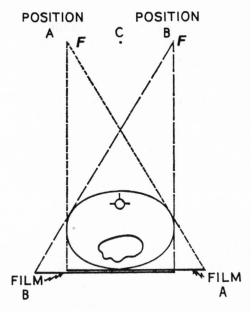

Figure 20.5. Stereoradiography. Two films are exposed separately, one with the tube focus at *A,* and the other with the focus at *B.* Note that the object is not moved. The focus positions are at equal distances from the center *C.*

some observers find it difficult to fuse the images unless the ratio is reduced to $1/13$, or even $1/16$. However, the resulting apparent depth of the stereoscopic image will be less than that with the larger ratio of $1/10$.

The *direction* of the tube shift relative to the anatomic area should be perpendicular to the dominant lines; thus, chest stereoradiography requires a tube shift across the ribs. With low-ratio grids, tube shift perpendicular to the grid strips should entail no significant difference in the density of the two radiographs if the tube has been correctly centered to the grid. But with a tube shift parallel to the grid strips, there may be a difference in the densities of the radiographs due to *anode cutoff* or *heel effect.* Also, recorded detail will be different in the two radiographs because the size of the effective focus will differ in the two positions. This is shown in Figure 20.6. But with a *high ratio Bucky grid such as 12 or 16,* because of the criticality of centering, the shift *must be parallel to the long axis of the table* to avoid off-center cutoff.

We must be careful to open the collimator so as to cover the films in both positions of the tube. If the beam is collimated excessively, the tube will have to be tilted to cover both films.

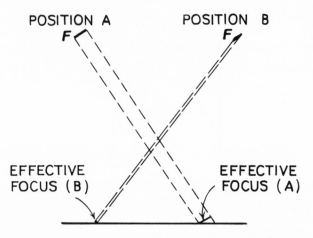

Figure 20.6. Difference in size of the projected or effective focus when the tube is shifted parallel to the long axis of the tube. Note that in position *B* the effective focus is smaller and therefore recorded detail is better than in position *A*. But the density of the radiograph will be less in position *A* because of anode cutoff (heel effect).

The steps in stereoradiography may now be summarized:

1. Center accurately the part to be radiographed.
2. Determine the total shift of the tube for the given focus-film distance. Suppose this shift is to be 4 in. (that is, 1/10 of 40 in.).
3. Determine the correct direction of shift.
4. Now shift the tube one-half the total required distance, away from the center. In this case, 1/2 × 4 = 2 in. Make the first exposure.
5. With the patient immobilized in the same position, change the cassette. (For chest stereoradiography, patient should suspend respiration.)
6. Now shift the tube the total distance, in this case 4 in., in a direction exactly opposite the first shift, and make the second exposure. (This is the same as shifting the tube one-half

the total distance to the opposite side from the center point.) The exact method of shifting is shown in Figure 20.7.

Figure 20.7. Method of shifting the tube in stereoradiography. In *A*, the tube has been shifted one-half the total distance to one side of the center, *C*, for the first exposure. In *B*, it has been shifted the full distance in the opposite direction for the second exposure.

7. Process the films.
8. The stereoradiographs are now ready for viewing.

Viewing Stereoradiographs. There are various methods of viewing a pair of stereoradiographs so that they are perceived three-dimensionally. These will now be described.

The films can be viewed stereoscopically without auxiliary equipment. They are placed side by side in illuminators, in the same relative position as they were "seen" by the x-ray tube, and with a horizontal shift. The observer then attempts to fuse the images by "crossing" his eyes, but not many are able to do this successfully.

A number of optical devices facilitate stereoscopic viewing. They all have the capability of shifting the image of one of the stereoradiographs onto its mate. The simplest device, a 30° or 40° *glass prism,* is available at optical supply houses. Figure 20.8 shows how a prism bends the light rays coming from one radiograph so that they seem to come from the other one, thereby superimposing the images. To be viewed properly, the stereoradiographic pair is held up with the tube side facing the observer; in other words, the eyes see the radiograph just as the tube did. At the same time, the stereoradiographs are positioned so as to represent a *horizontal shift of the tube.* With a vertical tube shift, as in radiography of the chest, the radiographs would have to be turned 90°, the chest then appearing to lie on its side. On one radiograph, the image appears *farther from the left hand edge;* this radiograph was made with the tube in the left position, and is therefore placed in the *left illuminator.* The other radiograph, exposed with the tube in the right position, is placed in the right illuminator. The observer now holds the prism between the thumb and index finger of the right hand in front of the right eye, with the *thinnest portion near the nose,* as shown in Figure 20.8. (If preferred, the prism can be held with the left hand in front of the left eye, again with the thinnest edge near the nose.) By slightly adjusting the position of the prism and stepping forward and backward, the observer soon succeeds in fusing or blending the images. This method requires very little practice, is inexpensive, and provides a convenient *portable monocular stereoscope.* If preferred, two 20° prisms may be used, one being held before each eye, again with the thinnest part near the nose; this is the simplest type of *portable binocular stereoscope.*

Figure 20.8. Basic principle of stereoradiographic viewing. The glass prism bends the light rays from stereoradiographic 2 in such a way as to superimpose its image on stereoradiograph *1.* This facilitates the fusion of the images to provide depth perception.

The more elaborate stereoscopes, such as the floor model **Stanford**® and **Wheatstone**® units, are modifications of the types just described, making use of prisms or mirrors to displace the images. Because of their bulk and high cost, they have been largely replaced by various types of small *hand-held binocular stereoscopes.* Some of these operate on the Stanford, whereas others use the Wheatstone principle. With the Stanford system, the stereoradiographs are placed in the illuminators in the same way as for the 40° prism. The same procedure holds for the Wheatstone system, except for the *added step* of flipping each radiograph over, around a vertical axis; the image in the left-hand illuminator is now nearer the left edge of the radiograph, whereas that in the right-hand illuminator is nearer the right edge.

One must be careful to place the stereoradiographs in the illuminators correctly, as described above, to achieve a genuine stereoscopic effect. Only then will an anteroposterior radiographic projection appear to be anteroposterior, and conversely. For example, with a chest stereoradiographed in a posteroanterior position, the anterior ribs should appear to curve away from the observer. Such verification, which is important in the relative localization of lesions or foreign bodies, can be simplified by taping an identifying marker— "stereo"—to the table top or cassette holder, to indicate the part that was farthest from the tube during radiography.

There is wide variation in the frequency with which stereoradiography is performed, depending on the preference of the individual radiologist. In fact, there has been a decline in the use of stereoradiography in recent years. However, stereoradiography helps not only in localizing a lesion or a foreign body but also in improving the perception of its shape, structure, and spatial relationship to other anatomic parts.

TOMOGRAPHY

In ordinary radiography a three-dimensional object—the body —is represented on a two-dimensional film. In effect, the object has been compressed virtually to zero thickness in the direction of the x-ray beam so that the images of a number of structures are superimposed on each other in the radiograph. Not infrequently, this makes radiographic interpretation difficult, if not impossible.

We have three methods of separating such superimposed images through modification of ordinary radiography:

1. ***Increased Distortion.*** We can separate confusing images by simply rotating the patient or by changing the direction of the x-ray beam. Thus, we use an oblique projection of the gall bladder to separate its shadow from that of the vertebral column or gas-filled bowel.

2. ***Decreased Focus-film Distance.*** When structures are relatively far apart along the axis of the x-ray beam, we can use a very short focus-film distance. This produces more geometric blurring (see page 342) of the images of structures farther from the film than of structures nearer the film, so the latter remain reasonably sharp. An example is radiography of the mandible in the posteroanterior view with a very short focus-film distance, blurring the image of the cervical vertebrae.

3. ***Motion of a Part.*** When two structures are directly aligned in the x-ray beam and the undesired one happens to be movable, we can set it in motion and blur its image while the desired image remains sharply defined. For example, the dens (odontoid process) of the second cervical vertebra can be well shown in the antero-posterior projection by having the patient move his/her jaw during the exposure.

While the above methods may succeed, they often do not. In fact, they fail completely when the desired structure is buried within a denser one, as exemplified by a cavity inside a densely consolidated or scarred part of the lung. Here we make use of a principle that departs from ordinary radiography and is called ***tomography.***

Tomography provides a reasonably sharp image of a particular structure, while images of structures lying in front of or behind it are blurred beyond recognition. Ideally, the desired image stands out sharply in a hazy sea of blurred shadows. ***Tomography simply consists of motion of the tube and film in opposite directions in a prescribed manner during the exposure.***

It is of interest that the principles of tomography, one of the outstanding innovations in radiology, were discovered independently in France by Bocage (1921), and Portes and Chasse (1922); in the Netherlands by Ziedses des Plantes (1921); and in the

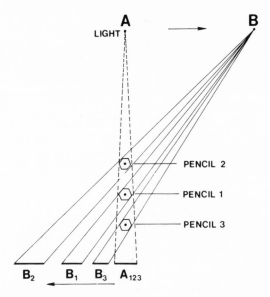

Figure 20.10. The effect of motion of a source of light on three objects lined up as shown. In position A, the images of all three pencils are superimposed, falling on the same spot as shadow A_{123}. In B, with pencil 1 at the pivot (fulcrum) level, if the light source moves toward the right and the film moves to the left at the same speed as shadow B_1, this shadow will remain sharp. The shadow of pencil 2, B_2, moves faster than the film and is blurred out. The shadow of pencil 3, B_2, moving slower than the film, is also blurred out. Note that the shadow of pencil 2 is larger than that of pencil 1, whereas the shadow of pencil 3 is smaller than that of pencil 1.

the focus-film distance to the focus-objective plane distance must be constant throughout the excursion of the tube to keep magnification constant during tube travel.

To satisfy these conditions, the tube and the Bucky tray must be connected by a rigid rod that allows them to rotate about a pivot or *fulcrum.* There must also be movable *joints* or *linkages* between the rod and the tube carriage and between the rod and the Bucky tray. A simple drawing of a *rectilinear* ("linear") tomograph appears in Figure 20.12. Only images of points in the plane of the fulcrum (objective plane) that are parallel to the film remain in constant position on the film and show good recorded detail. Images of points lying in planes above or below the objective plane are

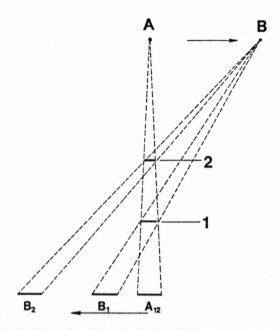

Figure 20.11. Principle of tomography. At focal spot position A, the radiographic images of structures *1* and *2* are superimposed on the film at A_{12}. When the tube is shifted to B and the film moves in the opposite direction so that the axis of rotation (pivot) of the x-ray beam is at level *1*, the image of *1* at B_1 will have a constant position on the film and will be *sharp*. In other words, A_1 and B_1 will strike the same spot on the film. But image B_2 will shift relative to B_1 and will blur out. (In practice, the tube is moved from position B through A to a corresponding point on the opposite side of A during the exposure.)

blurred in proportion to their distance from the objective plane. Such blurred images vary in size and shape and, ideally, are less visible than the sharper image of the objective plane. Figure 20.13 shows how the radiographic image of a point, *P*, outside the objective plane shifts on the film relative to the position of the image of a point, *E*, inside the objective plane.

In Figure 20.14 you see a schematic diagram of a simple rectilinear tomograph with the standard terminology and symbols used by the International Commission on Radiologic Units and Measurements (ICRU).

Thickness of Section. A tomogram is really a radiograph of a slice or **slab** of tissue rather than of a plane of zero thickness. Since

Figure 20.12. Simplified diagram of a rectilinear tomograph.

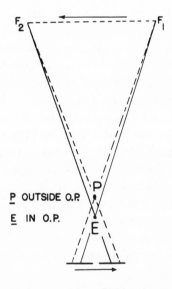

Figure 20.13. Relative shift of images of points lying outside (*P*) and within (*E*) the objective plane during tomographic excursion. Note that the image of point *E* retains the same location on the film, while the image of point *P* moves across the film and blurs. *O.P.* = objective plane.

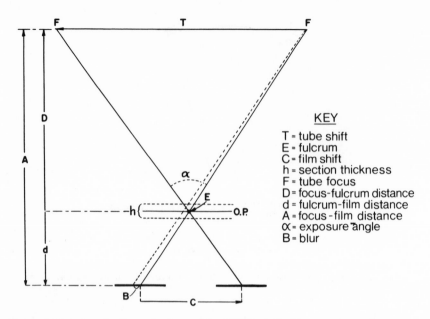

Figure 20.14. Standard terminology of the *ICRU* applicable to tomography.

blurring gradually increases at greater distances from the objective plane (ie, level of fulcrum) there is no distinct boundary between the tomographic section (slab) and its surroundings. Therefore we arbitrarily choose the boundary planes so that images of points in them have a certain amount of blurring and no more. Thus, *we define the tomographic section as the slab between these two planes of maximum permissible blur.* Obviously, the tomographic images of all points in the tomographic section will be sharper than the images of points beyond the boundary planes. If the maximum permissible blur has been properly chosen, say 0.5 mm, the images of all points within the slab will have acceptable recorded detail. Note that blur refers to the actual width of the blurred boundary of an image.

Two factors affect the thickness of section *h* for a given maximum permissible blur *B:*

1. *Exposure Angle*—the angle through which the central ray moves during the actual exposure; that is, the angle, at the fulcrum, made by the central ray between the beginning and the end of the

exposure. This definition applies regardless of whether the motion is rectilinear (straight line) or pluridirectional. It is to be emphasized that *the larger the exposure angle the thinner the tomographic section,* and conversely (see Figure 20.15). Note also that the angle through which the *tube* moves exceeds the exposure angle because tube motion starts before the exposure begins, and stops after the exposure ends.

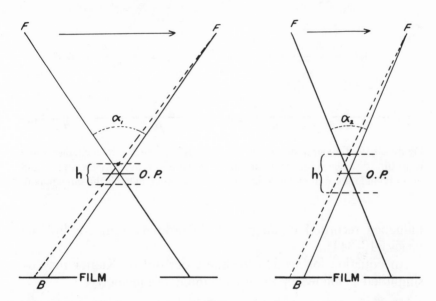

Figure 20.15. Thickness of tomographic section increases with a decrease in exposure angle. The blur *B* of the limit of the thicker section in the right-hand diagram is the same as that of the thinner section in the left-hand diagram; thus, the recorded detail is equal at the upper and lower boundaries of the thick and thin section.

2. *Focus-film Distance* — with a *constant exposure angle,* a change in focus-film distance does not affect section thickness (see Figure 20.16). (When tube excursion is stated as amplitude, that is, the *distance* the tube shifts rather than the exposure angle, section thickness does depend on FFD, but amplitude is now obsolete as a measure of tube excursion.) Focus-film and object-film distance

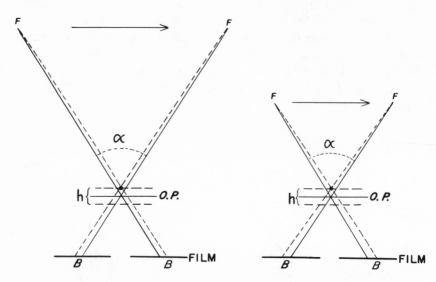

Figure 20.16. Tomographic section thickness is not affected by a change in the focus-film distance if the exposure angle remains constant. At the upper and lower boundaries of the tomographic sections, recorded detail is the same in both cases.

influence recorded detail just as in ordinary radiography (see pages 340–341).

An equation for section thickness derived by Kieffer may be simplified as follows by the use of simple trigonometry:

$$h = \frac{B}{tan\ 1/2\alpha} \qquad (3)$$

where h = section thickness
            B = maximum permissible blur
            α = exposure angle in degrees

If we select a reasonable maximum blur such as 0.5 mm, then Table 20.1 shows the approximate thickness for various exposure angles. When plotted graphically, these data generate the curve shown in Figure 20.17. Note that section thickness decreases as exposure angle increases. At the same time, a thinner section will have less subject contrast than a thicker one.

Figure 20.17. Relationship of tomographic section thickness to exposure angle. Note that the *section thickness increases as the exposure angle decreases.*

TABLE 20.1
RELATION OF SECTION THICKNESS TO EXPOSURE ANGLE

Angle	Section Thickness
	mm
50°	1.1
40°	1.4
30°	2.0
20°	3.0
10°	6.0
5°	11.0

Tomographic Image. A tomogram consists of two parts. First, it presents good recorded detail of the tomographic section, which we shall call the **tomographic image.** Second, it contains the blurred images of points outside the tomographic section, called **redundant shadows,** which greatly influence the quality of the tomographic image. Since the redundant shadows are generated by a moving x-ray tube, tomographic image quality ultimately depends on the **path of the tube during the exposure.** The more uniform the blurring of the redundant shadows, the better the recorded detail will be. An example of nonuniform blurring is the streaking of the image in rectilinear tomography.

Thus, tomographic image quality depends ultimately on (1) the recorded detail of the tomographic section and (2) the uniformity of blurring of the redundant shadows.

Types of Tomographic Motion. The four most important types of motion are shown in Figure 20.18. They may be summarized briefly as follows:

1. *Rectilinear*—tube and film move in straight lines parallel to each other, but in opposite directions (see Figure 20.18A). In other words, the movement is *plane-parallel.* This type of motion is often called, simply, *linear.*

2. *Curvilinear*—tube and film in their respective arcs in the same vertical plane (see Figure 20.18B).

3. *Vertical*—tube and film move in opposite directions along a line perpendicular to (or at some angle to) the objective plane (see Figure 20.18C).

4. *Pluridirectional*—tube and film move in parallel planes in circular, elliptical, hypocycloid, spiral, sinusoidal, or random paths (see Figure 20.18D). This movement is also *plane-parallel.*

Effect of Type of Motion on Blurring of Redundant Shadows. As we have already stated, the blurring pattern of the redundant shadows is an important factor in tomographic quality. Since the blurring pattern, in turn, depends on the type of tomographic motion, we shall now discuss this aspect of tomography.

Rectilinear tomography is the simplest and most commonly used system. Here, *maximum blurring of redundant shadows and most effective tomography occur when the dominant axis of the tomographed structure lies perpendicular to the tube shift* (see Figure 20.19). Conversely, *minimum blurring and least effective tomography occur when the dominant axis is parallel to the tube shift.* For example, in anteroposterior tomography of the vertebral column, the lateral vertebral margins, being parallel to the tube shift, will appear sharp in *all* sections without blurring of structures outside each section; therefore, these margins are not truly tomographed. But recorded detail of the vertebral plates, oriented as they are perpendicular to the tube shift, will be sharp only for the selected tomographic section, while the images of other sections will show various degrees of blurring; only the vertebral plates will be truly tomographed. If the vertebral column were arranged with its long axis across the table, the lateral margins would be tomographed and the plates would not. A reasonable compromise would be to place such elongated objects as the vertebral column, sternum, and long bones with their long axis *diagonally* on the table.

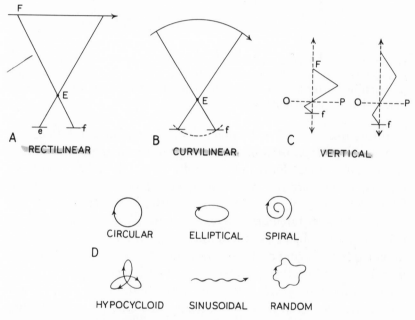

Figure 20.18. Types of tomographic motion.

From the preceding discussion we can see that rectilinear tomography, despite its simplicity and easy availability, has certain deficiencies. In practice, we find:

1. *Incomplete blurring of points outside the tomographic section.* This becomes worse as the orientation of elongated structures approaches parallelism with the direction of tube shift. It accounts for the *streaking* that is so objectionable with rectilinear tomography, for example, in the examination of the facial bones

2. *Elongation of the section image in the direction of tube shift,*

Figure 20.19. Relation of degree of blurring of redundant shadows to the direction of tube shift. Note that maximum blurring occurs when the tube is shifted perpendicular to the long axis of the object, and that no blurring occurs when the tube is shifted parallel to the axis.

resulting from distortion by angular displacement of the image.

3. *Incomplete formation of the image of the tomographic section.* Radiographic image formation generally follows the *Law of Tangents;* that is, image-forming rays are those which pass tangential to (skim) the edges of object elements in the body. The greater the number of such tangential rays, the more closely will the image conform to the object. An ideal tomograph would therefore be one in which the blurring rays arise from an infinite number of sources, thereby providing the greatest number of image-forming rays for points in the tomographic section. This situation does not exist in rectilinear tomography, so the tomographic image is incompletely formed. (See Littleton.)

Pluridirectional tomography uses complex motion of the tube and film. As already described, the incomplete image formed in rectilinear tomography is accompanied by linear streaking in the direction of tube shift due to parallelism of some of the object elements in the tomographic section. This can be overcome by moving the tube and film in a complex pattern while maintaining their paths parallel to each other. During such excursion of the tube, some component of motion is always perpendicular to the border of any structure in the path of x rays, regardless of its orientation. But such equipment is extremely expensive and is necessarily limited to certain procedures, such as the examination of the middle and inner parts of the ear. Therefore, most Radiology Departments must depend on rectilinear tomography, which is generally satisfactory if we keep its limitations in mind.

The most common types of pluridirectional or complex motion are shown in Figure 20.18D and include:

1. *Circular*—redundant shadows may be ring-like, giving rise to double margins and fictitious sharp cutoff at image margins by the incomplete blurring of rounded objects. This is especially true if the diameter of the x-ray path approaches that of the object.

2. *Elliptical*—results are intermediate between circular and rectilinear paths.

3. *Spiral*—excellent blurring of redundant shadows, but spiral motion is limited mechanically to small exposure angles.

4. *Hypocycloidal*—follows a "cloverleaf" path as in Figure 20.18D. It provides the best recorded detail in the tomographic image and the most uniform (nonstreaking) blur in the redundant shadows, with a good range of exposure angles. Hypocycloidal motion provides sections about 1.3 mm thick with an exposure angle of 48°, but three-phase equipment is mandatory to keep exposure times reasonably short. The Law of Tangents is fulfilled, in that x rays originate from virtually an infinite number of points during tube travel (Littleton).

Limitations of Tomographic Equipment. One of the main problems in the design of tomographic equipment is that of lost motion or "play" at the linkages (joints). Each linkage causes a certain amount of lost motion because it is impossible to have an absolutely tight fit which still permits the required motion at the linkage. As the number of linkages increases so does the total lost motion, since the individual lost motions are additive. Thus, the least amount of lost motion may occur in the rectilinear system.

We are concerned with lost motion because it contributes to loss of recorded detail. With the large number of linkages in the pluridirectional systems, much care must be used in their construction to minimize play at the joints. This has been accomplished to a surprising degree in modern pluridirectional tomographs such as the Polytome.™

As shown in Figure 20.20, the effect on recorded detail in the tomogram depends on the location of the lost motion. When present

Figure 20.20. Effect of the various locations of lost motion on the tomographic image. The wavy lines show the sites of lost motion.

1. *At the fulcrum*—maximum impairment of recorded detail occurs here because the effect is magnified in the film plane.

2. *At the Bucky tray linkage*—blurring equals the lost motion because the latter is essentially at the film plane.

3. *At the x-ray tube linkage*—minimum impairment of recorded detail occurs because it is minified at the film plane.

Limitations of Materials. The emulsion thickness of ordinary double-emulsion films adversely affects recorded detail in thin-section tomography with large exposure angles, in which sections measure 1 to 2 mm thick. Double-emulsion films are also subject to crossover (see pages 305–306), which causes a slight further impairment of recorded detail. This may be improved with single-emulsion films, but larger exposures are required. In ordinary tomography where section thickness is greater than 5 mm, emulsion thickness does not appreciably impair recorded detail.

Applications of Tomography. As we observed at the beginning of this section, tomography is indicated whenever the desired radiographic image would be obscured by the images of structures lying in front or behind, or whenever the desired structure lies within a denser structure. Included are lesions of the chest, sternum, dens, temporomandibular joints, upper thoracic spine (lateral), thoracic spine pedicles, cholecystography and cholangiography, nephrotomography, orbits, middle and inner ears, and others. Figure 20.21 shows a typical setup in rectilinear tomography. A metal rod (behind the table) connects the tube and Bucky tray through a movable linkage at each end. The rod is provided with a pivot or *fulcrum* which is adjustable at various heights above the table and determines the *objective plane.* Because the rigid rod pivots at the fulcrum, motion of the tube in one direction causes the Bucky tray to move in the opposite direction with proportional displacement of the tube and film during the entire range of motion. Tube travel is activated by a motor through a switch located in the control booth.

To obtain a tomographic series, we place the patient in the required position and localize the desired structure by appropriate radiographs. Next, we adjust the fulcrum for various heights above the table, corresponding to the series of objective planes needed to include the volume of interest. At each level of the fulcrum we expose a tomogram—commonly called a *cut.* Usually, the separation of successive fulcrum heights (and objective planes) is 0.5 or 1.0 cm, depending on the size and nature of the structure being investigated. Ordinarily, the exposure angle is 30°, but there are certain exceptions which will be discussed later. In this manner, we obtain a series of tomograms in which at least one should show the desired structure with optimum recorded detail. For example, a series of tomograms of the dens (odontoid process) should include one that depicts the dens with optimal recorded detail, while the remaining ones will display it with decreasing clarity until it disappears.

The *exposure* in tomography exceeds that in ordinary radiography of the same region because of the obliquity of the beam during most of the tube excursion, with consequent increase in the average focus-film distance and thickness of part. Although the increase in tomographic exposures varies with the area of interest and the

Figure 20.21. Rectilinear tomography. The tube is shifted during the exposure in the direction of the upper arrow, while the film moves in the opposite direction. The fulcrum level is selected at the level of the desired objective plane, *b.* The image of *b, b$_s$,* moves with the film, always striking the same spot. Its image is therefore sharp. But the image of *a, a$_s$,* constantly moving over the film during the exposure, is blurred out.

type of tissue, it is usually one and one-half to two times the corresponding conventional exposure.

Multitomography (multisection radiography). First proposed by Ziedses des Plantes in 1931, multitomography produces a set of tomograms of different sections simultaneously, with one sweep of the x-ray tube. This requires a special multisection or "book" cassette equipped with a series of pairs of graded intensifying screens, a film being placed between each pair of screens. Thus, a multisection cassette accommodates multiple films. Each pair of screens is separated from its neighboring pair by 0.5 or 1.0 cm balsa wood or polyester foam spacer, depending on the desired separation. Because of the decrease in intensity of the x-ray beam as it passes through the cassette (mainly by absorption in the films and screens), the speed of the screens is graded so that the slowest are on top and the fastest at the bottom.

Figure 20.22 shows the principle of multitomography. Because x rays diverge, spacers between the screen pairs are slightly thicker than the separation of the objective planes. Spacer thickness (more strictly, separation of the films) can be calculated by the formula:

$$S_F = \frac{AS_L}{D} \qquad (4)$$

where S_F = separation of films
          A = focus-film distance
          S_L = separation of objective planes
          D = focus-fulcrum distance

Commercially available multisection cassettes provide three or five pairs of screens with 0.5 or 1.0 cm spacers.

Multitomography has the advantage of saving time, since several tomograms can be obtained with a single excursion of the x-ray tube. At the same time, it has the distinct disadvantage of producing tomograms with poorer contrast and recorded detail, especially toward the bottom of the cassette, as compared with a set of individual tomograms.

It has been erroneously stated that multitomography provides a large saving in exposure of the patient. Actually, radiation exposure of the patient is little more for a multitomographic series (with screens) than for a set of individual tomograms containing the same number of films. The explanation rests on the fact that there is a limit to the speed of the fastest available screens which are at the bottom of the book cassette; hence, to balance the radiographic exposures, the uppermost screens must be very slow, with resulting overall increase in exposure. The *apparent* reduction in exposure of the patient during multitomography results from the higher kV which could just as well be used in ordinary tomography with a similar saving in patient exposure.

Plesiotomography. Introduced by McGann, a radiographer, plesiotomography is a convenient and useful refinement of multitomography. The prefix *plesio* means *near* or *close*, indicating that

Figure 20.22. Multitomography. Simultaneous "cuts" of objective planes I, II, and III.

the tomographic cuts are close to each other. A plesiotomographic cassette contains four pairs of speed-graded screens *without* added spacers; the screens themselves provide a spacing such that separation of the tomographic sections is approximately *1 mm.* Intensifying factors of the screen pairs, from top to bottom, are about 22.5, 32, 48, and 68. These cassettes are available in 8 in. × 10 in. and 10 in. × 12 in. sizes. The application of plesiotomography in the diagnosis of eighth nerve tumors in the internal auditory canal is described in McGann's paper. However, the procedure can be simplified by dividing the cassette in half (instead of quarters) to show both canals at the same time.

Plesiotomography has its main application in studies of the internal and middle ear. Most of the important structures are demonstrated, including the external auditory canal, malleus, incus, semicircular canals, internal auditory canal, and mastoid antrum. Eighth nerve tumors and cholesteatomas can be shown by this method when conventional methods fail. A plesiotomographic cassette is relatively inexpensive and should be available in all Radiology Departments without access to a pluridirectional tomograph.

Zonography. First proposed by Ziedes des Plantes in 1931, zonography is simply tomography with a *small exposure angle* — 5° to 10° — producing a thick section. For example, with a tomographic angle of 10° section thickness is 6 mm, and with 5°, 11 mm. Such a thick section, called a *zonogram,* superficially resembles an ordinary radiograph. It has better contrast and recorded detail than a conventional tomogram made with a tomographic angle of, say, 30°. Zonography is helpful when (1) the obscuring structures are far from the objective plane and (2) thin sections are not needed. Examples of structures usually suitable for zonography include the sternum (thoracic spine far removed), temporomandibular joint (opposite joint far removed), nephrotomography (thin sections usually not needed), and cholangiography (thin sections not needed). Zonography is ordinarily ill-advised in studies of the lungs because small cavities may be missed. (See Ettinger for practical use of zonography.)

Autotomography. Mention should be made of this variety of tomography, which does not require special equipment. Instead of moving the tube and film during the exposure, we can sometimes move the anatomic part and produce excellent tomograms of centrally located anatomic structures. In 1949 Ziedses des Plantes introduced head movement in pneumoencephalography, which has since come to be known as *autotomography.* It improves delineation of the aqueduct and fourth ventricle during air encephalography. With ordinary radiography, these structures are obscured by the dense bone at the base of the skull. Because of their location virtually at the axis of rotation of the head, they will blur very little when the head is rotated during radiographic exposure in the lateral view; whereas structures lying farther laterally will blur in proportion to their distance from the center. Figure 20.23 shows diagrammatically the technic of autotomography.

Patient Exposure in Tomography. In general, the surface dose for a given tomographic exposure is of the same order of magnitude as that for ordinary radiography, but is distributed over a larger area of the body. As already mentioned, patient exposure with multitomography is not much more than that with a sequential series of individual tomograms with the same number of films.

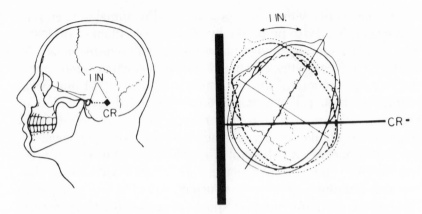

Figure 20.23. Autotomography. The head is rotated during the exposure, and only images of points in the axis of rotation of the head appear sharp on the film. This procedure is especially useful in air studies of the aqueduct and fourth ventricle. (From Selman, J.: *Skull Radiography.* Springfield, Charles C Thomas Publisher, 1966.)

Precautions during tomography are the same as for conventional radiography—adequate filtration (HVL 3 mm Al), high kV, collimation, shielding of gonads, and optimum processing of films. Under these conditions, and because its use is relatively limited, tomography adds an insignificant amount of radiation to the general population.

COMPUTED TOMOGRAPHY

In ordinary radiography soft tissues are classified as having "water" density. Except for fat, soft tissues do not differ sufficiently in density to provide adequate contrast. In fact, anatomic structures must have a density difference of at least 10 percent to be shown in ordinary radiography, and so we cannot differentiate between such structures as liver and muscle, nor can we see soft-tissue detail within the kidneys or brain. Conventional tomography also has limited usefulness in this regard. We can, of course, use contrast media to expand the diagnostic capabilities of routine radiography.

In 1961 a neurologist, William H. Oldendorf, suggested a method of detecting small density differences among soft tissues (ie, low contrast) by elaboration of tomography, but digital computers were not available to put his ideas into practice. Then, in 1971, Godfrey Hounsfield, a research physicist at EMI, Ltd, in Middlesex, England, installed in a London hospital a *computerized tomographic unit* which he had designed. This proved to be the first major advance in radiology since the discovery of x rays.

Computed tomography (CT) is a complex application of the law of tangents which states that in conventional tomography image quality improves with the number of image-forming rays passing tangential to an anatomic object over its entire border. However, this applies to structures whose density differs sufficiently from their surroundings to provide adequate subject contrast. But with CT each slice (ie, tomographic section) is scanned by a collimated x-ray beam in a circular path around the body over a range of 180° or 360°, depending on the design of the equipment.

An x-ray tube is mounted on a support known as a *gantry* which rotates around the patient (see Figure 20.24). The exit beam for each position of the tube is received by one or more very small radiation detectors mounted on the gantry, directly opposite the tube. There are two kinds of detectors: one is solid, such as a sodium iodide or bismuth germanate crystal coupled to a photomultiplier tube (see pages 506–507); the other is a gas-filled (eg, xenon) ionization chamber. The total attenuation ("absorption") by structures that differ almost imperceptibly in density (ie, extremely low contrast) is measured for each position of the tube and detector. In other words, an extremely large amount of data—approaching 100,000 counts—is accumulated for each tomographic section and then rapidly computerized in a number of stages to yield a tomogram. Such data processing requires a digital computer. The resulting tomogram reveals exquisite recorded detail of internal structures of each section, whereas with ordinary tomography they would appear as water density without visible internal structure.

We may summarize this introductory discussion as follows:

1. Numerous x-ray projections are made of each of a series of successive contiguous tomographic sections at intervals over an arc of 180° or 360°, depending on equipment design.

2. Images are received by appropriate detectors in the form of "counts."

Figure 20.24. Basic arrangement of a computed tomography (CT) scanner. As the x-ray tube moves in an arc around the patient during the exposure, its narrowly collimated beam produces a tomographic section or slice. The exit or remnant radiation strikes a detector from many thousands of directions, and the resulting information is processed by a computer which reconstructs an image of the section. The tube and detector are mounted opposite each other on a rigid gantry so that the detector always remains directly opposite the tube focus. (Adapted from *The Fundamentals of Radiography,* 12th ed, Eastman Kodak Company.)

3. The tremendous amount of accumulated data is processed by the computer to yield a tomogram of internal structures with superb recorded detail, impossible with conventional tomography.

We shall now describe some of the important features of CT scanners.

Types of Scanning Motion. CT scanners have undergone rapid evolution in design over four "generations" or stages, in a period of about ten years. However, we shall limit our discussion to two major types of motion.

1. *Rotation and Translation.* The EMI scanner originally designed by Hounsfield combined two kinds of motion: rotation around the body, alternating with translation (ie, rectilinear motion) across it, as shown in Figure 20.25. In other words, the x-ray tube moves

over an arc of a specified number of degrees (part of a circle) and then moves in a straight line. This sequence is repeated over the entire arc of 180° (one-half circle), with the x-ray tube activated *only during translation.* The closely collimated x-ray tube and detectors are maintained directly opposite each other at all times by the rigid gantry, which is free to rotate. A pair of solid detectors is mounted side by side so that with each full rotation-translation of the tube and detectors, two tomographic sections are obtained simultaneously. The original EMI scanner used a narrow "pencil" x-ray beam and required about 5 minutes for each section pair, or 25 minutes for a whole brain scan. This scanner used an oil-immersed 120-kV x-ray tube with a stationary anode and a large focal spot.

2. *Rotation with a Pulsed Beam.* CT scanners have undergone rapid improvement in design to shorten scanning time and enhance

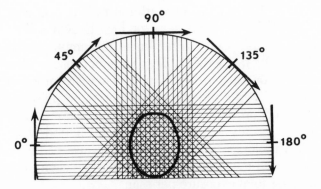

Figure 20.25. Simplified diagram of the scan pattern of the first-generation EMI CT scanner, which used rotation-translation motion. At each designated angle, at one-degree intervals, a pencil beam of x rays enters the patient and the exit or remnant radiation is picked up by a pair of collimated detectors arranged side-by-side directly opposite the x-ray tube, on the other side of the patient. Scanning x-ray exposure occurs only during the linear motion of the tube as indicated by the arrows. After each scan, the gantry rotates one degree without x-ray exposure, and exposure is again made during linear motion in the new position. With 160 measurements of transmitted radiation, multiplied by 180 degrees of rotation, the total number of measurements is 28,800. These are assigned CT numbers and processed by the computer to a final reconstructed image. In the second-generation scanner the pencil beam was replaced by a fan beam and multiple detectors to speed up scanning time.

recorded detail. In a rotating scanner (see Figure 20.26) the x-ray beam is fan shaped, the long axis of the x-ray tube being perpendicular to the width of the beam; this makes the x-ray distribution in the beam more uniform by avoiding the heel effect. At all times during a scan, the beam covers the full width of the section being scanned. Opposite the x-ray tube is mounted a row of detectors, either in a segment of a circle or in a complete circle. In the former arrangement, the array of about 30 detectors moves with the tube, but in opposite directions, because they are mounted on the same rotating gantry. In the *full-circle* array, there is a ring of about 600 stationary detectors with the tube mounted just within the circle (see Figure 20.27). The tube moves over a full circle, 360°. Both systems, known as third- and fourth-generation scanners, respectively, have greatly increased the speed of the examination, thereby reducing motion blurring. The brain can be scanned at the rate of about 2 seconds per section. Although the fan beam increases the amount of scattered radiation in comparison with the pencil beam, each detector has its own collimator (as does the x-ray tube itself) to minimize the amount of scattered radiation reaching the detector. These scanners use rotating anode tubes with 0.6 or 1.0 mm focal spots. They are programmed to deliver x rays intermittently in 300 bursts or pulses for each tomographic section. With each pulse lasting about 3 msec (0.003 sec), the tube is only activated over a total period of 1 sec per section. This prolongs tube life, allows the use of a small focal spot for improved recorded detail, and shortens scan time by permitting a larger total exposure per scan.

The detectors in the later generation scanners are of two types. One is a bismuth germanate crystal coupled to a photomultiplier tube, which counts the x-ray photons reaching it in much the same way as a radionuclide scintillation detector. The bismuth germanate crystal has greater efficiency in absorbing photons and also has less afterglow than a sodium iodide crystal. The other type of detector is an ionization chamber filled with the heavy inert gas, xenon, under pressure; the gas molecules are ionized in proportion to the intensity of the detected x rays (proportional region, Figure 22.8). Gas-filled detectors have virtually no afterglow and can be miniaturized, but they are slightly less efficient and stable than a

ROTATION

Figure 20.26. Third-generation CT rotational scanner with a fan beam and an array of thirty detectors. Mounted on a gantry, the tube and detectors rotate together around the patient. Note that the detectors always remain directly opposite the x-ray tube focus. Readings of the transmitted radiation (exit or remnant) are made continuously and processed by the computer during rotation of the gantry through a complete circle (360°). The x-ray beam is restricted by a beam-limiting device to a thin fan shape, and the detectors are also well collimated. This type of scanner markedly shortened scanning time.

crystal detector. The exit radiation from each tomographic section is absorbed by the detector and the resulting pulses in the photo-multiplier tube counted automatically. Each count is assigned a preprogrammed number—*CT number*—by the computer. A CT number is not proportional to the number of x-ray photons absorbed in the detector but rather to the total attenuation of x rays that have traversed the tissues in that segment of the tomographic section. Thus, the greater the absorption in the tissues, the higher will be the CT number.

Although, as we have stated, CT reveals internal structures having low inherent contrast, lesions which differ a great deal from their surroundings are more readily detected. Further improvement is achieved by intravenous injection of iodinated contrast media in the vascular system or by ingestion of opaque media, a

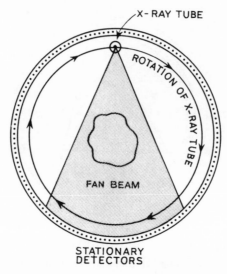

Figure 20.27. Fourth-generation CT scanner. The x-ray tube rotates full circle (360°) while about 600 detectors remain in a stationary array. Note that the beam is fan shaped.

process known as *contrast enhancement.* Contrast may be enhanced even further by delayed scanning, as with hematomas.

Image Reconstruction. This is a complex mathematical process carried out by the computer in which the image is first reconstructed as a digital image (ie, expressed in attenuation or CT numbers) and then changed to a conventional gray-scale image. The image of the section is broken up into a number of tiny picture elements called *pixels,* which are projections of solid cores of tissue known as *voxels* (volume elements) as shown in Figure 20.28. As we have just explained, the computer counts the light flashes in solid detectors, or ions in ionization detectors, as the radiation that has traversed each voxel reaches the corresponding detector. The computer instantaneously assigns a *CT number* to each pixel, based on the counts received by the corresponding detector. CT numbers are not absolute values but are relative to the attenuation by water, which is assigned CT number 0. CT numbers usually range from +1000 for bone to −1000 for air or gas. Thus, the computer produces a digital (numerical) image, that is, one in which the attenuation by tissue in the tomographic section is represented by numbers. Figure 20.29 shows how a single projection (tube and detector in a particular position) of a rectangular object might appear in terms of CT numbers. Note that the image pixels consist of higher CT numbers than the neighboring ones because we have chosen an object that is denser than its surroundings. But if the object were less dense than its background, its pixels would be represented by lower CT numbers.

VOXEL   **MATRIX**

Figure 20.28. Explanation of imaging terms. A *voxel* is a volume element — a geometrically defined portion of the tissue section through which the beam has passed. The projection of a voxel, corresponding to its smallest side, is called a *pixel* or picture element in the *matrix*, which represents the tomographic image of the tomographic section.

We have just seen how a single projection appears in CT numbers. Reconstruction of the whole image of the section from ***multiple projections*** can be accomplished in several ways. These have become extremely complex and we shall not try to describe them. The simplest method, ***back projection,*** is no longer used in modern CT scanners, but it does provide a relatively simple concept of the principle. Image reconstruction requires, first of all, the handling of an immense amount of data by the computer. Figure 20.29 shows a single projection of a rectangular solid object in a row of pixels. The CT number for each square pixel is proportional to the sum of the object densities (ie, total absorption) in the voxel through which that portion of the radiation has passed. In back projection, a "magic square" consisting of pixels in, for example,

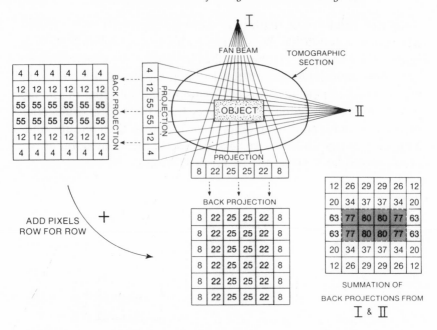

Figure 20.29. Simplified explanation of image reconstruction by a CT scanner. The corresponding pixel CT numbers (ie, numbers assigned by the computer to the radiation attenuation in each voxel) from each back projection are added as shown. The larger the number of projections and back projections resulting from rotation of the gantry around the volume of interest, the better will be the recorded detail in the reconstructed image. This is consistent with the principle in ordinary radiography that recorded detail improves with increased information, provided that noise does not increase as well. When the computer changes the CT numbers to a *gray scale* (analog image), we then have a recognizable tomogram.

nine rows across and nine columns down (81 pixels altogether) forms the basis of the image and is called a matrix (see Figure 20.29). Actually, a matrix may consist of a great number of pixels, such as $80 \times 80 = 6400$, for better recorded detail. In Figure 20.29 we see that the row of CT numbers from one projection is repeated in each succeeding row. Now let us assume that the gantry has been rotated 90° and another exposure made. The second matrix resulting from this back projection is shown on the left. Now the numbers in the corresponding squares (ie, corresponding pixels) are added to give the summated matrix shown on the far right of the figure. This procedure is repeated for each position of the tube as the gantry rotates. The more such projections that are added to the matrix, the better the recorded detail. Figure 20.29 shows the final matrix obtained by the summation of four projections; it reveals the digital image of the rectangular solid. It should be mentioned that image quality is further improved by programming the computer to make a number of important corrections.

Finally, the computer converts the digital image to a gray-scale image to resemble a conventional tomogram, except that it has incomparable recorded detail. Figure 20.29 shows the gray-scale image of the tomographic section obtained by the four projections. In practice, the computer controls allow the operator to increase or decrease image contrast at will.

Medical Applications of CT Scanning. Although CT scanning was first applied to the examination of the brain, it has also revolutionized the diagnosis of lesions in virtually all parts of the body; to name a few: head and neck, chest, abdomen, and vertebral column. In the brain, normal structures are readily depicted — gray and white matter, ventricles, and subarachnoid and subdural spaces. Lesions in the brain are also well shown — tumors, infarcts, abscesses, hematomas, edema, hydrocephalus, cerebral atrophy, and calcifications. Contrast enhancement brings out structural details that would otherwise remain invisible. While there is still an important place for radionuclide imaging and conventional angiography, CT has become the predominant noninvasive diagnostic procedure. In fact it can demonstrate lesions that would otherwise be undiagnosable, short of craniotomy.

Lesions in the abdomen and chest that are particularly amenable to detection and evaluation by CT scanning include tumors of various kinds. In the abdomen, liver, biliary tree, and kidneys can be studied by CT, but ultrasound may be superior in some instances. An important application of CT in the abdomen at present is in the detection of pancreatic tumors and enlarged retroperitoneal lymph nodes. In fact, CT has assumed a prominent role in staging Hodgkin's and non-Hodgkin's lymphoma, as well as other malignant tumors, by virtue of its ability to discover enlarged lymph nodes containing metastatic tumor.

XERORADIOGRAPHY (XEROGRAPHY)

In 1937, C. F. Carlson invented *xerography* (pronounced "zero-"), a radically different kind of photocopying process. Not long afterward the xerographic method was applied as a substitute for film in radiography where it became known as *xeroradiography.*

The xerographic *principle* depends on the fact that semiconductors such as selenium, while ordinarily behaving as insulators, become conductors when struck by light or x rays. A typical xerographic plate consists of *selenium* coated on a sheet of metal, usually aluminum. In use, the aluminum is electrically grounded.

To make a *xeroradiograph* or, in short, a *xerogram,* a positive electrostatic charge is first applied evenly to the selenium surface. Next, the charged plate is placed under the anatomic part and the proper x-ray exposure made, just as in film radiography, although the exposure factors are different. In any area of the plate struck by x-ray photons, the selenium loses positive charges through the grounded aluminum backing, the amount of charge neutralization depending on the x-ray exposure. Thus, the selenium loses much of its charge in areas beneath soft tissues which transmit large numbers of photons, whereas it loses relatively little charge in areas underlying bone, which transmits few photons.

With this system we obtain an *electrostatic latent image* consisting of areas varying in the density of positive charges remaining on the plate after exposure. These densities are then converted to a visible or manifest image by spraying the plate with a toner—a fine cloud of negatively charged blue plastic powder that sticks to the various areas on the plate in amounts depending on the size of the residual positive charge. A permanent image is obtained by pressing a sheet of clear plastic or plastic-coated paper against the plate, thereby transferring the blue powder to the plastic, which is then peeled off the plate.

After it has been cleaned and subjected to 45 seconds of heating or *relaxation,* the plate can be re-used. Heating eliminates residual images that may appear as "ghosts" on the next xerogram.

At present, xerography has its main application in mammography (see pages 364–368) but is useful also in the examination of small bones, as well as in tomography of the larynx and upper part of the trachea. It has the following important advantages over film radiography where it is applicable:

1. *Recorded Detail Enhancement.* Xerograms have a unique property called *edge effect,* an accentuation of the borders between images of different densities. This produces an apparent increase in local contrast and recorded detail. The edge effect is caused by the "theft" of powder by the denser area from the less dense area along the border (electrical "fringe" phenomenon). As a result, details stand out strikingly, resembling bas relief. The edge effect becomes more pronounced as overall contrast is increased; therefore, low or medium kV technics are preferred. It is especially important in accentuating the image of tiny calcium deposits or *microcalcifications,* present in about 30 percent of breast cancers.

2. *Low Over-all Contrast.* Despite the apparently high contrast caused by the edge effect, the over-all contrast of xerograms is *low* in comparison with ordinary radiographs. The low contrast and the edge effect together produce xeromammograms in which details stand out boldly and all structures, from fat to bony ribs, are clearly seen with a single exposure. Although xeromammograms, after adequate experience of the observer, are easier to interpret than film mammograms, early comparative studies show them to yield about the same degree of diagnostic accuracy. However, experts still disagree about the relative merits of the two types of mammography.

3. *Wide Latitude.* Xeroradiography is characterized by wide exposure latitude, so that variation of about 10 kV at 80 kV in examinations other than mammography has only a slight effect on xerogram quality. At the same time, a wider range of densities can be depicted on a single plate, facilitating interpretation.

4. *Magnification Effect.* Not entirely explained is the phenomenon of magnification of microcalcifications and other fine structures, making them much easier to detect.

5. *Rapid Process with no Liquid Solutions.* Processing is complete in ninety seconds in the xerographic processor in a light room. No plumbing is required, since this is entirely a dry process.

6. *Less Patient Exposure in Mammography.* With suitable technic, xeromammography effects substantial reduction in patient exposure. Excellent xeromammograms are obtainable at 44 to 48 kV and

300 mAs with 2 mm filtration, giving a midplane breast dose of about 0.45 rad for an average two-view examination. With a special low-dose film-screen system, the corresponding dose is 0.15 rad (Jans et al, 1979). With the older method using special fine-grain film, the breast dose was 8 to 15 rads!

7. *Positive or Negative Image Mode.* By proper selection of charge, we can obtain either positive or negative xerograms. Furthermore, these can be transferred to film or paper, depending on the preference for viewing by transmitted or reflected light, respectively.

Xerography has several limitations. One is the artifacts caused by dust or imperfections in the plate, which may resemble micro-calcifications in mammograms. Another is that xerography cannot be used at present in the examination of large parts because of the large exposures that are needed as compared with film-screen systems. Another problem is the specialized service required for proper operation of the xerographic unit, although minor repairs can be made by the radiographer after a short course in maintenance of the equipment.

PHOTOFLUOROGRAPHY (PHOTORADIOGRAPHY)

In photofluorography, the x-ray beam, after traversing the chest, falls on a special fluoroscopic screen at the end of a light-tight hood. A high speed camera at the other end photographs the fluoroscopic image, producing a miniature photoradiograph. This provides economical radiography of the chest for large volume throughput.

A photofluorographic apparatus (see Figure 20.30) may include:

1. *X-ray Control, Transformer, and Tube* having a capacity of 200 to 500 mA at 100 kV. A rotating anode with high thermal rating is essential for a large volume of chest radiography, as is automatic exposure control.

2. *Fluorescent Screen* emitting *blue light* of sufficient intensity to be photographed. The screen measures 14 × 17 in. and is backed by lead glass to absorb x rays, at the same time allowing the light from the screen to pass to the camera.

3. *Light-tight Hood,* placed between the fluorescent screen and

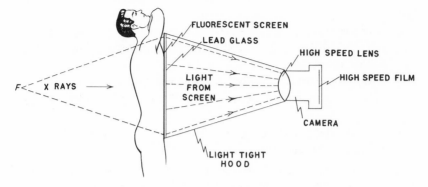

Figure 20.30. Essential parts of a photofluorographic unit.

the camera, is shaped like a truncated pyramid, larger at the screen and tapering toward the camera.

4. *High-speed Camera* such as the Odelca®, receiving the light from the fluorescent screen. The lens has tremendous light-gathering ability—a Bouwers concentric mirror optical system with a cone lens—because the light emitted by the screen is of extremely low intensity.

5. *Photographic Film*, high speed, loaded into the camera with the ability to record the fluoroscopic image. Two film sizes are available: 70 mm and 100 mm.

Excellent radiographs are obtained with exposures of $1/10$ to $1/2$ second. The grain of the fluorescent screen is effectively reduced by minification of the image, since the film image is much smaller than the screen image.

The advantages of photofluorography include: (1) the through-put of a large patient load, (2) the excellent image quality, (3) the small storage space needed for the miniature radiographs, and (4) the economy of small film size. Photofluorography was at one time widely used in mass surveys of the chest to detect unsuspected pulmonary diseases such as tuberculosis and cancer, as well as for routine x-ray examinations of the chest on admission of patients to hospitals. It is no longer recommended in the United States for these purposes because of low cost-effectiveness and exposure of large numbers of people to x rays.

QUESTIONS

1. Discuss fluoroscopic image intensification. Compare it with ordinary fluoroscopy. What is the advantage in using a cesium iodide phosphor?
2. What is meant by stereoscopic vision?
3. How do we determine the correct tube shift in stereoradiography?
4. List the steps in making and viewing stereoradiographs.
5. Describe the principle of tomography.
6. Define tomographic section; fulcrum; objective plane; tomographic image; redundant shadows; exposure angle.
7. Discuss the various types of tomographic motion. Compare their advantages and disadvantages.
8. Explain the main modifications of tomography: zonography; multitomography; plesiotomography; autotomography.
9. What is the comparative exposure with multitomography and with a series consisting of an equal number of individual tomograms?
10. How should tomographic equipment be activated, for maximum safety of personnel?
11. How is tomographic section thickness defined? Explain the factors that influence section thickness.
12. How does computed tomography resemble and differ from ordinary tomography?
13. Describe briefly the main features of three types of CT scanners.
14. Define voxel; pixel; back projection.
15. Explain the xerographic process and list the advantages and disadvantages of xeroradiography as compared with ordinary film radiography.
16. Show with the aid of a completely labeled diagram, the essential parts of a photofluorographic unit for chest radiography. Why is it no longer recommended for mass surveys and admission radiographs of the chest?

CHAPTER *21* RADIOACTIVITY AND RADIUM

O NE OF THE OUTSTANDING ACHIEVEMENTS of the late nineteenth century was the discovery that certain elements had the unique property of giving off penetrating and ionizing radiation. In 1896, Henri Becquerel found that the heavy metal *uranium* emitted rays that passed through paper and darkened a photographic plate in a darkened room. Soon after, Marie Curie and her husband Pierre began looking for other elements that might behave in a similar way. In 1898, after two years of extraordinary hardship and personal sacrifice, they announced their discovery of *polonium* and *radium,* new elements which emitted radiation. Not only did this discovery open new therapeutic opportunities in medicine, but it also expanded immeasurably our knowledge about the structure of matter. The term *radioactivity* was applied by Marie Curie to the special behavior of these elements.

RADIOACTIVITY

Unstable Atoms

The accepted designation of nuclear structure is *nuclide, defined as a nuclear species with a particular number of protons and neutrons, and having a particular energy state.* Radioactive nuclides, known also as *radionuclides,* are exceptional in that they have *unstable nuclei,* which means that their nuclear structure is inherently changeable. In the process of undergoing such spontaneous change, called *radioactive decay* or *disintegration,* they give off *ionizing radiation.*

Why are certain nuclides naturally radioactive? The precise answer is unknown, but there are a number of theories. Nuclear

475

particles exist in energy levels, analogous to those of orbital electrons that occupy various energy levels outside the nucleus. Transition of particles within the nucleus to lower energy levels in radionuclides are also accompanied by the release of radiation. In naturally occurring nuclides with a high atomic number (above 81), nuclear energy is large enough to allow random escape of nuclear particles, usually accompanied by electromagnetic radiation (gamma rays). Such nuclides are unstable and as they give off radiation they change into other nuclides. It is uncertain which particular nucleus of a sample of nuclide will decay at any particular instant, but a *constant fraction of those present will decay in a given time interval* (eg, per sec). This fraction, called the *decay constant* (other terms: *deexcitation, disintegration, or transformation constant*), *is the same for all samples of a given radionuclide but is different for different radionuclides.* The decay constant of a radionuclide cannot be changed without extreme difficulty.

Radioactivity, then, may be defined as the ability of certain nuclides—radionuclides—to (1) emit ionizing, penetrating radiation while (2) undergoing spontaneous, uncontrolled decay.

There are two kinds of radioactivity—natural and artificial—but, as we shall see, they both obey the same laws. *Natural radioactivity* is a property of naturally occurring radionuclides such as radium. *Artificial radioactivity* pertains to artificial radionuclides such as radiocobalt; these are nuclides that have been made radioactive by irradiation of the stable form with subatomic particles (neutrons, deuterons, etc) in special high energy devices such as the nuclear reactor or cyclotron.

The *artificial radionuclides,* to be discussed more fully in the next chapter, make up an impressive array of material that has important application in biologic research, clinical medicine, and industry.

Radioactive Series

The naturally occurring radionuclides can be grouped in three series or families, based on their parent elements: (1) *thorium,* (2) *uranium,* and (3) *actinium.* Each of these gives rise, by spontaneous decay, to a series of nuclides characteristic of that series. The chain of breakdown of the successive nuclides always occurs in exactly the same way and at a fixed rate. Some daughter nuclides, such as thorium A (^{216}Po), decay at extremely rapid rates and are therefore difficult to isolate; others, such as radium, in the uranium series, decay very slowly and can more readily be obtained in pure form. Radium has had an important place in the treatment of certain types of cancer. Radium and its offspring comprise the last descendants of the uranium series.

RADIUM

Properties

Since the behavior of radium, which has been useful in cancer therapy, exemplifies that of other radioactive nuclides, our discussion will deal mainly with this element. Radium, a heavy metal having a silvery-white appearance when pure, behaves chemically like barium and calcium. It belongs to the uranium radioactive series and has atomic number 88 and mass number 226. Because its radioactivity persists unchanged when combined with other elements, it is available only in the form of one of its salts — usually *radium chloride* ($RaCl_2$) — which are far more easily prepared than the pure metal.

Types of Radiation

There are three different kinds of radiation emitted by radionuclides: (1) alpha particles, (2) beta particles, and (3) gamma rays. A given radionuclide may emit all of these radiations or only one or two of them. Various members of the radium series, as will be shown below, give off one or more of these radiations. Alpha and beta particles ionize matter directly, whereas gamma rays do so indirectly, like x rays.

1. **Alpha particles** are simply *helium nuclei* (ie, helium ions) consisting of two protons and two neutrons. Since this gives them an atomic number of 2 and a mass number of 4, they can be represented by the symbol $^4_2$He. Alpha particles, having a large

mass and two positive charges, strongly ionize the atoms of matter through which they pass. Upon accepting two electrons, an alpha particle becomes a neutral helium atom:

$$\text{alpha particle} + 2 \text{ electrons} \rightarrow \text{helium atom}$$
$$\text{He}^{++} + 2\text{e}^- \rightarrow \text{He}$$

Alpha particles leave the nucleus at high speeds, 1.5×10^7 to 3.0×10^7 meters per sec (9,000 to 18,000 miles per sec) but do not penetrate matter for any appreciable depth because of their strong ionizing ability; in fact, they are absorbed by an ordinary sheet of paper.

2. **Beta Particles,** often called beta rays, consist of high speed *electrons* represented by the symbol e^- or β^-. Ejected from the nucleus at speeds approaching that of light rays, they are able to penetrate matter to a greater depth than alpha particles, their maximum range in tissue being 1.5 cm. In fact, 0.5 mm of platinum or 1 mm of lead is required to stop these beta particles. They are used in therapy, mainly for superficial skin lesions in small areas. Beta particles are less strongly ionizing than alpha particles.

3. **Gamma rays** are high energy electromagnetic waves (photons). For example, the gamma rays of radium have an average energy of 0.83 MeV, equivalent to 1.5 million volt (MV) x rays. They travel with the speed of light and are much more penetrating than alpha or beta radiation. Gamma rays are physically identical to x rays, the difference being that gamma rays originate within atomic *nuclei,* whereas x rays arise from electronic processes outside nuclei. Since gamma rays are electromagnetic waves (and photons), they are not deflected by a magnetic field. They ionize matter in the same way as x rays by first releasing fast electrons, which, in turn, cause much stronger ionization along their paths. The application of radium in therapy most often depends on the gamma radiation, the alpha and beta particles being removed by appropriate absorbing filters.

The Radium Series

When an atom of radium decays, it does not disappear but changes to another nuclide, that is, it undergoes *radioactive*

transformation. Let us "look into" an atom of radium and see what happens during its radioactive transformation. The atom ejects an alpha particle, which carries a charge of $+2$ because of its two protons. Since the atomic number of radium is 88, that of the atom remaining after the emission of an alpha particle is $88 - 2 = 86$. Furthermore, the mass number of radium is 226 and that of the ejected alpha particle is 4, so the mass number of the daughter atom is $226 - 4 = 222$. Thus, the daughter atom differs from its parent radium; it is the element ***radon,*** which has atomic number 86 and mass number 222 and is the first decay product of radium:

1 radium atom $\rightarrow$ 1 radon atom $+$ 1 alpha particle
$$^{226}_{88}\text{Ra} \rightarrow {}^{222}_{86}\text{Rn} + {}^{4}_{2}\text{He}$$

Note that the sum of the mass numbers (superscripts) of the products radon and alpha particle equals the mass number of radium. The same holds for the atomic numbers (subscripts), so the equation is balanced.

The radon atom is radioactive, decaying to a different radionuclide, which in turn decays to still another radionuclide, and so on. This chain of decay goes on until a stable atom is left (in this case a metal, ***lead***). Figure 21.1, showing the radium series, is included mainly to indicate pertinent data and not to tax your memory. Note that the radiation emitted by the radium element itself is limited to alpha particles; radium element also emits a gamma ray, too weak to be of use in therapy. Beta and penetrating gamma rays first appear with radium B (lead isotope) and C (bismuth isotope). Since a sealed source of radium reaches a state of ***equilibrium*** with its descendants after approximately thirty days (ie, the same number of atoms of a particular daughter is appearing as is disappearing in a given time interval) and then actually consists of a mixture of these decendants, we speak loosely of radium as emitting all three types of radiation. However, it is the ***radium series*** as a whole that emits all three types of radiation. Whether we start with radium or radon gas there is soon a sufficient accumulation of radium B and C to give appreciable intensities of beta and gamma radiation.

	URANIUM	RADIUM	RADON	RADIUM A	RADIUM B	RADIUM C	LEAD
				POLONIUM	LEAD	BISMUTH	
Atomic No.	92	88	86	84	82	83	82
Mass No.	238	226	222	218	214	214	206
Half Life	4.5×10^9 yr	1622 yr	3.8 da	3 min	26.8 min	19.7 min	stable

alpha ... alpha ... alpha ... beta gamma ... alpha beta gamma

Figure 21.1. Successive decay products of radium, shown from left to right. These make up the radium series which is the last part of the uranium series. Data on radium D, E, and F have been omitted.

Radioactive Decay

As we have already indicated, radionuclides such as radium undergo nuclear decay (synonyms *transformation, disintegration*), emitting one or more types of radiation while changing to another nuclide. The radioactive **decay scheme** is a diagrammatic method of representing the process (see Figure 21.2). The parent radionuclide radium (Ra) should be drawn at the top. An arrow points downward and to the **left,** because the daughter nuclide radon (Rn) has a smaller atomic number than its parent. Each nuclide symbol has a superscript and a subscript indicating its mass number and atomic number, respectively. Finally, the type of radiation should be indicated by its symbol near the arrow, in this case by an α for the alpha particle.

In the case of **beta decay,** the daughter nuclide has a larger atomic number than the parent, so the arrow points downward and to the **right.** With **gamma-ray emission** the atomic number of the daughter nuclide remains unchanged, so the arrow points **vertically downward.**

Decay Constant

Radioactive transformation occurs as a random process, that is, we cannot predict which particular atom will undergo nuclear decay at any instant. Starting with a given quantity of radium (or other radionuclide), the activity (number of disintegrations per

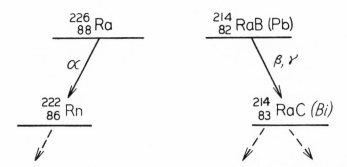

Figure 21.2. Decay schemes of radium 226 and radium B (lead 214). Only the first decay product is shown in each instance. By convention, when the product nuclide has a lower atomic number than the parent, the arrow points downward and to the left, as is the case when radium decays to radon. When the product nuclide has a larger atomic number than the parent, the arrow points downward and to the right, as occurs with the decay of radium B (lead 214) to radium C (bismuth 214). Note the two arrows below radium C—this is an example of branching decay by alternate routes.

second) decreases with time, but the **rate at which the activity decreases remains constant** (does not change). There are two ways of specifying the decay rate. One is the **decay constant** which is derived by a special branch of mathematics called calculus; to find the amount of activity remaining after a particular time interval requires the use of a special (exponential) equation.

The other way of indicating decay rate is **fractional decay**, that is, the fractional decrease in activity per given time interval. In other words, fractional decay means that if one gram of a radionuclide decreases 10 percent in one day, 0.9 g remains. At the end of the second day the 0.9 g will also decrease by 10 percent, leaving 90 percent of 0.9 g or 0.81 g, etc.

The decay constant is not the same as fractional decay unless fractional decay happens to be very small, about 0.2 or less (Pfalzner). Both are constant and unique for any particular radionuclide (see pages 476, 482). For example, the decay constant λ (Greek lambda) is 4.27×10^{-4} per yr for Ra, and 0.181 per day for Rn. But note that fractional decay for Rn is 16.6 percent per day; its decay constant 0.181 per day can be used only in the equation for exponential decay.

Half-Life

The caption *half-life* appears in Figure 21.1. This is a term which *denotes the length of time required for one-half the initial amount of a radionuclide to decay.* For example, suppose we have 1 gram of radium at the start. Referring to Figure 21.1, note that its half-life is 1622 years. This means that it will have gradually decayed to one-half its present mass in 1622 years; or, in 1622 years, there will be only 0.5 g of radium left. In another 1622 years, it will again have been reduced by one-half; that is, it will be one-fourth the original amount, or 0.25 g. Notice that the half-life is constant for any given radionuclide, and that the half-lives of different radionuclides show wide differences. Thus, the half-life of uranium is 4.5 billion years, while that of radium A is three minutes.

In any radioactive series, after equilibrium has been reached among all the daughter nuclides, the quantity of any one member of the series is larger if its half-life is longer. Thus, if we start with a radium sample, radium having the longest half-life in its series, will be present in largest amount; whereas radium A (polonium 218) with a half-life of three minutes will be present in smallest amount.

As we have already indicated, there is no way of predicting which radium atom will decay at a given instant. However, we know statistically that in 1622 years one-half the atoms in a given amount of radium will have decayed. Thus, half-life is really a *statistical* concept indicating the time it takes for radioactive decay of one-half the atoms on the basis of pure chance.

It is of interest that the decay constant λ of Ra (or of any radionuclide) can be derived from its half-life T by the following equation:

$$\lambda = 0.693/T$$

Substituting 1622 yr, the half-life of Ra,

$$\lambda = 0.693/1622 = 4.27 \times 10^{-4}/\text{yr}$$

This is the value of Ra half-life quoted above.

Average Life

Although we cannot determine which atom of a radionuclide will decay at any particular instant, we do have a simple way of computing the probable survival time or life expectancy of an individual atom, similar to the determination of life expectancy by life insurance companies. This, the average life T_a, is simply the reciprocal of the decay constant

$$T_a = 1/\lambda$$

For example, the decay constant of Rn is 0.181/day, so the average life is $1/0.181 = 5.5$ days.

Radon

When an atom of radium decays and emits an alpha particle, an atom of radon remains:

1 radium atom → 1 radon atom + 1 alpha particle

Radon is a radionuclide that exists as a colorless heavy gas. Figure 21.3 shows the decay curve of radon, as well as the derivation of its half-life. As already noted, fractional decay is constant with time.

Because of its convenient half-life of 3.8 days and the availability of gamma rays from its daughter radionuclides, radon was at one time used in implant therapy in the form of "seeds." These were prepared by collecting the radon gas in thin gold tubes and then pinching off and sealing short segments about 3 to 5 mm long. However, because of problems with radiation safety during manufacture and possible leakage of the seeds, radon is no longer available in the United States, having been replaced by artificial radionuclides such as gold 198, iridium 192, and tantalum 182.

RADIOACTIVE EQUILIBRIUM*

A radionuclide decay series is said to be in *radioactive equilib-*

---

*Portions of this section are from Selman: *The Basic Physics of Radiation Therapy*, 2nd Ed., 1976. Courtesy of Charles C Thomas, Publisher, Springfield, Illinois.

Figure 21.3. Decay curve of radon, semilogarithmic plot. The half-life is 3.83 days.

rium when, in a sealed source, the rate of appearance of each daughter equals its rate of decay; that is, the amount being formed per second equals the amount decaying per second. However, a distinction is made between **secular** and **transient equilibrium.**

In **secular equilibrium** the parent nuclide has a much longer half-life than any of its daughters; radium is an example. Because of its long half-life, radium furnishes a virtually inexhaustible supply of daughter nuclides. These accumulate until secular equilibrium has been reached (after about thirty days), provided the radium was first sealed in a leakproof container such as a needle or tube. Now the daughters are present in constant amounts. Since the use of radium in gamma-ray therapy depends on RaB (radiolead) and RaC (radiobismuth), and their amounts are constant at equilibrium, the gamma-ray output of the sealed source is constant, thereby simplifying dosimetry. Furthermore, the half-life of the sealed source is the same as that of the parent radium — 1622 years.

Radon is an example of a radionuclide which reaches **transient equilibrium** with its descendants because it has a relatively **short half-life** of 3.83 days. Upon reaching transient equilibrium at about five hours after being sealed, radon and its decay series continue to undergo rapid decay, with the same half-life as the parent radon. Therefore, the gamma-ray output decreases appreciably in a period of days. On the other hand, the gamma-ray output of a radium source remains constant because of its extremely long half-life relative to treatment time.

RADIUM DOSAGE IN BRACHYTHERAPY

Radium and its substitutes have an important place in the treatment of certain accessible cancers. But because gamma-ray dosage decreases rapidly with distance, treatment must be carried out with the sources close to the tumor. This is known as **brachytherapy** (*brachy* = short), which obviously means treatment at short distances. In brachytherapy, radium or its substitutes are usually encapsulated in a suitable container, such as a needle, tube, or grain, and applied to a surface, imbedded in the tumor, or inserted into a body cavity. Long-lived radionuclides like radium are removed after a predetermined dose has been delivered.

The effect of ionizing radiation on a given tissue depends on the amount of energy absorbed by the tissue, and this, in turn, is related to the radiation exposure to which the tissue has been subjected. In order to specify radiation exposure we must have certain precisely defined units which provide all the essential information. Such a system must be sufficiently accurate to permit the comparison of various treatment methods and the evaluation of treatment results. Besides, it must provide the radiologist with a means of exchanging information with his colleagues.

Basic to any **gamma-ray dosage system** is the **time-intensity factor.** With radium, this is the product of the exposure time by the amount of radium in the applicator. Thus, if 10 mg of radium element are applied for twenty-four hours, the time-intensity factor is $10 \times 24 = 240$ milligram-hours (usually abbreviated mg-hr). The gamma-ray activity of a **radium** source is essentially constant during any treatment period because of its very long half-life.

The time-intensity factor requires a more general unit of activity than the "milligram" used with radium. It so happens that this unit, the millicurie, represents approximately the activity of 1 milligram of radium. The millicurie (mCi) is defined as 37 million disintegrations per second (3.7×10^7 dps). This unit applies to all radionuclides. In the new International System of Units (S.I.) the unit of activity is the becquerel (Bq), defined as 1 dps.

Short-lived artificial radionuclides, such as gold 198, decay very fast (half-life of ^{198}Au is 2.7 days), so this factor must be taken into account by conversion to the radium equivalent. Thus, 1 mCi of ^{198}Au, when allowed to decay completely, is equivalent to 26.5 mg-hr or mCi-hr of radium.

After calculation of the time-intensity factor, that is, the number of mCi-hr of radon or radium, we must then determine the radiation *exposure* at the site of the lesion. The radiation exposure depends not only on the time-intensity factor, but also on the *distribution* of the radium in the tissues, the *volume of tissue irradiated,* and the *filtration* of the applicator. In surface treatment, one must consider the *area* of the surface, its *shape,* the *distribution* of the radium in the applicator, the *distance* of the applicator above the surface, and the *filtration* of the applicator. The exposure rate of gamma radiation at a distance of 1 cm from a point source of 1 mg of radium filtered by 0.5 mm of platinum is 8.25 R/hr. This observation has enabled the physicist and radiologist to express radium (or other radionuclide) exposure in R. If the radium in a surface applicator, or in needles inserted into the tissues, is distributed according to certain plans, such as those of Paterson and Parker, or of Quimby (revised), the minimum exposure of the lesion per 1000 mg-hr or mCi-hr can be found from the tables published by these authors. The *absorbed dose* in rads can then be derived by multiplying the exposure in R by the appropriate conversion factor, f, for the *gamma rays of radium* ($f = 0.96$ for soft tissue; 0.92 for bone):

$$\textit{absorbed dose } (rads) = 0.96 \times \text{R } \textit{in soft tissue}$$
$$= 0.92 \times \text{R } \textit{in bone}$$

In the early 1900s, treatment dosage was expressed in terms of "skin erythema units," based on the threshold erythema dose — the smallest dose that, when applied to the anterior surface of the forearm, would produce faint reddening of the skin. A single exposure of about 1000 R with 1 to 2 million volt radiation delivers a threshold erythema dose. To get the same result with x rays having a half-value layer of 1 mm Cu would require 680 R; and with half-value layer 1 mm Al, 270 R.

TYPES OF CONTAINERS FOR BRACHYTHERAPY

There are several types of containers for radium or its substitutes. Such containers, when loaded with the radioactive material, are called *sources*. The planning and execution of radiotherapy is the responsibility of the radiotherapist and physicist, but since the technologist may be called upon to aid in assembling sources into suitable applicators, we shall briefly describe some of the more frequently used forms.

Most radium sources have a platinum-iridium wall. This serves two purposes: (1) it acts as a filter and (2) permits the use of radium in the desired form.

Filtration

The radium series emits three types of radiation, differing in penetrating ability. Any metal container will absorb the alpha particles because of their low penetrating ability; this is desirable because the strongly ionizing alpha particles would produce severe local reactions without reaching very far into the lesion being treated. The beta particles have a greater penetrating ability, so a monel metal container with a 0.05 mm wall may be used to absorb the alpha particles and still permit beta-particle treatment of superficial lesions.

If we need gamma radiation only, then the alpha and beta particles can be removed by filtration with 0.5 mm platinum, usually alloyed with iridium. Heavier filtration than this reduces gamma-ray intensity by 2 percent per 0.1 mm additional platinum thickness.

Containers

The various types of containers for radium and its substitutes will now be described.

1. **Implants** ("seeds"). When radon was available for implant therapy, it was sealed in tiny gold capillary tubes measuring about 5 mm long. These were left in the tissues permanently. However, artificial radionuclides have replaced radon for this purpose. Examples include gold 198, iridium 192, and iodine 125.

2. **Needles.** These are hollow platinum-iridium tubes with a point at one end and an eye for threading at the other. The platinum-iridium alloy is harder and stronger than pure platinum. Radium chloride is first sealed in platinum cells, which are then encased in the hollow needle shaft, to form the **_permanent type needle_** (see Figure 21.4). Total filtration of the needle and cell usually equals 0.5 mm platinum. Many prefer cesium 137 as the radioactive source, encased in stainless steel needles having a wall thickness of 1.0 mm.

POINT   RADIUM

PLATINUM WALL   EYE

Figure 21.4. Radium needle. The wall is actually a platinum-iridium alloy, stronger than pure platinum. Sealed within the needle is the radium in the form of a salt, usually radium chloride.

3. **Tubes.** These resemble needles but are usually larger and are rounded at both ends, one of which has an eye for threading. Tubes usually have a wall thickness of 1.0 mm platinum-iridium and are loaded with radium chloride. Many prefer cesium 137 encased in stainless steel tubes with a wall thickness of 1.0 mm.

4. **Plaques.** These are flat, hollow applicators, having one face made of thin monel metal (0.05 mm), on the inner surface of which is permanently spread a layer of radium chloride. Plaques can be obtained with any desired activity to provide a source of beta particles for the treatment of very superficial skin lesions. Filters may be added to remove the beta particles for gamma-ray

therapy. Strontium 90, a beta-particle emitting artificial radionuclide, is used in superficial therapy of certain eye lesions.

PROTECTION

The protection of personnel from radium radiation will be described in greater detail in Chapter 23. However, it must be emphasized that the best protection is *distance*. Radium applicators should never be picked up with the fingers. Loading of applicators, as well as other manipulations, must be performed by the use of long forceps. Radium should be stored in a lead container of proper thickness and should be transported in a lead-lined carrying case provided with a long handle.

Because of the long half-life of radium, the form in which it is used (usually radium chloride crystals), and the accumulation of radon gas, accidental breakage of an applicator or needle is fraught with serious radiation hazard. For this reason, artificial radionuclides that give off gamma rays of suitable energy and can be prepared in the form of seeds or wires are being used more and more as radium substitutes. At present, cesium 137 is available in encapsulated needles and tubes, iridium 192 as seeds enclosed in nylon ribbons, and gold 198 and iodine 125 in the form of implantable grains or seeds. They differ in their gamma-ray energy, so dosage has to be adjusted in terms of milligram-radium-equivalent (mg-Ra-eq).

LOSS OF RADIUM

In some cases the technologist may be held responsible for the transportation and storage of radium. This requires constant vigilance, since lost radium may be difficult to trace. The search for lost radium may require the services of a radiation physicist or other qualified person, using some type of survey meter (see pages 579–580). Lost radium must be found because it entails a serious radiation hazard.

Questions

1. Define radioactivity. By whom was it discovered? Named?
2. Give an example of a decay scheme. What is meant by the statement "decay rate is constant?"
3. What makes some nuclides radioactive? Where do the ionizing radiations come from during radioactive decay?
4. Discuss radioactive series.
5. If a radioactive atom emits a beta particle, what change occurs in the atomic number? Atomic mass number?
6. How does the emission of a gamma ray affect the atomic number? Atomic mass number?
7. Briefly discuss radioactive equilibrium.
8. How does artificial radioactivity differ from natural?
9. To what radioactive series does radium belong?
10. Discuss the importance of radium in radiology.
11. Name and describe the three types of radiation emitted by various radionuclides. In the radium series, which members emit gamma rays that are useful in therapy?
12. Describe the basic steps involved in computing gamma-ray dosage in brachytherapy. Why and how does this have to be modified with short-lived radionuclides?
13. What is the main purpose of a filter in a radium source? Which metal is most often used to filter radium?
14. Define half-life; average life.
15. Define curie; millicurie; becquerel. State the symbols for each.
16. Describe the four main types of implant containers (sources).
17. Why is it so important to find lost radium?
18. Discuss the use of artificial radionuclides as radium substitutes. Which ones are available and in what forms?
19. What are the advantages of radium substitutes over radium itself?

CHAPTER *22* *ARTIFICIAL RADIONUCLIDES*

I N CHAPTER 4 we learned that matter is made up of extremely small particles called *atoms.* The concept of atomic structure has become extraordinarily complex, but for our purpose we may now review it in simplified form—a central core or *nucleus* containing almost the entire mass of the atom and, surrounding the nucleus, the *orbits* or paths in which the negative *electrons* are in continual motion. The nucleus has two main constituents, *protons* and *neutrons,* collectively referred to as *nucleons.* A proton is a positively charged particle whose mass is nearly 2000 times that of an electron. A neutron has nearly the same mass as a proton but carries no charge.

All matter is made up of one or more simple entities called *elements.* The atoms of any particular element have a characteristic and distinct number of positive charges or *protons* in the nucleus and an equal number of negative charges or *electrons* in the orbits around the nucleus. The number of nuclear protons is called the *atomic number.* Notice that the atomic number is specific for a given element; all atoms of any one element have the same atomic number. Atoms of different elements have different atomic numbers.

Since the nucleons are responsible for the mass of an atom, the *mass number* of a particular atom has been defined as the total number of nuclear protons and neutrons. For example, hydrogen with one nuclear proton has a mass number of 1, and helium with two protons and two neutrons has a mass number of 4.

Isotopes

As we have stated before, all the atoms in a given sample of a particular element have the same atomic number, that is, the same number of nuclear protons (their chemical behavior is also identical).

491

However, all the atoms in this sample do not necessarily have the same mass number—total number of protons **and** neutrons. Since the number of protons is the same, the difference in mass number must be due to a difference in the number of **neutrons.** Such atoms whose nuclei contain the same number of protons, but different numbers of neutrons, are called **isotopes.**

The following equations show how a radionuclide differs from its isotope only in the number of nuclear neutrons:

$$\text{nuclide} = x \text{ protons} + y \text{ neutrons}$$
$$\underline{-(\text{isotope} = x \text{ protons} + z \text{ neutrons})}$$
$$\text{nuclide} - \text{isotope} = y - z \text{ neutrons}$$

Note that there is not an unlimited variety of isotopes of any particular element; as they occur in nature, there may be only two, or three, or several. However, the numerical ratio of the different isotopes is nearly constant for each element.

Since all the isotopes of an element have the same atomic number, they have the same chemical properties. The gas hydrogen, for example, has three isotopes (see Figure 4.5): ordinary hydrogen or **protium** with mass number 1, **deuterium** (heavy hydrogen) with mass number 2, and **tritium** with mass number 3. As would be anticipated, these three forms of hydrogen have the same atomic number—1—and identical chemical properties.

The term **nuclide** refers to a species of atom having in its nucleus a particular number of protons and neutrons. Accordingly, we can say there are three distinct hydrogen nuclides.

Artificial Radionuclides

In recent years many artificial radionuclides have been produced, a number of which happen to be radioactive. These decay to entirely different elements while emitting ionizing radiation, as described above. Radioactive isotopes have the same **chemical** properties as their stable counterparts, differing only in their mass number (number of nuclear neutrons) and radioactive nature. We prefer to speak of radioactive nuclides or **radionuclides** rather than radioisotopes, since they are nuclides that happen to be radioactive.

Artificial radionuclides are produced by irradiation of stable nuclides by subatomic particles such as neutrons or deuterons in an atomic reactor or cyclotron, respectively. A neutron is an uncharged particle having a mass number of 1. A deuteron is a heavy hydrogen nucleus having a single positive charge and a mass number of 2. The irradiated nucleus captures a neutron or deuteron, becoming unstable, that is, radioactive.

When the daughter element differs from the parent, the process is called *transmutation.* An example of the transmutation of an ordinary, stable element to a different radioactive element will make this process more easily understandable. Ordinary sulfur is changed, during neutron irradiation, to radioactive phosphorus:

$$\text{sulfur} + \text{neutron} \rightarrow \text{phosphorus} + \text{hydrogen}$$
(stable)   *(radioactive)*

$$^{32}_{16}\text{S} \;+\; ^{1}_{0}\text{n} \;\rightarrow\; ^{32}_{15}\text{P} \;+\; ^{1}_{1}\text{H}$$

In each term of the equation, the lower number or *subscript* represents the atomic number, and the upper number or *superscript* represents the mass number. The sum of the superscripts on one side of the equation equals that on the other side. The same holds true for the subscripts. Knowing that the atomic number of phosphorus is always 15, we can express radioactive phosphorus as ^{32}P. Since it has a specific number of protons (15) and neutrons (17) in its nucleus and therefore a particular species of atom, it is an example of a *radionuclide* or *radioactive nuclide.* ^{32}P is unstable because its nucleus contains a surplus neutron (ordinary nonradioactive phosphorus is ^{31}P) and it therefore decays to ordinary sulfur, emitting a beta particle (negative electron) in the process:

$$^{32}_{15}\text{P} \rightarrow {}^{32}_{16}\text{S} + {}^{0}_{-1}\text{e} + \tilde{v}$$
beta particle   *antineutrino*

At the present time, there is no way of altering the type of radiation emitted by a given radionuclide, natural or artificial.

Another method of inducing artificial radioactivity is to irradiate stable atoms with deuterons (heavy hydrogen nuclei) in a cyclotron. However, this is not a major commercial source of medical radionuclides.

Nuclear Reactor

As mentioned above, radionuclides can be produced by exposing stable nuclides to a flow of neutrons—*neutron flux.* In fact, this is how artificial radioactivity is often induced both for medical and industrial use. One type of nuclear reactor (see Figure 22.1) depends on the fission (splitting) of nuclei of uranium 235 (^{235}U), an isotope of ordinary uranium (^{237}U), by extremely slow, environmental neutrons (see Figure 22.2). These neutrons have a very small average kinetic energy, about the same as that of the molecules of air at the prevailing temperature and are therefore called *thermal neutrons.* When a thermal neutron is captured by a ^{235}U nucleus, the nucleus splits into fragments of various sizes while emitting one to three neutrons plus 200 million electron volts (MeV) of energy:

Figure 22.1 Simplified concept of nuclear reactor using uranium 235 as the fuel.

$$^{235}U + {}_0^1n \rightarrow \frac{\text{sum of masses of}}{\text{nuclear fragments}} + 1 \text{ to } 3\,{}_0^1n + 200\,\text{MeV}$$

The splitting of the ^{235}U atom in this manner is termed *fission.* Fast neutrons emitted during fission must be slowed to thermal energy to facilitate their capture by other ^{235}U atoms which, in turn, undergo fission. Graphite blocks are used as moderators to slow the neutrons. The liberation of one to three neutrons each time a neutron is captured and the rapid multiplication of this process constitute a ***chain reaction,*** accompanied by the release of a tremendous amount of energy in an exceedingly small interval of time.

Figure 22.2. Fission of uranium 235 by slow (thermal) neutrons, resulting in a nuclear chain reaction. This differs from radioactive decay in the production of large nuclear fragments, as well as radiation, during fission.

If a piece of ^{235}U is large enough to permit more neutrons to be emitted than can escape from the surface, the mass will explode.

Thus, for the reactor to operate properly, the mass of ^{235}U must be *critical,* that is, just large enough for the fission process to continue at a steady rate, but still not so large as to go out of control or *go supercritical.* Fission rate can be varied by the use of boron or cadmium *control rods;* these have a strong affinity for neutrons, and adjustment of the depth to which the rods are inserted into the reactor regulates the size of the *neutron flux* (flow). Normally, the reactor's operation is adjusted by the cadmium control rods to maintain the fission process at the desired level without letting the reactor go out of control. Note that the "fuel" of the reactor is not pure ^{235}U, but rather natural uranium, of which only about $1/140$ is ^{235}U, enriched by the addition of ^{235}U.

Since the neutron carries no charge, it is not repelled by the positively charged nucleus; in fact, as a neutron approaches a nucleus there is actually an attractive force between them. Neutrons entering stable nuclei render them unstable. Thus, when placed in drawers and inserted into the reactor (see Figure 22.1), stable nuclides are exposed to neutron flux and changed to radionuclides through *neutron capture.*

The use of the nuclear reactor for the production of radionuclides will now be exemplified by typical equations.

1. *Transmutation Reaction*—a different element is produced from the one entering the reaction, the latter being called the *target element* (see Figure 22.3). This reaction is designated as an

NEUTRON → $^{32}_{16}$S (16p 16n) STABLE SULFUR → $^{32}_{15}$P (15p 17n) RADIO- PHOSPHORUS + $^{1}_{1}$H PROTON

Figure 22.3. Transmutation of sulfur to radiophosphorus by neutron capture.

(n,p) reaction because a neutron enters the nucleus and a proton (hydrogen nucleus) leaves it. The ^{32}P can be separated chemically from sulfur in *carrier-free* (pure) form.

$$\underset{\text{stable sulfur}}{^{32}_{16}\text{S}} \quad + \quad \underset{\text{neutron}}{^{1}_{0}\text{n}} \quad \rightarrow \quad \underset{\text{radioactive phosphorus}}{^{32}_{15}\text{P}} \quad + \quad \underset{\text{proton}}{^{1}_{1}\text{H}}$$

2. **Radiative Capture** — the product nuclide is a radioactive isotope of the target nuclide and can be separated from it only with great difficulty. Contaminated by its stable isotope, the product radionuclide resulting from neutron capture is not carrier-free.

$$\underset{\substack{\text{stable}\\\text{cobalt}}}{^{59}_{27}\text{Co}} + \underset{\text{neuron}}{^{1}_{0}\text{n}} \rightarrow \underset{\substack{\text{radioactive}\\\text{cobalt}}}{^{60}_{27}\text{Co}} + \underset{\text{gamma ray}}{\gamma}$$

This is an (n, γ) reaction because a neutron enters the nucleus and a gamma ray is emitted. On decaying, ^{60}Co changes to ^{60}Ni, while gamma rays and beta particles are given off.

3. **Fission Products** — various radionuclides representing the fragments of the ^{235}U nuclei that have undergone fission. They are actually "waste" products of the nuclear reactor, some of which can be separated chemically and used in medicine. In fact, they provide the main source of iodine 131 (^{131}I), cesium 137 (^{137}Cs), and strontium 90 (^{90}Sr), all three having medical application.

Properties of Artificial Radionuclides

Some of the more important properties of artificial radionuclides will now be discussed. They decay in much the same manner as radium (see Chapter 21), and they differ widely in their decay rates.

Types Of Radiation. The radiations emitted by radionuclides have been described on pages 477–478. But those artificial radionuclides that are of medical interest emit only beta particles or gamma rays with beta particles.

Beta particles are fast-moving electrons ejected from the nuclei of certain radionuclides, actually arising from neutron decay:

$$\underset{\text{neutron}}{^{1}_{0}\text{n}} \rightarrow \underset{\text{proton}}{^{1}_{1}\text{H}} + \underset{\text{electron}}{^{0}_{-1}\text{e}} + \underset{\text{antineutrino}}{\tilde{v}}$$

For example, ^{32}P is a pure beta emitter, decaying as follows:

$$^{32}_{15}\text{P} \rightarrow ^{32}_{16}\text{S} + \underset{\text{beta particle}}{^{0}_{-1}\text{e}} + \underset{\text{antineutrino}}{\tilde{v}}$$

A few radionuclides emit **positrons** — positively charged electrons. Beta particles cause significant ionization in tissues where they are for the most part absorbed. They cannot be detected directly by special external counting devices, although the brems radiation resulting from interaction with atomic nuclei can be so detected.

Gamma rays are electromagnetic in nature and are identical to x rays. Carrying no charge, they do not ionize directly but release primary electrons in the tissues by interaction with atoms. Gamma-ray emission is frequently accompanied by beta particles; thus, ^{60}Co and ^{131}I give off both gamma and beta radiation. External radionuclide detection by Geiger or scintillation counters depends on gamma radiation which usually has sufficient penetrating ability to pass completely out of the body.

Units of Activity. The rate at which a radioactive sample decays is its *activity*, measured in units called *curies* (Ci). *One curie is an activity of 3.7 (10)^{10} disintegrations per second (dps).* Smaller units representing decimal fractions of the curie are usually more convenient. One millicurie (mCi) is an activity of 3.7 (10)^7 dps, and one microcurie (μCi) is 3.7 (10)^4 dps.

The S.I. unit of radioactivity is the *becquerel* (*Bq*), defined as 1 dps; thus, 1 Ci = 3.7 (10)^{10} Bq. In this country, the S.I. system has not yet met with wide acceptance except for the gray, which is the unit of absorbed dose.

Specific Activity. A given sample of a radionuclide may not be carrier-free; that is, it may also contain the stable isotope. The *specific activity* of such a sample is defined as its activity (due to the radionuclide present) divided by its total weight. For example, if 10 g of stable cobalt irradiated in a nuclear reactor for a specific time acquires an activity of 55 Ci, then the specific activity of the resulting ^{60}Co sample is 55/10 = 5.5 Ci/g. In actual practice, the specific activity of ^{60}Co teletherapy sources may reach about 200 Ci/g.

Radioactive Decay

All radionuclides undergo a decrease in activity with time. The rate of decrease is exponential and is specific for any given radionuclide. So, regardless of the number of such atoms initially present in a sample, a certain fixed fraction will decay in a particular time interval. For example, if the initial number of atoms is 1 million, and the decay rate for the radionuclide is 0.5 per sec, then 500,000 will have decayed in 1 sec. In the next second, 0.5 of the remaining 500,000 atoms, or 250,000, will have decayed, etc. At present, there is no practicable method of changing the decay rate of radionuclides (see pages 480–481 for a discussion of fractional decay *vs* decay constant).

Half-life. In nuclear medicine there are three kinds of half-lives: physical, biologic, and effective. These depend on the method of measuring a radioactive sample over a period of time. Such curves for ^{131}I are shown in Figure 22.4.

Figure 22.4. The three types of decay curves and corresponding half-lives for ^{131}I. In this example, the effective half-life is about five days and the biologic half-life about thirteen days. The physical half-life is constant—8.05 days.

1. *Physical Half-life (T)* is defined as the time required for a given radioactive sample to decay to one-half its initial activity. For example, with an initial activity of 10 mCi (3.7×10^8 Bq) the physical half-life is the *time* it takes for the activity to decrease to 5 mCi (1.85×10^8 Bq) as measured outside the body (*in vitro*). Examples of physical half-lives include: ^{131}I 8.1 days; ^{32}P 14.3 days; ^{60}Co 5.2 years.

Let us see how physical half-life is actually measured. First we measure the activity of a sample of the selected radionuclide by counting the number of decay events (disintegrations) per min by means of a suitable counter (see pages 503–510) under standard conditions, and subtract the background counting rate. This is the initial net counting rate. We repeat the procedure several times at suitable intervals over a period longer than the half-life. Finally, we plot the data, with counting rate as a function of time elapsed since the initial count; the resulting curve is shown in Figure 22.5. To find the half-life, we locate the point on the vertical axis corresponding to one-half the initial counting rate, then trace a horizontal line to the curve and, from the point of intersection, a vertical line to the horizontal axis where the final point of intersection locates the half-life. The physical half-life is constant for a particular radionuclide and is related to the decay constant; in fact, half-life T can be derived from the decay constant λ by the following equation:

Figure 22.5. Physical decay of ^{131}I (semilogarithmic plot to obtain a straight-line curve.) With an initial net counting rate of 500 counts per min the half-life is the time required for the counting rate to decrease to 250 c/m. For ^{131}I this is 8.1 days.

$$T = 0.693/\lambda \tag{1}$$

Or, knowing the half-life, we can derive the decay constant by rearranging equation (1) as follows:

$$\lambda = 0.693/T \tag{2}$$

There is also a useful formula for the fraction of a radioactive sample remaining after n half-lives: $1/2^n$. Thus, if a sample of ^{131}I has an activity of 100 mCi, what fraction remains after twenty-four days? Since the half-life of ^{131}I is 8.1 days, the stated time approximates $24/8 = 3$ half-lives. The fraction remaining at the end of this time is

$$1/2^n = 1/2^3 = 1/8$$

The activity remaining is then 100 mCi $\times$ $1/8$ = 12.5 mCi.

2. **Effective Half-life** (T_e) is that due to both physical and biologic decay and is always less than the physical half-life. It is obtained from the curve plot of a series of absolute counting rates over a particular part of the body at suitable intervals after administration of a radionuclide. Effective half-life relates to physical half-life T and biologic half-life T_b as follows:

$$1/T_e = 1/T + 1/T_b \tag{2}$$

This can be rearranged as follows:

$$T_e = \frac{T\,T_b}{T + T_b} \tag{3}$$

and in words

$$\text{effective half-life} = \frac{\text{physical half-life} \times \text{biologic half-life}}{\text{physical half-life} + \text{biologic half-life}}$$

3. **Biologic half-life** (T_b) is the time required for a given deposit of radionuclide in the body or a particular organ to decrease to one-half its initial maximum activity, due only to biologic utilization and excretion, and disregarding physical decay. It can be computed from equation (2), which may be rearranged as follows:

$$1/T_b = 1/T_e - 1/T \tag{4}$$

For example, we know that ^{131}I has a physical half-life of 8.1 days. Suppose we find by absolute counting that the effective half-life of sodium iodide 131 in the thyroid gland is six days. Substituting these values in equation (3),

$$1/T_b = 1/6 - 1/8.1 = 0.167 - 0.123 = 0.044$$
$$T_b = 1/0.044 = 23 \text{ days, } \textit{the biologic half-life}$$

Application of Artificial Radionuclides in Medicine

Artificial radionuclides can be used in medicine because they react in the body just like their stable isotopes. For example, the body cannot tell the difference between radioactive iodine and stable iodine. But once a radionuclide has entered the body, it acts as a radioactive tag that allows it to be detected, and its course through the body traced, by special instruments; or, alternatively, it can be detected in the blood, secretions, or excretions within or outside the body. Furthermore, it can be measured with reasonable precision in most instances. In this chapter, only basic principles will be covered. We shall also touch upon the use of radionuclides in therapy, which depends on the fact that sometimes, as with iodine in the thyroid gland, a radionuclide will concentrate selectively in certain organs. Under such circumstances, a sufficiently large dose can be given to irradiate effectively the target organ.

The following outline summarizes the medical uses of radionuclides according to various indications:

1. *Diagnosis*—general procedure
   a. Compound tagged with radionuclide (radioactive isotope of a normal element substituted for it in the compound).
   b. Injected or ingested in tracer amount—small enough to be diagnostic, but not large enough to deliver intolerable radiation exposure.
   c. Body cannot distinguish between radioactively tagged compound and its stable counterpart.
   d. Fate of tagged element determined by counting with special instruments (GM counter; scintillation counter; scintiscanner; gamma camera)
      (1) Externally as ^{123}I, ^{131}I, or ^{99m}Tc, thyroid gland; ^{99m}Tc in various compounds, brain, lung, skeletal system, liver, kidneys.

(2) Excretions as in counting urine in Schilling test for pernicious anemia.

(3) Secretions as in measuring ^{131}I output in saliva.

2. *Therapy* — methods

a. *Chemical*

(1) Selective absorption as ^{131}I in thyroid gland: ^{131}I given orally in therapeutic amount; selectively absorbed in target organ — thyroid — which is irradiated by deposited radionuclide, in this instance, 90 percent of therapeutic dose from beta particles, 10 percent from gamma rays.

(2) Differential absorption as ^{32}P in malignant tumors.

(3) Colloidal dispersion as ^{198}Au in the reticuloendothelial system.

b. *Physical*

(1) External as ^{60}Co and ^{137}Cs in teletherapy, shown in Figure 22.21; and ^{90}Sr in contact therapy, shown in Figure 22.22.

(2) Interstitial as ^{137}Cs needles; ^{192}Ir seeds; ^{198}Au grains; ^{125}I seeds; ^{182}Ta wires.

(3) Intracavitary as ^{137}Cs tubes; ^{32}P-chromic phosphate in pleural or peritoneal malignant effusions.

Radionuclide Instrumentation

The basic procedure in any quantitative diagnostic radionuclide study is to count, with an appropriate detecting or counting instrument, the number of photons or ionizing particles it receives and detects from a radioactive source in a specified interval of time and with a defined geometric arrangement. The source may be either an organ in the body or a specimen outside the body, depending on the examination being conducted.

A general formula for radionuclide counting may be expressed as follows, ***provided the sample and the standard are counted under identical conditions:***

$$\frac{\text{mCi in sample}}{\text{mCi in standard}} = \frac{\text{net counting rate in sample}}{\text{net counting rate in standard}}$$

The net sample counting rate, R_S, is the difference between the total counting rate, R_T, and the background counting rate, R_B.

$$R_S = R_T - R_B \qquad (5)$$

We obtain the background counting rate after having removed the sample and all other radioactive sources from the counting range of the detector. The counting rate is the total count divided by the elapsed time. In any radionuclide procedure, the background counting rate must be subtracted from the total to obtain the net counting rate, unless the background is negligibly small.

We must have a method of counting the individual radiations emitted by a radioactive source. The same devices, with modifications, can be used to count both photons and charged particles. These devices consist of (1) the radiation detector plus its related electric circuitry and power supply and (2) the instrument for registering the number of counts.

Radiation Detectors. The two main types of detectors, which differ completely in principle, are the *Geiger-Muller* or *GM tube* and the *scintillation detector.* A detector with its related electrical circuitry is often referred to as a *counter;* thus, GM counter; scintillation counter.

1. *GM Tube.* This is an electronic pulse-type device that can detect individual ionizing particles or photons. It consists of a central wire *anode* and a cylindrical *cathode* enclosed in glass (see Figure 22.6). Within the tube is a suitable gas, often argon and alcohol under reduced pressure of about one-eighth atmosphere. The GM tube operates within a range of about 1,000 to 1,500 volts. There are two general types of GM tubes—end-window and side-window (see Figure 22.7). Radiation enters the end-window tube at one end and is therefore said to be *directional.* On the other hand, radiation enters a side-window GM tube at any point around its circumference and is therefore *nondirectional.*

The characteristic curve of a GM tube is shown in Figure 22.8. Although this curve is typical of all GM tubes, it may vary in numerical detail from one tube to another.

Photons or beta particles entering the tube cause ionization of the contained gas. With an applied potential of 800 to 1100 volts, the ions undergo sufficient acceleration to cause further *ionization*

Figure 22.6. Simplified diagram of an end-window GM counter.

Figure 22.7. A. End-window type of GM tube. B. Side-window type. *A* is anode, *B* is bead, *W* is window.

by collision with other atoms, resulting in an electrical discharge along the central wire anode. This discharge is manifested by a "pop" in the audio circuit. In this voltage range (800 to 1100 for this particular GM tube), the number of pops or counts per second is independent of the applied voltage but increases with the number of photons or beta particles entering the tube—this is the *GM region* of the characteristic curve (see Figure 22.8). Here, each entering photon or beta particle is detected as an individual count.

Such a counter can be used to detect the presence of photons or beta particles and, under suitable conditions, determine their

Figure 22.8. Characteristic curve of one type of GM tube. The voltage may be different for other GM tube. The operating voltage should correspond to about the middle of the pleateau.

quantity. A GM counter displays high efficiency in detecting beta particles but low efficiency (about 1 to 2 percent) in detecting gamma radiation. Its efficiency in detecting gamma rays can be improved by coating the cathode with bismuth.

While the GM counter is still used in certain types of survey meters (see pages 579–580), it has been replaced by the much more efficient and dependable scintillation counter in nuclear medicine. It will be described in the next section.

2. *Scintillation Detector.* Early in the present century, ionizing radiation was found to produce flashes of light or *scintillations* in certain crystals. Application of this principle gave us the scintillation counter, which turned out to be a much more efficient detector of gamma rays than the GM counter.

A scintillation counter conducts the light flashes, produced by gamma photons in a detector crystal, through a Lucite® channel to a photomultiplier tube. This consists of a photocathode and about eleven accelerating anodes or *dynodes* in series, as shown in Figure 22.9. The electrons liberated in the photocathode are accelerated serially along the photomultiplier by the dynodes, eventually giving rise to a pulse in the external circuit. One pulse occurs for each entering photon, provided the latter has a certain minimum energy; the size of each pulse is proportional to the energy of the photon

Figure 22.9. Diagram of a scintillation counter. Incoming radiation produces flashes of light (scintillations) in the detector crystal, one flash per photon. The light flashes are conducted by the Lucite channel to the light-sensitive cathode where photoelectrons are released. These are then accelerated by a series of dynodes (anodes) and are detected as pulses by the counting circuit after they strike the plate.

entering the crystal. Since the scintillation counter has a dead time of only about 5 microsec, it is capable of tremendous counting rates. Also, its high degree of sensitivity permits the counting of sources having extremely small activities.

Most scintillation counters have a thallium-activated sodium iodide detector crystal. However, anthracene crystals are available, especially for beta particles. The larger the volume of the crystal, the greater is the sensitivity or counting rate for a given activity. Crystals vary in diameter from a few mm for the measurement of exposure rates near sealed radioactive sources, to 15 in. (38 cm) for rapid imaging of large organs such as the brain or liver.

The *well counter* is a scintillation counter specially modified for measuring samples of low activity. A hole bored in the detector crystal of a well counter can accommodate a small bottle containing the radioactive sample (see Figure 22.10). Because the crystal surrounds the sample on the sides and bottom, the well counter is extremely sensitive; in fact, it can count a source with an activity as low as 10^{-5} μCi (microcurie). At the same time, the high sensitivity requires heavy lead shielding (usually about 5 cm Pb) to minimize background effects.

Figure 22.10. Well counter, using a well crystal in a scintillation counter. Thick lead shielding is required to reduce the background counting rate.

Measuring Devices for Radiation Counters. Special electronic devices receive and register the rapid pulses arising in the circuit of a GM or scintillation counter on exposure to ionizing radiation. There are two main types of such meters: (1) scaler and (2) rate meter.

1. *Scaler.* This is a recording unit with four main components: an electronic scaling circuit, a mechanical register, a high voltage supply, an interval timer, and a "window" or channel selector that limits the counting to radiation in a desired energy range. The *scaling circuit* responds very rapidly to pulses in the GM or scintillation detector (to which it is connected) by lights which flash successively and show accumulated accounts. A *mechanical register* is also included to record multiples of 10, 100, or 1,000, according to the scale selected (see Figure 22.11), in the *decade scaler.*

The scaler includes a *high-voltage supply* for the counter as well as a voltage stabilizer to minimize fluctuation in the counting rate.

Two types of *timers* are available to determine the time element in the counting rate which is defined as follows:

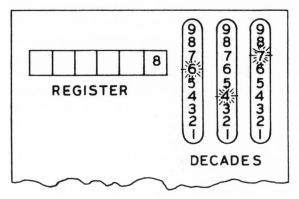

Figure 22.11. Panel of a decade scaler. The reading here totals 8,647 counts.

$$\text{counting time} = \frac{\text{number of counts}}{\text{elapsed time}}$$

A *preset timer,* set for a desired time interval, automatically terminates the counting at the end of the elapsed time. The other type, the *preset counting* timer, is set for a predetermined number of counts; when this number of counts has been accumulated, the timer automatically stops the counting process and indicates the time that has elapsed.

2. *Rate Meter.* Operating on a different principle from the scaler, the rate meter indicates the counting rate in counts per minute by means of a needle moving over a calibrated scale. In a sense, it averages the rate at which the pulses arrive from the GM or scintillation counter.

Due to the random nature of radioactive decay, wide fluctuations in the counting rate (and indicator needle) occur from instant to instant, especially with sources of low activity. To stabilize the indicator needle and improve accuracy, enough time should be allowed for the rate meter to accumulate a sufficient number of counts.

The rate meter circuit contains a variable capacitor on which the pulses build up a charge, in parallel with a variable resistor, which permits gradual leakage of the charge. The product of the capacitance and the resistance of the circuit (*RC*) is called the *time constant.* As the capacitance and the resistance are increased by means of a control knob, the time constant increases, the charges leak away more slowly, and the needle remains steadier. However, it also takes the needle longer to come to rest (or reach its equilibrium position for a particular counting rate); hence, more time has to be allowed for the needle to come to rest before the reading is taken. For an accuracy of 2 to 5 percent, the elapsed time should be *four times the time constant.* For example, if the selected time constant is 10 sec, then one must wait $(4 \times 10) = 40$ sec before reading the counting rate, which will then have an accuracy of 2 to 5 percent.

The rate meter supplies the high voltage for the operation of a GM or scintillation counter. A separate timer is not required because the counting rate is shown directly in counts per minute.

A rate meter can be used both for routine counting and for radiation surveys in health physics. It is also especially useful in recording a continuous process, such as the progressive loss or uptake of a radionuclide, when connected to a *chart recorder.* This has a continuous roll of paper on which are recorded, in ink, the instantaneous fluctuations of a lever arm activated by the pulses arriving at the rate meter. Multiple channels are available, as in the scaler, to permit selection of the energy "window" of the radiation to be counted and so avoid counting radiation having energies outside the range delimited by the window.

Sources of Error in Counting

Various errors are inherent in the counting process, the most important ones being (1) statistical errors and (2) recovery time of the counter.

Statistical Errors. Since radioactive decay—a purely random process—obeys the laws of chance, statistical errors affect the accuracy of a given counting rate which, after all, reflects the rate of decay of a radioactive source. As a general rule, it is well to remember that the *reliability* (or reproducibility) *of a given count depends on the total number of counts recorded.* If the same sample is counted repeatedly under identical conditions, the counts will differ from each other because of chance variations (statistical fluctuation). How, then, can we tell which count is correct and how much it differs from the ideal or "true" count? Actually the answer lies in specifying a certain statistical reliability of a given count. Only the important elementary concepts will be included here.

1. **Standard Deviation,** σ (Greek letter "sigma"), is defined as follows:

$$\sigma = \pm \sqrt{N} \text{ (approx.)} \tag{6}$$

where N is the total number of counts recorded in a given run. The standard deviation means that if we take the range $N \pm \sqrt{N}$, or the range of values from $N - \sigma$ to $N + \sigma$, there is about a two to one chance that the true count would lie somewhere within this range. For example, if the total count is 6400,

$$\sigma = \pm \sqrt{6400} = \pm 80$$

There is about a two to one chance that the true count falls between $6400 - 80$ and $6400 + 80$, or between 6320 and 6480.

2. **Percent Standard Deviation** ($\%\sigma$). It is often more convenient to express σ as a percentage of the total count:

$$\%\sigma = \frac{\pm \sqrt{N}}{N} \times 100$$

$$\%\sigma = \pm \frac{100}{\sqrt{N}} \tag{7}$$

or,

$$\%\sigma = \pm \frac{100}{\sigma}$$

In the preceding numerical example,

$$\%\sigma = \pm \frac{100}{\sqrt{6400}} = \pm \frac{100}{80} = \pm 1.3\%$$

The final count may then be stated as $6400 \pm 1.3\%$; there is, again, a two to one chance that the true count lies between these limits. Figure 22.12 shows a curve plot of the percent standard deviation as a function of the total number of counts.

We can easily demonstrate that the percent standard deviation becomes smaller (ie, reliability becomes greater) as the total number of recorded counts is increased. Suppose we count a given

Figure 22.12. Variation in percent standard deviation relative to the total number of counts.

sample long enough to accumulate 2500 counts. Then,

$$\%\sigma = \pm \frac{100}{\sqrt{2500}} = \pm \frac{100}{50} = \pm 2\%$$

If the same sample is counted long enough to accumulate only 100 counts, then,

$$\%\sigma = \pm \frac{100}{\sqrt{100}} = \pm \frac{100}{10} = \pm 10\%$$

Thus, the percent standard deviation is simply 100 divided by the square root of the number of counts. The percent standard deviation for a given **total count** also applies to the **counting rate** based on that total count.

In actual practice, with preset timing, we count a sample for a predetermined interval of time; and we also count the background, but not necessarily for the same interval. We then compute the counting rate by simply dividing each count by its corresponding time. The true sample counting rate R (without background), is equal to the gross sample counting rate (including background) R_T, minus the background counting rate R_B,

$$R = R_T - R_B \tag{8}$$

As a rule, to keep the percent standard deviation as small as possible, the ratio R_T/R_B should be as large as possible, preferably at least 9.

In counting a radioactive sample we must know how long the sample and the background must be counted in order to achieve a desired percent standard deviation in the "true" or net sample counting rate. This information can be obtained from the following equation:

$$\%\sigma_s = \pm \frac{100\sqrt{R_T/t_T + R_B/t_B}}{R_T - R_B} \tag{9}$$

where $\%\sigma_s$ = desired percent standard deviation of the net counting rate of the sample
    R_T = total counting rate, including background
    R_B = background counting rate
    t_T = time required to count sample, including background
    t_B = time required to count background

But, another relationship is needed—the ratio of the sample counting time to the background counting time—for maximum reliability. This is covered by:

$$t_T/t_B = \sqrt{R_T/R_B} \tag{10}$$

For example, if the counting rate of the sample is 900 cpm (counts per min) and that of the background is 100 cpm, $\sqrt{900/100} = \sqrt{9} = 3$, so the sample must be counted three times as long as the background. Note that, as mentioned earlier, the sample counting rate here is nine times the background counting rate. This was specified above for the minimum ratio that provides acceptable reliability.

Let us now apply these equations to an actual problem. Suppose the counting rate of a sample to be 900 cpm and that of the background 100 cpm. How long should the sample and background be counted to provide a net counting rate with a standard deviation of $\pm$ 2%? First we apply equation (10),

$$t_T/t_B = \sqrt{900/100} = 3$$
$$t_B = t_T/3$$

Next we make use of equation (9), substituting 2 for $\%\sigma_s$,

$$2 = \frac{100\sqrt{900/t_T + 100/t_B}}{900 - 100}$$

Now substituting $t_T/3$ for its equal, t_B (found above),

$$2 = \frac{100\sqrt{900/t_T + 100 \times 3/t_T}}{800} = \frac{\sqrt{1200/t_T}}{8}$$

Transposing and then squaring both sides,

$$(16)^2 = 1200/t_T$$
$$t_T = 4.7 \text{ min} \approx 5 \text{ min}$$
$$t_B = t_T/3 = 1.5 \text{ min} \approx 2 \text{ min}$$

The total number of counts accumulated in these time intervals are:

$$\text{total sample count} = N_T = 900 \times 5 = 4500 \text{ counts}$$
$$\text{background count} = N_B = 100 \times 2 = 200 \text{ counts}$$

The technologist should always be aware of the standard deviation of any counting procedure, so as to appreciate its reliability.

Frequently, the problem is the reverse of that described above; we may need to know the percent standard deviation of a net counting rate after the gross and the background counts have been measured. This can be readily calculated from equation (9).

Recovery Time of Counter. As already mentioned in the discussion of GM and scintillation counters, a high counting rate may incur an error owing to the inability of the counter to detect radiation during a tiny interval of time following a pulse. This interval is called the ***dead time*** or ***recovery time*** of the counter— the higher the counting rate, the greater the likelihood that two ionizing events may occur so closely in time that only one is detected. A simple formula gives the approximate percentage correction for the dead time at extremely high counting rates:

$$\%C = 100\,\frac{R_\tau}{1 - R_\tau} \tag{11}$$

where $\%C$ is the percentage correction that must be added to the observed counting rate R, to obtain the corrected counting rate, and τ (Greek letter "tau") is the dead time of the counter in question. For example, with a GM counter having a τ of $2(10)^{-4}$ sec, an observed counting rate of 200 cps should be corrected as follows:

$$\%C = 100 \frac{200 \times 2 \times 10^{-4}}{1 - 200 \times 2 \times 10^{-4}}$$

Performing the indicated multiplication first,

$$\%C = \frac{4}{1 - 0.04} = \frac{4}{0.96} = 4\%$$

The corrected counting rate is then

$$200 + 200(0.04) = 208 \text{ cps}$$

With a scintillation counter having a dead time of $(10)^{-6}$ sec, the correction factor is only about 1 percent even with an extremely high counting rate of 500 cps (the corresponding correction with a GM counter would be approximately 11 percent).

Efficiency and Sensitivity of Counters

The ability of a particular counter to detect radiation is generally known as its *efficiency.* But as we have seen, radioactive decay is a random process accompanied by the emission of radiation. In order to detect all of the radiation, the source would have to be placed completely within a special type of counter.

Sensitivity of Counters. In practice, a counter is placed at some distance from the source, which may be an organ or sample having sufficient activity. Because the radiation is emitted in all directions, the counter cannot receive it all, but can "see" only some of the radiation coming toward it, as in Figure 22.13 Furthermore, of the radiation actually entering the counter, only a fraction produces ionizing events and is detected. For example, an ordinary GM counter will detect about 1 to 2 percent of the entering gamma rays, although this can be improved by coating the cathode with bismuth. These two negative aspects of efficiency—the inability of a counter to "see" all the radiation and its failure to detect all the radiation that enters it—are embodied in *counter sensitivity f* defined by the following equation:

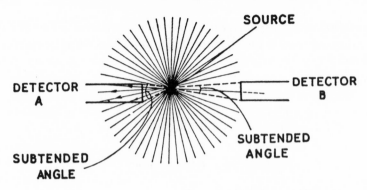

Figure 22.13. Angle of acceptance. The closer the counter is to the source, the greater is the number of photons entering it. Thus, detector *A* would record a higher counting rate than detector *B* with the same radioactive sample.

$$f = \frac{\text{counting rate}}{\text{activity}} \qquad (12)$$

Bear in mind that sensitivity is related to a given geometric arrangement of the source and the counter. Note that sensitivity may be expressed as counts per sec per μCi, or counts per min per mCi, or any other convenient combination of units. Sensitivity can be used to convert counting rate to activity of a sample, by rearrangement of equation (12),

$$\text{activity} = \frac{\text{counting rate}}{f} \qquad (13)$$

provided the same geometric setup, counter, and radionuclide are used as in the initial determination of sensitivity. It also permits the computation of the sample activity needed to obtain a desired counting rate.

The preceding discussion applies primarily to the determination of the sensitivity of a particular counting system. In actual practice, there are two additional factors that influence the counting rate when counting is done over the body. One is attenuation of the radiation as it passes through tissues or other matter, on its way to the detecting instrument. The other is the scattering of radiation from nearby objects, with entrance of this scattered radiation into the detector. We can minimize these factors by using radionuclides whose radiation is not appreciably attenuated, and by keeping the counting system isolated from scattering material. The influence of scattering can be further controlled by narrowing the energy window of the detecting system to match the energy of the primary radiation.

Minimum Detectable Activity. We sometimes need to know the smallest quantity of a radionuclide that a counter can detect to a reasonable degree of reliability, with a given geometric arrangement and type of counter. According to the ICRU, the minimum detectable activity is that activity which, in a given counting time, records a number of counts on the instrument equal to three times the standard deviation of the background count in the same time interval. The equation specifying minimum detectable activity, A_{min}, is

$$A_{min} = \frac{3}{f}\sqrt{R_B/t_B} \tag{14}$$

where $\sqrt{R_B/t_B}$ is the standard deviation of the background counting rate, and f is the sensitivity of the counter. Since $R_B = N_B/t_B$, we can rearrange as $t_B = N_B/R_B$. Substituting this value of t_B in equation (14),

$$A_{min} = \frac{3\,R_B}{f\sqrt{N_B}} \tag{15}$$

N_B is the number of background counts recorded in a preselected interval of time, usually about ten minutes. For example, if, with a particular geometric arrangement, f is 2000 cps per μCi, R_B 4 cps, and N_B 2500 counts in 10 min, then the minimum detectable activity is

$$A_{min} = \frac{3 \times 4}{2000 \times \sqrt{2500}} = \frac{3}{500 \times 50} = 0.0001\,\mu\text{Ci}$$

Note that the sensitivity and minimum detectable activity both depend on the geometric arrangement of the source and counter, the type of counter, and the radionuclide being counted. Therefore, calibration of the equipment should be carried out separately for each counting setup and each radionuclide in use in the department.

Geometric Factors in Counting

In counting a radionuclide sample, we must take into account (1) *the distance between the source and the counter,* (2) *the presence of scattering material* in the vicinity of the source, (3) *the collimation of the counter,* and (4) *the size of the source.* Figure 22.13 shows how a source gives off radiation in all directions. The inverse square law of radiation applies (approximately because not a point source), so that the nearer the counter is to the source, the more radiation it "sees." Matter near the source gives rise to scattered radiation, which may be detected by the counter and give a falsely high counting rate. Collimation affects the fraction of emitted radiation reaching the counter. Figure 22.14 shows the response of the same counter with two different degrees of collimation. As the collimator is narrowed, the counting rate decreases, but the area of maximum sensitivity depends only on the diameter of the collimator hole. On the basis of this principle, a counter can be so collimated that it can detect, in the thyroid gland, small nodules whose activity is different from that of the surrounding gland. But collimation must not be so severe that the counter fails to see the entire organ, as in measuring radioiodine uptake by the thyroid gland (see Figure 22.15).

A *focused collimator* (see page 528 and Figure 22.18) provides maximum sensitivity for a particular degree of collimation, making it much more efficient than a single hole collimator.

Because of the fact that sensitivity depends so intimately on the geometric arrangement of the source and counter, equipment should be standardized and used under an identical geometric setup.

Methods of Counting

Two methods of counting, whether this is to be done on specimens outside the body, or over certain areas of the body, include (1) absolute counting and (2) comparative counting, both of which we shall now describe. But note that health authorities require calibration of all test doses before they are given to the patient.

1. **Absolute Counting.** In principle, this is similar to the method

Figure 22.14. Effect of collimation on sensitivity of scintillation counter. In *A*, with less collimation, the counting rate is higher because the angle of view is large and the crystal "sees" a larger total area than in *B* where collimation is more severe. However, the area of maximum sensitivity depends on the size of the collimator opening (and not on the depth of the crystal within the collimator); this is the same in *A* and *B*. (*Modified from* Quimby, E. H., Feitelberg, S., and Silver, S.: *Radioactive Isotopes in Clinical Practice.* Philadelphia, Lea & Febiger, 1968.)

of determining the sensitivity, *f*, of a counter. First we measure sensitivity with a standard known radioactive source (similar to the one to be counted in the patient or specimen) in the same geometric setup to be used with the clinical material. Suppose the standard source under these geometric conditions has an activity of 1 μCi and a net counting rate of 3000 cps. Then $f = 3000$ cps per μCi. If, now, we count the specimen under identical conditions (same radionuclide and geometric setup), and find a net counting rate of 1000 cps, then according to equation (13),

$$\text{activity of sample} = \frac{\text{counting rate}}{f} \mu\text{Ci}$$

Therefore,

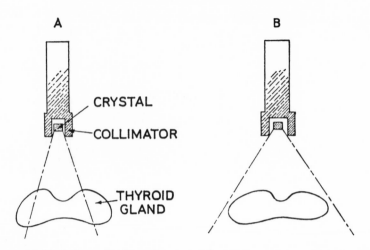

Figure 22.15. Effect of collimation on angle of view of a counter. In *A*, the collimation is so restrictive that the counter does not "see" the entire gland and the counting rate will therefore be too low. In *B*, with less severe collimation, the angle of view covers the entire gland and a more accurate counting rate will be obtained. (*Modified from* Quimby, E. H., Feitelberg, S., and Silver, S.: *Radioactive Isotopes in Clinical Practice.* Philadelphia, Lea & Febiger, 1968.)

$$\text{activity of sample} = \frac{1000}{3000} = 0.33 \, \mu\text{Ci}$$

2. Comparative Counting. In clinical radionuclide studies utilizing the tracer method, we usually count the sample and standard separately under identical conditions. These net counting rates are then compared directly, the specimen counting rate being expressed as a percentage of the standard. Comparative counting may be exemplified by tracer studies of the radioiodine uptake by the thyroid gland. A predetermined dose of radioiodine is given to the patient and, after the appropriate time has elapsed, the counting rate over the thyroid gland is measured at a fixed distance (for example, 20 cm) with the "window" set for the proper energy range. The same dose as that given the patient is now measured separately in a neck "phantom" (see Figure 22.16) at the same distance. After correction of both counting rates for background,

$$\% \text{ thyroid uptake} = \frac{\text{net thyroid cpm}}{\text{net standard cpm}} \times 100 \qquad (16)$$

Figure 22.16. Diagram of a standard neck phantom, made of Lucite. The standard radioiodine capsule is placed in the 1-inch well.

This procedure is carried out at two, six, and twenty-four hours, but additional studies are usually indicated, including chemical laboratory tests and thyroid scintiscanning.

Important Medical Radionuclides

We shall now summarize the properties of some of the more important radionuclides used in medicine.

Radioactive Iodine. Iodine 131 (^{131}I), the most commonly used radioisotope of iodine, has a physical half-life of 8.1 days and emits 364-keV gamma rays and 183-keV (av.) beta particles. Obtained mainly by separation from the fission products of the nuclear reactor, ^{131}I as sodium iodide is used especially in the diagnosis and treatment of diseases of the thyroid gland. The therapeutic effect of ^{131}I in hyperthyroidism and certain thyroid cancers depends mainly on the **beta particles,** whereas tracer and scanning studies depend on the **gamma rays,** which are much more penetrating and can be detected outside the body with a GM or scintillation counter.

Another radioisotope of iodine—[123]I*—is preferred for uptake and imaging studies of the thyroid gland. Produced in the cyclotron by deuteron irradiation of tellurium, it has a half-life of 13.2 hr.

---

*Data by courtesy of Medi-Physics, Inc., 900 Durham Avenue, Plainfield, NJ 07080.

Iodine 123 decays by electron capture and then emits 159-keV gamma rays, but no particles. Its main advantage, aside from the favorable energy of its gamma rays, lies in its short half-life which permits the administration of larger activities than with ^{131}I, but with a substantially smaller dose to the thyroid gland. For example, a 400-μCi imaging dose of ^{123}I gives an absorbed dose of about 20 rads to the normal thyroid gland, as contrasted with about 130 rads from a 100-μCi dose of ^{131}I, a really significant difference.

Radioactive Phosphorus. Phosphorus 32 has a half-life of 14.3 days and emits 700-keV (av.) beta particles. It is prepared mainly by neutron irradiation of stable sulfur in a nuclear reactor (see page 496). After administration in suitable form orally or intravenously, ^{32}P tends to concentrate in the bone marrow, spleen, liver, and lymph nodes. It can therefore be used in the treatment of certain blood disorders, mainly polycythemia rubra vera, a condition in which the bone marrow produces an excess of red blood cells. Phosphorus 32 suppresses the overproduction of these cells. Intravenous ^{32}P as phosphate delivers a whole body dose of about 1.5 rads per mCi during the first three days, and thereafter, about 2.5 rads per mCi to soft tissues and 25 rads to bone (Shapiro).

Technetium 99m. The radionuclide ^{99m}Tc has a short, though convenient, half-life of six hours. Its gamma radiation, having a relatively low energy—140 keV—is easily collimated and at the same time has adequate penetrating ability to pass through the body and reach the detector. Technetium 99m is at present used mainly as the pertechnetate salt in aqueous solution. Because of the short half-life and the absence of beta radiation, large doses can be given with relatively little exposure to the patient; for example, 10 mCi intravenously for brain imaging delivers a whole body dose of about 0.12 rad. As a result we can achieve high counting rates and good resolution of the scan images. By far the greatest application of ^{99m}Tc, tagged to glucoheptonate is in brain imaging, although it is being widely used in other areas such as bone imaging with ^{99m}Tc-tagged phosphorus compounds, liver imaging with ^{99m}Tc-tagged sulfur colloid, and lung imaging with ^{99m}Tc-tagged albumin aggregate. It is useful in the form of sodium pertechnetate in diagnostic studies of the thyroid gland.

We should mention the ***technetium "cow,"*** a molybdenum (^{99}Mo) generator which decays to ^{99m}Tc. Each day 0.9 percent sodium chloride solution is passed through the generator, dissolving out the ^{99m}Tc; this is called "milking" the "cow." The resulting ^{99m}Tc is filtered during the milking process and, after calibration, is ready for use.

Radioactive Cobalt. Cobalt 60 (^{60}Co), a radioisotope of cobalt 59, is produced in a nuclear reactor. It has a half-life of 5.2 years and emits gamma rays of two energies—1.17 and 1.33 MeV (average 1.25 MeV)—and a low energy beta particle (av. 96 keV). Cobalt 60 is available in a variety of forms for brachytherapy (short distance therapy)—needles, beads, and wires—as a substitute for radium. More recently, cesium 137 has been found to surpass ^{60}Co for this purpose. Large ^{60}Co teletherapy units are designed for use in external irradiation.

Vitamin B_{12} or cyanocobalamin contains cobalt as a part of its molecular structure; when this compound is tagged with the radionuclide ^{57}Co, it is symbolized by ^{57}CoB$_{12}$ and is the agent that is widely used in the Schilling test for pernicious anemia (see pages 525–526).

Radioactive Gold. The radionuclide, gold 198 (^{198}Au) in colloidal form, has been used as a liver imaging agent. It has a half-life of 2.7 days and emits a 412-keV gamma ray and 316-keV (av.) beta particles. As usual with scanning radionuclides, the gamma rays are the ones that are utilized. Virtually all of the energy is deposited in the liver which receives an absorbed dose of about 7 rads from an administered activity of 150 μCi of ^{198}Au. Radiogold has been virtually replaced by ^{99m}Tc sulfur colloid for liver imaging. However, it is still commercially available in the form of grains for permanent implantation therapy of certain accessible cancers.

Radioactive Iron. Of the two radioisotopes of iron, ^{59}Fe and ^{55}Fe, the former is generally more useful in diagnosis. Iron 59, produced by neutron irradiation of stable iron in the nuclear reactor, has a physical half-life of 45 days and emits gamma rays of three different energies, 98 percent of which are 1.29 and 1.10 MeV. It also emits beta particles with an average energy of 118 keV. Various compounds containing ^{59}Fe are used as tracers to study the absorption and storage of iron and its rate of appearance in the red blood cells, especially in anemia. A diagnostic intravenous dose of 5 μCi of ^{59}Fe delivers a small total-body dose—about 0.16 rad. The corresponding value for oral administration is much less—0.014 rad in normals and 0.1 rad in iron-deficient individuals. The largest dose as far as individual organs are concerned is about 1 to 1.7 rads to the testes.

Radioactive Chromium. The radionuclide chromium 51 (^{51}Cr) is used in the form of chromate to determine red cell volume in polycythemia and in patients undergoing extensive surgery and to determine red cell survival in hemolytic anemias. Chromium 51 has a physical half-life of 27.8 days, and emits a 320-keV gamma ray and 242-keV (av.) beta rays. In the chromate form, this nuclide tags red cell, whereas in the chromic form it labels blood plasma.

Examples of the Use of Radionuclides in Medical Diagnosis

It is beyond the scope of this book to give a detailed account of the numerous diagnostic procedures in the Nuclear Medicine Department. Instead, we shall include examples of the more important procedures based on various principles; these will include (1) *uptake by an organ*, (2) *excretion*, and (3) *dilution*. Organ imaging will be discussed in the next section.

1. **Uptake or Tracer Studies.** As mentioned earlier, the thyroid gland has a strong affinity for iodine. If radioactive iodine is taken it will normally be trapped in the thyroid gland over a period of twenty-four hours, its concentration depending on the functional capacity of the gland. Obviously, before such a test can be run, the patient must avoid the intake of ordinary stable iodine (^{127}I), as well as drugs that are known to suppress the activity of the thyroid gland. Such restriction may require weeks or months, depending on the type of drug; radiopaque media containing iodine may interfere with further iodine uptake for several months.

Depending on the type of equipment, a tracer activity of 2 μCi to 5 μCi of ^{131}I is taken orally in the morning by the fasting patient. A phantom simulating the neck should be available, made of Lucite or hard paraffin according to ICRU specifications (see Figure 22.16). A plastic test tube containing a standard of the same activity as that given the patient is placed in the hole in the phantom. At prescribed intervals, preferably two, six, and twenty-four hours, counting rates are taken at the same fixed distance—20 cm—from the thyroid and from the phantom (comparative counting). The window is set for a range of 354 to 375 keV. Each time, a body background count should also be made over the lower end of the thigh, which resembles the tissues of the neck without the thyroid; the thigh counting rate should be subtracted from the thyroid counting rate each time. The percent uptakes at each counting session (two, six, twenty-four hr) are computed from the following equation:

$$\% \text{ thyroid uptake} = \frac{100 \text{ (neck } R_T - \text{ thigh } R_T)}{\text{phantom } R_T - \text{ room } R_B} \qquad (17)$$

where R_T is the total counting rate of each item, and R_B is the background counting rate.

Figure 22.17 shows typical uptake curves obtained in various functional states of the thyroid gland. There is significant overlap of normal and abnormal values at both ends, this being more serious in the hypothyroid (low) range (see Table 22.1). Still, the thyroid uptake of radioiodine is an extremely useful measure of thyroid gland function, especially when combined with supplementary chemical and radiochemical studies, and radionuclide imaging.

When available, ^{123}I is preferred for uptake and imaging studies of the thyroid gland because of the much smaller absorbed dose as compared with [131]I (see pages 521–522).

2. **Excretion of a Radionuclide by the Body.** An example is the Schilling test for *pernicious anemia*, performed with cyanocobalamin (vitamin B_{12}) labeled with the radionuclide cobalt 57 ([Co57]). Normal persons readily absorb this vitamin from the gastrointestinal tract, storing it in the liver within four to seven days. However, patients with pernicious anemia cannot absorb it because they lack *intrinsic factor*, which is normally secreted by the stomach. The fasting patient is first asked to void, the urine specimen being saved as a pretest control. The patient then swallows a capsule containing 0.5 μCi of [57]CoB_{12} with one-half glass of water (patient must not have received ordinary B_{12} orally or parenterally during the preceding two days). One hour later, a large dose of ordinary, stable B_{12}—1000 μg—is given intramuscularly to flush any absorbed radioactive B_{12} through the kidneys and into the urine, which is

Figure 22.17. Representative iodine 131 uptake curves in the three functional states of the thyroid gland. Actually, there is no sharp dividing line between the normal (euthyroid) and abnormal (hypo- and hyperthyroid) states.

Table 22.1
RANGE OF 24-HR UPTAKES OF [131]I
BY THE THYROID GLAND.
IN VARIOUS FUNCTIONAL STATES*

Euthyroid (normal)	5%–30%
Hyperthyroid	more than 30%
Hypothyroid	less than 5%

* These values are typical; actually, there may be much more overlap of the normal and abnormal than that shown here. Other tests are usually necessary to establish the diagnosis.

collected for 24 hours in a 1-gallon plastic bottle with a screw cap. Urine collection must be complete. If the urine volume is less than 1 liter, it is made up to exactly 1 liter; if more than 1 liter, a 1-liter sample is poured into another bottle. Next, the same activity of standard as that originally given the patient is made up to 1 liter in the same type of bottle. The standard bottle and the patient's specimen bottle (1 liter) are each counted in contact with the crystal of a scintillation counter and calculations are made as follows:

if original volume of urine was less than 1000 ml,
make volume up to 1000 ml, and

$$\%\text{absorption} = \frac{\text{urine } R_T - \text{background } R_B}{\text{standard } R_T - \text{background } R_B} \times 100 \quad (18)$$

if original volume of urine was more than 1000 ml,
take 1000-ml sample and

$$\%\text{absorption} = \frac{\text{urine volume (urine } R_T - \text{background } R_B)}{1000 (\text{standard} \quad R_T - \text{background } R_B)} \times 100$$

$$(19)$$

Absorption in normal individuals exceeds 5 percent. If absorption is less than 5 percent the examination should be repeated after four days, intrinsic factor being given at the same time as the $^{57}\text{CoB}_{12}$ capsule. In the presence of pernicious anemia, the absorption should increase to a level above 10 percent.

3. **Dilution Tests with Radionuclides.** When a radioactive nuclide in a given volume of solution is mixed with an unknown larger volume of water, the nuclide obviously becomes diluted. If the net counting rate r_s per ml of the original sample volume v_s is known, and the net counting rate R_s per ml of the larger volume is measured under the same conditions as the original sample, then the larger volume V_s can be computed by means of the following equation:

$$VR_s = vr_s \quad (20)$$

This equation summarizes the *dilution principle*, used to determine circulating blood volume. A small activity of 5 μCi of radioactive iodine-tagged human serum albumin (RISA) is injected intravenously, most often into an antecubital vein. After an interval of about ten minutes to allow for admixture with the circulating blood, 5 ml of blood is withdrawn from the opposite antecubital vein, oxalated, and counted in a well counter. The same volume, 5 ml, of a dilute standard (5 μCi in 1 liter) is counted in the same way. Both are corrected for background. The circulating blood volume is then obtained from the following equation:

$$\text{blood volume in ml} = \frac{\text{cpm/ml standard} \times 1000}{\text{cpm/ml blood}} \qquad (21)$$

Standard tables give predicted normal values of blood volume. The plasma volume can be found by separating the plasma from the sample and counting it in the same manner as the whole blood. After appropriate correction, red cell volume is obtained by subtracting plasma volume from whole blood volume.

Radionuclide Scanning and Imaging

Any procedure which mechanically maps the distribution of a radionuclide within the body, from points outside the body, is called *radionuclide scanning* or *scintiscanning.* The efficiency of *automatic rectilinear* scanners may be high, especially in the presence of high counting rates. Scanning is by no means foolproof, since errors may arise in equipment, method, or interpretation. Considerable experience is necessary to qualify one to interpret the results. We must note that scans are not quantitative—they simply display relative counting rates over various parts of an organ or region.

Rectilinear scanners are equipped with a scintillation counter provided with a multiple hole *focused collimator,* shown in Figure 22.18. Such collimators consist of a block of heavy metal such as tungsten in which are bored multiple holes whose directions converge toward a point within the body at some fixed distance from the face of the detector. A small zone of maximum sensitivity exists near this focal point, the distance between it and the face of the collimator being called the *focal distance* of the collimator. The great advantage of the focused collimator lies in providing *maximum sensitivity for a given degree of collimation.*

The scintillation counter and its collimator move automatically back and forth over the selected region of the body, recording the counting rates of the administered radionuclide on x-ray film as photographic dots, and on special paper as ink or burn dots. The higher the counting rate in a given area, the closer will be the grouping of the dots. In addition, there is a system for adjusting the background counting rate to increase the contrast in the scan and, within limits, make it easier to detect small abnormalities.

Figure 22.19 shows a block diagram of a rectilinear scintillation scanner.

Figure 22.18. Diagram of a shielded scintillation detector and focusing collimator for rectilinear scanning.

Figure 22.19. Block diagram of a rectilinear scintillation scanner.

One of the main limitations of the rectilinear scanner is its inability to display momentary changes in radionuclide distribution within the area of interest; in other words, the rectilinear scanner produces only *static* (stationary) images. A different type of imaging system is needed to display not only an entire organ or region at once as a static image but also the deposition and disappearance pattern of a radionuclide over a period of time. Several available devices have been designed to perform dynamic studies, and also shorten the time needed for ordinary static imaging. The *Anger gamma camera,* using a large detector crystal which measures about 15 in. (38 cm) in diameter (ordinary scintillation crystals are 3 or 5 in.), can detect and record simultaneously the radioactivity over a fairly large area, without mechanical scanning. Another such device, the *autofluoroscope,* consists of a bank of many detector crystals. A Polaroid® camera as well as 70-mm and 35-mm roll film, and a Microdot® System, serve to display the scintigram produced by both types of cameras. Note that the term *imaging* rather than scanning should be used for diagnostic studies with these cameras. The recorded image is called a *scintiphoto.*

At present, scanning and imaging are used mainly in the following studies, although new applications are continually under investigation:

1. **Thyroid Gland**—^{131}I or ^{123}I (see page 522) in the form of sodium iodide—for detection of functioning and nonfunctioning nodules, the former being "hot nodules" because they appear dark on the scan or scintiphoto; and the latter being termed "cold nodules" because they appear as light areas in the scan. About 10 to 15 percent of cold nodules turn out to be malignant tumors. Scanning and imaging also show the size, shape and location of the thyroid gland. Technetium 99m as sodium pertechnetate is also used as a thyroid imaging agent.

2. **Brain**—^{99m}Tc DTPA and ^{99m}Tc glucoheptonate (ie, these compounds tagged with technetium 99m) provide a high counting rate, good differential uptake between most lesions and the normal brain, and relatively small radiation dose to the patient. Brain imaging is useful in the detection of tumors (primary and metastatic), subdural hematomas, vascular abnormalities, granulomas, infarcts, and abscesses. In general, brain lesions take up *more* radionuclide than the adjacent normal tissue, so that they appear as darker areas in the image—so-called "hot" areas.

3. **Liver**—several imaging agents are available, of which the most widely used include ^{99m}Tc as a sulfur colloid. Liver imaging is particularly useful in finding not only metastatic and primary neoplasms but also certain degenerative diseases such as cirrhosis. Lesions replacing normal liver tissue usually take up *less* radionuclide and appear lighter than the normal tissue—so-called "cold" areas. Liver scintiphotos also aid in the study of liver function, and in determining the size, shape, and position of this organ.

4. **Kidney**—Hippuran® tagged with ^{131}I is used for the evaluation of renal function, and ^{99m}Tc DTPA and ^{99m}Tc glucoheptonate for renal imaging.

5. **Lung**—macroaggregated serum albumin tagged with ^{99m}Tc (^{99m}TcMAA) provides indirect evidence of pulmonary arterial emboli or thrombosis. The albumin particles are large enough to lodge temporarily in the normal pulmonary capillary bed, thereby indicating that blood is reaching the capillaries. In arterial embolism or thrombosis, capillary perfusion is blocked and the albumin particles do not reach the capillaries, a condition manifested in the scan by a "cold" area. However, differentiation from air cysts as in emphysema, from pleural effusions, and from tumor masses is difficult or impossible. Technetium 99m-tagged albumin microspheres have virtually replaced the above agent in lung imaging, operating on the same principle.

6. **Bone**—^{99m}Tc pyrophosphate or ^{99m}Tc medronate are excellent imaging agents for the skeletal system. Bone imaging has its greatest application in locating metastatic cancer in patients with a known primary lesion, often before there is x-ray evidence of skeletal metastasis. Owing to the incitement of osteoblastic activity by metastatic lesions, they appear as "hot" areas. However, they are not specific for malignant deposits; trauma, infection, Paget's disease and some benign tumors cause sufficient bone reaction to produce a similar image of increased activity.

7. **Miscellaneous**—thallium 201 as thallous chloride is proving to be valuable in imaging the heart to localize myocardial infarcts and determine their extent. Selenium 75 in the compound selenomethionine is being used in the diagnosis of parathyroid tumors. In patients with certain types of thyroid cancer, whole-body imag-

ing should be performed in a search for metastasis after an appropriate dose of iodine 131.

Radionuclides in Therapy

The use of radionuclides in therapy comprises the **internal** and **external** modes of administration. Only a few examples will be given in order to show the potentialities of this important form of treatment.

Internal Therapy with Radionuclides. Radioactive iodine (^{131}I) probably represents the most frequently used radionuclide for internal therapy. Its application is confined to the treatment of hyperthyroidism and certain types of cancer of the thyroid gland.

1. *Hyperthyroidism.* When ^{123}I or ^{131}I studies show overactivity of the thyroid gland—hyperthyroidism—a medical decision must follow as to the therapeutic approach, that is, medical, surgical, or radionuclide. If the latter is selected, a suitable oral dose of ^{131}I produces internal irradiation and partial destruction of functioning thyroid tissue. The dose is much larger than that for diagnosis, usually requiring an activity of about 4 to 8 mCi or more, depending on the type of gland, its size, and the uptake percentage. About 90 percent of the therapeutic effect of ^{131}I results from its beta particles (maximum energy 608 keV) and about 10 percent from its gamma rays (mainly 364 keV).

2. *Thyroid Cancer.* Approximately 10 percent of thyroid cancers have the structure and function that make them amenable to treatment with radioiodine. To stimulate metastatic lesions from thyroid cancer to take up ^{131}I, the gland itself should first be removed surgically or destroyed by a large dose of ^{131}I, provided it can take up enough of the administered dose. This is usually about 150 mCi, and it may have to be repeated one or more times. Because of the high activity and the amount of radionuclide excreted in the urine, stringent radiation safety precautions have to be observed in ^{131}I therapy of thyroid cancer.

External Therapy with Radionuclides. There are two main types: *teletherapy* and *contact therapy.* The former has, by far, the wider application.

1. *Teletherapy.* In this form of therapy, the source-to-surface

distance (SSD), that is, the distance from the source to the center of the treatment field on the skin, is 80 or 100 cm, more commonly the former. The most widely used source material, *^{60}Co,* has a half-life of 5.2 years and emits high energy gamma rays (1.17 and 1.33 MeV, equivalent to about 2 MV x rays). It also emits low energy beta particles which are removed by the steel capsule. The introduction of ^{60}Co therapy marked an important advance in the treatment of deep-seated cancer because the highly penetrating gamma rays (HVL = 11 mm Pb) can provide a large percentage depth dose resulting in relatively little skin reaction. Even greater improvement in depth dose has been achieved with the advent of the linear accelerator (4 to 25 MV). Figure 22.20 shows the comparative isodose curves obtained with a ^{60}Co teletherapy unit and a 4-MV linear accelerator. Note, in particular, the central axis 10-cm depth dose of about 55 percent with ^{60}Co, as contrasted with about 65 percent with 4-MV x rays. Beyond the improved percentage depth dose and skin-sparing effect of ^{60}Co gamma rays and of megavoltage x rays, a third advantage is bone-sparing— equal absorption of high energy photons per gram of bone and soft tissue, thereby reducing the hazard of bone damage.

The ^{60}Co *teletherapy irradiator* consists of pellets or slugs of ^{60}Co doubly encased in stainless steel and mounted in a heavy sphere of lead, tungsten, and uranium alloy to reduce the radiation exposure rate outside the sphere to the permissible value. A window in one side of the sphere, which can be opened or closed by remote control, serves as the port through which the gamma rays can be directed at the patient. Figure 22.21 shows a typical ^{60}Co teletherapy unit. The output of such a unit may be very large; for example, an 8000 rhm source delivers an exposure rate of 8000 R/hr at 1 meter. Such a source consists of about 8000 Ci of ^{60}Co. Because of the nearly monoenergetic gamma rays from this source, filtration is not used except for removal of the beta particles, this being provided by the steel capsule.

Less widely used at present is the ^{137}Cs (radiocesium) irradiator. Since the gamma rays of ^{137}Cs have an energy of 0.66 MeV, as contrasted with an energy of about 1.25 MeV for ^{60}Co, the depth dose is less with the cesium unit. For example, at a depth of 10 cm in tissue, the percentage depth dose with ^{137}Cs is about 25 percent

Figure 22.20. Comparison of isodose curves of cobalt 60 gamma rays and 4-MV linac x rays. Note the larger central axis depth dose with the higher energy 4-MV x rays. An SSD od 80 cm is shown in both cases for comparison, but an SSD of 100 cm is more often used with the 4-MV x-ray beam.

less than with ⁶⁰Co. Furthermore, the specific activity of ¹³⁷Cs, being much lower than that of ⁶⁰Co, requires closer treatment distances to keep the treatment time reasonably short; this further decreases the percentage depth dose. Despite these shortcomings, the ¹³⁷Cs irradiator has been available in some of the larger departments for therapy at intermediate depths.

2. *Contact Therapy.* Strontium 90 (⁹⁰Sr), an artificial radionuclide, is used in contact therapy, that is, with the applicator in direct contact with a superficial lesion. Figure 22.22 shows diagrammatically the construction of an eye irradiator. The radiation emitted by a ⁹⁰Sr applicator consists of beta particles only; their

Figure 22.21. Rotational cobalt 60 teletherapy unit with an isocontour shield. The latter always remains opposite the source during rotation, reducing the amount of protective barrier needed in the walls of the therapy room.

penetrating ability is so poor (av. energy 930 keV) that surface lesions of the front of the eyeball can be treated with a relatively small exposure of the highly sensitive lens. At a depth of 9 mm, the exposure rate becomes almost insignificant. Still, the dose to the lens of the eye may be sufficient to induce cataract formation. The half-life of ^{90}Sr is twenty-eight years. The source itself measures about 5 mm in diameter and is doubly sealed in a stainless steel container, filtered by thin layers of stainless steel and aluminum.

Table 22.2 summarizes the radionuclides most frequently used in medicine. Many others are available for specific purposes, and others may be found, in the future, to be superior to those in use today.

QUESTIONS AND PROBLEMS

1. Define isotope; radioisotope; nuclide; radionuclide; nucleon.
2. What is radioactivity? Artificial radioactivity?

Figure 22.22. Contact strontium 90 applicator.

3. Describe a nuclear reactor, including fission, chain reaction, and control.
4. Discuss the two main methods of producing radioisotopes in the nuclear reactor, with equations showing how ^{32}P and ^{60}Co are obtained. What is the principle source of ^{131}I?
5. Discuss the three types of half-life. State the simple formula for the fraction of a radionuclide remaining after a particular number of half-lives have elapsed.
6. Explain the construction, operation, and use of GM and scintillation counters. Define dead time.
7. Contrast the rate meter and scaler. What is meant by preset timing? Preset counting?
8. Discuss the sources of error in counting.
9. Suppose the gross sample counting rate (including background) to be about 200 cpm, and the background counting rate to be about 50 cpm. How many sample and background counts should be recorded, respectively, to bring about a 5 percent standard deviation in the net counting rate? How long would the sample and the background have to be counted?
10. The counting rate of a sample is 400 cps. If one were to use a GM counter with a recovery time of $2(10)^{-4}$ sec, what would be the counting rate, corrected for dead time? What would this be with a scintillation counter having a recovery time of $(10)^{-6}$ sec?
11. Discuss the efficiency of counters, including sensitivity and minimum detectable activity.

TABLE 22.2
SOME RADIONUCLIDES OF MEDICAL INTEREST

Nuclide	Symbol	Physical Half Life	Main Radiation		Use in Medicine
			$E\gamma$	$E\beta$	
			MeV	*MeV*	
Cesium 137	^{137}Cs	30 years	0.662	0.188	Teletherapy. Needles.
Chromium 51	^{51}Cr	27.8 days	0.320	0.242	Red cell volume and survival.
Cobalt 57	^{57}Co	270 days	0.122	—	Tagged vitamin $B_{12}(^{57}CoB_{12})$ in diagnosis of pernicious anemia.
Cobalt 60	^{60}Co	5.2 years	1.17 1.33	0.096	Teletherapy.
Gold 198	^{198}Au	2.7 days	0.412	0.316	Implant therapy as seeds or grains.
Iodine 123	^{123}I	13.2 hr	0.159	—	Diagnosis of thyroid disorders.
Iodine 131	^{131}I	8.1 days	0.364	0.183	Diagnosis and treatment of thyroid disorders. Localization of thyroid cancer metastases. Renal function test as iodohippurate.
Iron 59	^{59}Fe	45 days	1.10 1.29	0.118	Iron absorption and utilization. Iron appearance time in red cells in study of anemia.
Phosphorus 32	^{32}P	14.3 days	—	0.700	Treatment of polycythemia rubra vera. Treatment of certain metastatic bone tumors (esp. breast and prostate). Malignant pleural and pertioneal effusions.
Selenium 75	^{75}Se	127 days	0.270 0.140	0.011	Parathyroid imaging.
Strontium 90	^{90}Sr	28 years	—	0.196 0.937*	Contact therapy of superficial lesions of eye.
Technetium 99m	^{99m}Tc	6 hours	0.140	0.084	Imaging of brain, thyroid, liver, lung, bone, and kidneys.

$E\gamma$ is energy of principal gamma rays. $E\beta$ is average energy of beta rays.
*Refers to yttrium 90, always associated with strontium 90.

12. Explain the geometric factors in counting.
13. Name and explain the two principal methods of counting.

14. State the three basic procedures in medical radionuclide diagnosis, and cite examples of each.
15. State important facts about the radionuclides that are useful in medical diagnosis; therapy.
16. Discuss the application of radionuclides in diagnosis and therapy.

CHAPTER *23* *PROTECTION IN RADIOLOGY–HEALTH PHYSICS*

T HE HARMFUL EFFECTS of exposure to ionizing radiation were largely unsuspected at the time of the discovery of x rays and radium. However, the pioneer workers in this field soon recognized the injurious potentiality of such radiation. It is therefore surprising that so many of the early radiologists and technicians carelessly exposed themselves to x rays and radium, incurring serious local and general radiation injuries, which all to often resulted in death.

In the intervening years we have learned a great deal about radiation hazards and their prevention. As a result, protective measures have become ever more stringent, especially with the extensive use of radionuclides in medicine and industry, and nuclear reactors in the generation of electric power.

Every radiologic technologist should own and read the following *National Council on Radiation Protection and Measurements (NCRP) Reports,* obtainable from NCRP Publications, 7910 Woodmont Ave. Suite 1016, Bethesda, MD 20814:

No.
24 *Protection Against Radiations from Sealed Gamma Sources (1960).*
30 *Safe Handling of Radioactive Materials (1964).*
33 *Medical X-ray and Gamma-ray Protection for Energies up to 10 MeV—Equipment Design and Use (1968).*
34 *Medical X-ray and Gamma-ray Protection for Energies up to 10 MeV—Structural Shielding Design and Evaluation (1970).*
37 *Precautions in the Management of Patients Who Have Received Therapeutic Amounts of Radionuclides (1970).*
39 *Basic Radiation Protection Criteria (1971).*

40 *Protection Against Radiation from Brachytherapy Sources (1972).*
53 *Review of NCRP radiation Dose Limit for Embryo and Fetus in Occupationally Exposed Women (1977).*
66 *Mammography (1980).*

Other valuable booklets published by the U.S. Department of Health, Education, and Welfare, Bureau of Radiological Health, Rockville, MD 20852, include:

Gonadal Shielding in Diagnostic Radiology (1974).
Handbook of Selected Organ Doses for Projections Common in Diagnostic Radiology, No. 76-8031 (1976).

The most recent official requirements for radiographic equipment are included in the following publication, obtainable from Superintendent of Documents, U.S. Government Printing Office, Washington, DC 20402:

Code of Federal Regulations 21 (April 1, 1983).

What is the "safe" limit of exposure to radiation? It is doubtful whether any amount of radiation is really safe. However, an attempt will be made to answer this question on the basis of acceptable exposure limits, as well as to point out what steps can be taken to eliminate the risk of overexposure. The subject of protection or **health physics** will be taken up principally as it affects the **radiologic technologist** and the **patient.** A brief summary of electrical hazards in the Radiology Department will be included. Attention will also be directed to the use of radium and artificial radionuclides.

BACKGROUND RADIATION

A sensitive radiation detector, such as a GM counter, will indicate the presence of environmental ionizing radiation even in the absence of all known sources, such as radium, x rays, and radioactive nuclides. As it turns out, man has virtually no control over environmental radiation, which we call **natural background radiation,** and to which all matter, living and nonliving, is continuously exposed.

Natural background includes not only external sources of radiation, but also radioactive materials located within the body and even the detector itself. Let us survey the sources of natural background radiation, which may be classified as *external* and *internal.*

1. *External sources* comprise three categories. The first is the *cosmic rays,* which are of two types. The *primary cosmic rays,* arising in the sun and other stars, consist mainly of high energy protons (more than 2.5 billion electron volts), but also include alpha particles, atomic nuclei, and high energy electrons and photons. *Secondary cosmic rays* are produced by interaction of primary cosmic rays with nuclei in the earth's atmosphere and consist mainly of mesons (a type of nuclear particle), electrons, and gamma rays. Most cosmic rays observed in the laboratory are of the secondary type. They are so penetrating that they can pass through lead many meters thick.

A second external source of background radiation includes the *naturally radioactive minerals* within the earth. These occur in minute amounts almost everywhere in the earth's crust, including building materials, and in larger amounts where the minerals of uranium, thorium, and actinium have been deposited. It must be emphasized that terrestrial (earthly) background radiation varies from place to place; for example, in Kerala, India, it is about twenty times greater than that in most parts of the United States.

A third external source includes the radionuclides produced by interaction of cosmic rays with nuclides in the earth's atmosphere. The main products are carbon 14 and hydrogen 3 (tritium) resulting from capture of slow cosmic-ray neutrons by stable atmospheric nitrogen; and krypton 81 from a similar reaction with stable krypton.

2. *Internal sources* comprise the naturally radioactive nuclides incorporated in the tissues of the body, and in the materials of which the detector itself is constructed. The main naturally radioactive nuclides are potassium 40, carbon 14, and strontium 90.

To the natural background radiation must be added the *artificial radiation* arising from the following sources: medical and dental x rays; occupational, such as x-ray, radium, and radionuclide technology; environs of atomic energy plants; and atomic bomb

542   *The Fundamentals of X-ray and Radium Physics*

fallout. In contrast to natural background, man can exercise some measure of control over exposure to artificial sources.

Table 23.1 summarizes the average exposures of the general population of the United States on an annual basis as to the site of exposure, dose per exposed person, and the prorated exposure to the population as a whole (based on report fo Bureau of Radiological Health (HEW/FDA 1970). Obviously, the concern with these small exposures is with genetic effects appearing in future generations from damage to the reproductive cells, and with injury to the bone marrow. Bear in mind that these data are approximate and do not necessarily apply to a particular individual.

THE MAXIMUM PERMISSIBLE DOSE EQUIVALENT

It is obvious that a standard upper limit should be established for individuals exposed to ionizing radiations. This standard, the *maximum permissible dose equivalent (MPD)* may be defined *as the maximum dose of ionizing radiation which an individual may accumulate over a long period of time, or in a single exposure, and which carries a negligible risk of significant bodily or genetic damage.* It should be emphasized that the MPD is based on the balancing of risks versus benefits of radiation exposure.

As applied to technologists, radiologists, and other radiation workers, the *lifetime accumulated occupational MPD from x, gamma, or beta radiation to the whole body and to certain radiosensitive organs*—gonads, blood forming organs, lens of the eye, head, and trunk—shall not exceed

$$MPD = 5(N - 18) R \qquad (1)$$

where N is the attained age in years and is greater than 18. Strictly speaking, the dose unit should be the rem which will be discussed below. Since the R, rad, and rem do not differ much numerically in the case of x and gamma rays, we may use the R for protection surveys in radiology.

The MPD is actually a prospective exposure limit in that it sets the limit for future exposures. Thus, based on equation (1), the MPD for one week is 100 mR (0.1 R), and for one year 5 R. A cumulative exposure of 3 R is allowed in any 13-week period. The

TABLE 23.1
ANNUAL DOSE RATES FROM IMPORTANT SIGNIFICANT SOURCES
OF RADIATION EXPOSURE IN THE U.S. (*BEIR 1980*).

Source	Exposed Group	Body Portion Exposed	Average Dose (exposed persons)	Prorated over Population
			mrems/yr	mrems/yr
NATURAL BACKGROUND				
cosmic radiation	total population	whole body	28	28
terrestrial radiation	total population	whole body	26	26
internal sources	total population	gonads	28	28
		bone marrow	24	24
		Total (rounded)	80	80
MEDICAL X RAYS				
Patients				
medical diagnosis	adults	bone marrow	100	77
dental diagnosis	adults	bone marrow	3	1.4
		Total (rounded)	103	78
Personnel (occupational)				
medical	adults	whole body	320	0.3
dental	adults	whole body	80	0.05
RADIOPHARMACEUTICALS				
*Patients (diagnosis)**	adults	bone marrow	300	13.6
Personnel	adults	whole body	300	0.1
ATMOSPHERIC WEAPONS TESTING	total population	whole body	4-5	4-5

*The Environmental Protection Agency (Report ORP/CDS 72-1) estimates the exposure of patients during nuclear medicine procedures to be about 20 percent of the total radiation exposure in medical diagnosis.

hands and feet may receive as much as 75 R per year, but not over 25 R in any 13-week period (see Figure 23.1). If the exposure exceeds the prorated value of 1.25 R in any 13-week period, such exposure plus additional exposure during that year must be limited to 5 R. Note again that these limits apply only to radiation workers exposed to x or gamma rays.

Returning to equation (1), let us see how it applies in a specific case. What is the maximum cumulative whole body exposure permitted for a radiologic technologist who is 32 years

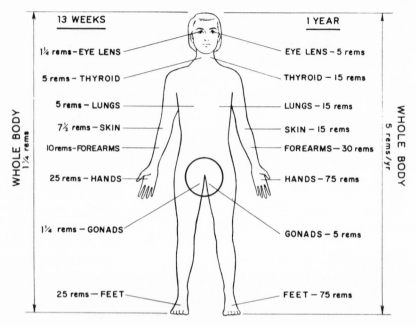

Figure 23.1. Maximum permissible dose equivalents (MPD) to various organs and to the whole body of radiation workers, for thirteen weeks (left column) and for one year (right column).

old? Applying equation (1) we find the MPD to be

$$5\,(32 - 18) = 70\ \text{R}$$

Note that the radiation exposure of x-ray personnel for their own diagnosis or therapy is *not* included in computing the MPD.

Table 23.2 summarizes the whole body MPDs for individuals under various conditions. Note that for occasional nonmedical exposure, and for limited populations, the MPD is one-tenth the occupational MPD. For the general nonmedical population the MPD is **5 R per generation** (30 yr), or 0.17 R per year. The MPD for occupationally exposed women has been arbitrarily set at 0.5 R for the entire duration of pregnancy (period of gestation). It must be emphasized that the quoted MPDs are maximum guidelines, and that exposures should be kept as far below these values as possible. This is known as the ALARA concept: "*as low as reasonably achievable.*"

TABLE 23.2
NONMEDICAL WHOLE BODY MAXIMUM PERMISSIBLE
DOSE EQUIVALENTS (MPDs) FOR INDIVIDUALS
UNDER VARIOUS CONDITIONS

Condition	MPD
	rem/yr
Occupational	5
Limited Population	0.5
General Population	0.17
Pregnancy (Occupational)	0.5 (duration of pregnancy)

MPD may be stated in terms of exposure in R for x, gamma, and beta radiation, which, for protection purposes only, is numerically the same as dose in rads. This holds because equal absorbed doses of these three types of radiation produce virtually the same effects in the tissues. However, to produce a given effect in tissues, a smaller absorbed dose (rads) is required with heavy particles, such as alpha particles and neutrons, than with x rays. Thus, *one rad of alpha particles or fast neutrons produces a greater tissue effect than one rad of x rays,* and it would therefore be incorrect to add the absorbed doses of such different kinds of radiation in arriving at the total MPD. To express on a common scale, for protection purposes only, the irradiation incurred by exposed persons for all types of radiation, the ICRU has introduced the quantity *dose equivalent* (*DE*). By definition, the *DE* is the product of the absorbed dose and appropriate modifying factors which depend on the particular radiation hazard involved. For our purposes, we need to consider the *quality factor* (*QF*) only. Thus,

$$DE = absorbed\ dose \times QF \qquad (2)$$
$$\text{rems} = \quad\quad \text{rads} \quad\quad \times QF$$

By introducing the appropriate value of *QF* in the equation we can convert rads to rems. The unit of *DE* is the **rem,** and the value of *QF* varies with the type of radiation. For x rays, gamma rays, and beta particles, *QF* has been arbitrarily assigned the value 1. Therefore

$$DE = \text{absorbed dose} \times 1$$

$$DE = 1\ \text{rad} \times 1 = 1\ \text{rem}$$
or, 1 rad = 1 rem *for x, beta, and gamma rays*

As indicated above, we may use R in place of rad for x, beta, and gamma radiation in protection surveys, but it is preferable to express organ dose in rads, as explained below (see pages 558–569). On the other hand, the *QF* for fast neutrons is 10; for example, 1 rad of fast neutrons is ten times as effective as 1 rad of x rays in producing cataract in the lens of the eye. Conversely, it takes ten times more rads of x rays than neutrons to produce the same effect. Therefore,

$$DE = \text{absorbed dose} \times 10$$
$$= 1\ \text{rad} \times 10 = 10\ \text{rems}$$
or, 1 rad = 10 rems *for fast neutrons*

This means that with fast neutrons, 1 rad gives a *DE* of 10 rems insofar as cataract induction is concerned. The *QF* for alpha particles is 20, so that 1 rad of this radiation gives a *DE* of 20 rems.

The rems of different kinds of radiation are equivalent (*DE*) and can be added. For example, if an individual were exposed to a mixture of radiations and received 1 rad from x rays, 1 rad from fast neutrons, and 1 rad from alpha particles, the total absorbed dose would be 3 rads. However, this would seriously underestimate the radiation hazard. By converting these doses to *dose equivalents,* we would obtain:

x rays	1 rad ×	1 =	1 rem
fast neutrons	1 rad ×	10 =	10 rems
alpha particles	1 rad ×	20 =	20 rems
		total	31 rems

Thus, the dose equivalent, in this case 31 rems, provides a more realistic measure of the radiation hazard when the quality factor is different from 1. However, under ordinary conditions in the Radiology Department exposure is limited to radiation with a quality factor of 1 so that the MPD may be stated in rads, or even in roentgens because 1 R is numerically equal to about 1 rad.

PERSONNEL PROTECTION FROM EXPOSURE TO X RAYS

Let us now turn to the problems associated with the *occupational* exposure of x-ray personnel, under three main headings:

1. Determination of radiation safety in the Radiology Department, called *radiation monitoring.*
2. Deleterious effects to the individual resulting from excessive exposure.
3. Protective shielding of radiographic and radiotherapeutic installations.

Radiation Monitoring. In the Radiology Department we can monitor whole-body exposure without special equipment or training (a qualified health physicist can do this more precisely, but not ordinarily required). Several devices are available. The most sensitive instrument, the *pocket dosimeter,* outwardly resembles a fountain pen but contains a thimble ionization chamber at one end. The exposure may be read by means of a separate electrometer; or, in the self-reading type, by means of a built-in electrometer. A dosimeter of this type, while sensitive to exposures up to 0.2 R (200 milliroentgens), is easily damaged and is unreliable in inexperienced hands. Besides, it does not provide a permanent record.

The *film badge* offers the most convenient method of personnel monitoring under average conditions. Commercial laboratories specialize in furnishing and servicing the film badges. The x-ray film badge consists of a dental film, covered by a copper and plastic filter to show the quality of the radiation, and allow conversion to tissue dose. The film is backed by a sheet of lead foil to absorb scattered radiation from behind the badge. It is usually worn on the clothing over the front of the hip or chest, but during fluoroscopy it should be worn at the neck, clipped to top of the front of the apron, to monitor exposure of the thyroid gland and eyes. Pregnant personnel should wear a second badge over the abdomen beneath the leaded apron during fluoroscopy and mobile radiography.

The laboratory regularly supplies a fresh badge, which, after being worn for the prescribed interval (usually one month), is returned to the laboratory for processing under standard conditions. Dosimetric comparison is then made with standard films exposed to known amounts of radiation. The resulting film exposure in roentgens is reported to the Radiology Department for permanent filing. Badges should never be exchanged among personnel and should be clearly marked for identification. With exposure levels well below the weekly MPD (0.1 R), the film badge should be worn and returned *monthly,* especially if the work load is reasonably constant. The one-month period is preferred because of convenience and greater accuracy of calibration.

Another kind of personnel monitor, the *thermoluminescent dosimeter* (TLD), depends on the ability of certain crystalline materials to store energy on exposure to ionizing radiation because of the trapping of valence electrons in crystal lattice defects. When the crystals are heated under strictly controlled conditions, the electrons return to their normal state, the stored energy being released in the form of light. Measurement of the light by a photomultiplier device gives a measure of the initial radiation exposure, since the two are very nearly proportional. The dosimeters should be returned to a commercial laboratory for readout, unless this can be done accurately on the premises. Lithium fluoride (LiF) is at present the most prevalent material for TLD. The many advantages of TLD over film badge monitoring include: (1) detectors are cheap and small—for example, 1 mm × 6 mm—and can be sealed in Teflon® to avoid mechanical damage, (2) direct reading available at any time, (3) response to radiation proportional up to about 400 R, (4) response almost independent of radiation energy from 50 kV to 20 MV (film badge is not), (5) response very similar to that of human tissues, (6) wide exposure range detectable—1 mR to 1,000 R, (7) accuracy about ±5 percent (film badge accurate to about ±50 percent, (8) feasibility of incorporating detector in jewelry to make it unobtrusive. For these reasons, it seems likely that the TLD will eventually become the method of choice in personnel monitoring.

On termination of employment all technologists must receive an appropriate summary of occupational exposure, regardless of the monitoring system. If reemployed, the technologist should present this summary report to the new employer.

Harmful Effects of Radiation. Why has health physics become so important in radiology? The answer lies in the fact that radiation is always harmful to tissues, the amount and nature of any damage being dependent on radiation quality (LET), absorbed dose, size and location of the treated region, and fractionation or number of days over which the treatment is administered. It is the differential damage to a given type of tumor as compared with that to normal tissues that underlies successful irradiation therapy. The term *therapeutic ratio* has been applied to the ratio of the dose the normal tissues can tolerate, to the dose needed to destroy the tumor. Remember that the therapeutic exposure of patients is a matter quite different from the small exposure that technologists may receive over a prolonged period of time. The latter problem concerns us here. *The objective of a program in health physics is to keep the exposure of personnel as far as possible below the maximum permissible level to avoid the slightest radiation injury.* But suppose overexposure is incurred; what sort of harmful effects may be anticipated? These are three in number: *local, general, and genetic.*

1. *Local Effects.* Small occupational exposures should not cause local changes in the skin. Several hundred rads of low energy x rays are required to produce erythema (skin reddening), but such a dose would be very unlikely except in a therapy patient. However, even with very small exposures repeated over a period of years, late irradiation effects may occur in the form of dry skin, which is subject to cracking, ulceration, and possible cancer induction. Another harmful effect is cataract (opacity) formation in the highly radiosensitive lens of the eye by an exposure of a few hundred rads.

2. *General Effects.* Whole body exposure to x or gamma radiation always entails the possibility of harmful effects. The blood-forming organs (bone marrow and lymphatic tissues) are especially susceptible. No certainty exists as to the presence of a threshold; that is, a minimum level of exposure below which there is no damage, and above which damage abruptly appears. Such *a threshold or lower limit has not been demonstrated.* We know that an absorbed dose of as little as 5 to 25 rads to the whole body in one exposure can produce chromosomal abnormalities; and in some individuals, a dose of 50 to 75 rads may cause detectable changes in the blood picture. Lymphocytes, leucocytes, and platelets are

most susceptible, in that order. Small doses to a large part of the body increase slightly the chance of inducing leukemia.

Evidence in laboratory animals indicates that chronic exposure to radiation causes *shortening of life span,* increasing in severity with increasing exposure. Statistical studies have failed to show conclusively a similar effect in humans.

Exposure during *pregnancy* is especially hazardous to the *conceptus* (embryo or fetus). Maximum sensitivity to the conceptus occurs during the *first trimester* (three months) of pregnancy, wherein an absorbed dose of the order of 10 rads may increase the incidence of congenital anomalies. Sensitivity to radiation gradually decreases beyond this period but never reaches zero. Therefore, radiologic procedures should be kept at a minimum consistent with medical necessity, particularly during the early months. Total exposure of the fetus throughout the period of gestation (pregnancy) shall not exceed 0.5 rem (0.5 R of x or gamma rays) and should, in fact, be as far below this level as possible.

Not likely to be encountered in the Radiology Department are the serious damaging effects produced by *acute whole body exposure to large amounts of radiation*—in the range of 100 to 1000 R or more to the whole body. Such exposures are more apt to occur accidentally in atomic energy installations and give rise to the *acute radiation syndromes.* Their severity depends on the size of the exposure. A *supralethal exposure* of about 600 to 1000 R to the whole body causes the "gastrointestinal" form of the acute radiation syndrome, consisting of nausea, vomiting, and prostration within one or two hours, followed by step-like rising fever. There is associated loss of appetite, intractable diarrhea, dehydration, and profound drop in the white blood count. Hemorrhages occur in the skin and intestinal tract, terminating in death from sepsis in one to two weeks. However, intensive treatment with transfusions, fluids, antibiotics, and bone marrow transplants from compatible donors make it possible for the victim to recover.

With a *midlethal exposure* of about 450 R the effects are somewhat less pronounced, about one-half the exposed individuals dying in one month from pancytopenia; this comprises the "bone marrow" form of the acute radiation syndrome. With a *sublethal exposure* of 100 to 300 R there may be mild nausea, vomiting, and malaise lasting about twelve to twenty-four hours. After a latent period of about three to five weeks, loss of hair occurs, although it usually regrows. There is a drop in all of the blood cell counts, and many individuals develop cataracts in two to six years. Most recover, but some enter a chronic stage, remaining feeble and anemic for months. Statistically, there is an increased incidence of leukemia in the survivors—about three to five times that in the unexposed population, as found in the survivors of the atomic bombing of Hiroshima and Nagasaki in World War II.

3. *Genetic Effects.* A serious problem associated with exposure to radiation is the *genetic hazard,* that is, the appearance of abnormalities in future generations. This results from the extreme vulnerability of the genetic material—*genes*—(particularly in the chromosomes of the sex cells) to radiation damage. There is no known safe lower limit of dosage, the damage being approximately proportional to the absorbed dose. Because of the transmission of genetic material to offspring during reproduction, it is obvious that any radiation-damaged genetic material will be similarly handed down. This becomes especially serious when large populations are exposed individually or in groups, so we must shield the gonads (ovaries and testicles) during diagnostic procedures whenever possible. Radiation damage to the genetic material is expressed as *chromosome aberrations* and *gene mutations.* The latter, being recessive, tend to be hidden by pairing with normal genes during reproduction, only to become manifest in subsequent generations. Many such mutants die very early in pregnancy and therefore never appear. Insofar as technologists are concerned, they are not subject to appreciable genetic damage if whole-body exposure remains well below the maximum permissible.

With careful monitoring, the likelihood of incurring radiation injury is virtually nonexistent. When, under *unusual* circumstances, damage to the blood-forming organs is suspected, corrective steps should be taken immediately. First, the affected individual should be removed from further exposure to ionizing radiation. Second, a trained health physicist should survey the Radiology Department and recommended the best means of eliminating the hazardous conditions. However, it must be emphasized here that even under suitably controlled conditions, each technologist must observe certain rules of conduct. In other words **even in the best controlled department, the technologist may incur overexposure, unless full use is always made of all available protective facilities.**

PROTECTIVE BARRIERS IN RADIOGRAPHIC
AND RADIOTHERAPEUTIC INSTALLATIONS

Radiation Sources. All x-ray tubes must be of rayproof type; that is, the manufacturer must enclose the tubes in a metal housing that reduces leakage radiation to a prescribed safe level. (Leakage radiation is that radiation which penetrates the protective housing.) The specifications for such protective enclosures are given in *NCRP Report #33.* Leakage radiation for the average *radiographic tube* shall not exceed an average value of 100 mR/hr at 1 meter, the required shielding being about 1.5 mm (about $1/16$ in.) lead. With *orthovoltage x-ray therapy tubes* (150 to 300 kV), the exposure rate from leakage radiation shall not exceed 1 R/hr at 1 meter. In addition to protective housing, the same report includes specifications governing collimation, exposure timers, filter systems, shielding of the patient, and other items.

Radioactive sources used in *teletherapy*—cobalt 60 and cesium 137—must be doubly sealed in stainless steel and leak-tested by the manufacturer, who must provide a certificate attesting to the absence of leakage. Thereafter, a qualified person must conduct leak tests every six months (this also includes semiannual leakage tests for sealed radium sources such as needles and tubes, and for strontium 90 eye applicators). A leak test for radioactive sources is performed by carefully wiping the collimator bars and edges of the final collimator aperture with a long-handled cotton applicator moistened with dilute detergent solution. The swab can either be sent in a special container to a commercial laboratory, or tested by the method of Rose—the cotton is held near the unshielded window of a GM survey meter (30 mg/cm^2 window). Any increase over background counting rate detected with earphones indicates a minimum leak of 10^{-9} Ci. A leak only ten times as great, that is, 10^{-8} Ci, will give thousands of counts per min and kick the indicator needle off the scale. When this occurs, the equipment must be promptly checked by a health physicist or other qualified person. Radium needles and tubes as well as strontium 90 applicators can be tested in the same way. In addition, radium needles and tubes should be placed in a stoppered test tube together with activated charcoal for twenty-four hours, after which time the charcoal is tested as above by Rose's method. Leaking needles must be returned promptly in adequately shielded, unbreakable sealed containers to the supplier for repair.

Wall Protection. This requires the use of built-in *protective barriers* of suitable radiation-absorbing material(s) to reduce radiation exposure to the permissible level. Wall protection should be planned in advance by a radiation physicist qualified in this field, to avoid expensive alteration after completion of the building; poor planning may result in excessive wall protection, which becomes unnecessarily expensive. However, it costs relatively little to reduce the exposure rate to 10 mR/week (ie, to 1/10 the present occupational MPD); many authorities recommend this degree of protection. A basic principle in permanent barriers is that joints and holes must be covered by the same or equivalent protective barrier as the wall. Proper wall protection varies with the *energy of the radiation* modified by certain factors described in *NCRP report #33*.

Terms that often apply to wall protection are "controlled" and "uncontrolled" areas. A *controlled area* is one that is under the supervision of the Radiation Safety Officer; an *uncontrolled area* is not.

There are four main types of radiation to consider in radiation protection:

Useful beam is the radiation passing through the tube aperture and the beam-limiting device, previously called the primary beam.

Leakage radiation includes all the radiation passing through the tube housing, other than the useful beam.

Scattered radiation is that which has undergone a change in direction during passage through matter.

Stray radiation is the sum of scattered and leakage radiation.

There are two kinds of wall barriers. A *primary protective barrier* is one whose atomic number and thickness suffice to reduce the exposure rate of the useful beam to the MPD. A *secondary protective barrier* is one whose atomic number and thickness suffice to reduce the exposure rate of the stray radiation to the MPD.

We may conveniently discuss wall protection in (1) radiography, (2) orthovoltage therapy, and (3) megavoltage therapy. Exact wall barrier thicknesses may be obtained for any particular installation from appropriate publications (*NCRP Report #34*) and with the aid of a *qualified expert*. However, we shall give an estimate of the type of barrier ordinarily needed in each general area.

1. *Radiography.* As a general rule, the **primary protective barrier**, that is, where the useful beam can hit the wall **directly**, in radiography up to 140 kV should consist of $1/16$ in. lead (Pb) extending 7 ft up from the floor when the x-ray tube is 5 to 7 ft from the wall. This barrier also takes care of leakage radiation, that is, radiation coming through the tube housing. A **secondary protective barrier** (covering areas exposed only to scattered and leakage radiation) requires $1/32$ in. Pb under the same operating conditions. This secondary barrier extends from the top of the primary barrier to the ceiling, but should overlap the primary barrier at least $1/2$ in. at the seam. Ordinary plaster often suffices as a secondary barrier without added lead, especially in large radiographic rooms. Control booths should have the same protection as walls, and radiation should scatter at least **twice** before reaching the opening of the booth.

2. *Orthovoltage X-ray Therapy* (200 to 300 kV range). A primary protective barrier of about $3/8$ to $1/2$ in. Pb should extend 7 ft up from the floor. The secondary barrier of $1/8$ in. Pb should overlap the primary barrier about $1/2$ in. and extend to the ceiling.

Shielding of the floor and ceiling in the above two types of installations depends strongly on beam energy and other factors, and must be determined in advance by a qualified expert.

The leaded glass observation port should have the same lead equivalent as the adjacent wall and should be overlapped about $1/2$ in. by the lead in the wall. Leaded glass must ordinarily be about four times as thick as sheet lead for equivalent protection; for example, 1 in. leaded glass is equivalent to $1/4$ in. sheet lead.

In wall construction, an economical material is the laminated lead building block. Another, possibly less expensive, method is to nail sheet lead with lead-headed nails between double studs placed flatwise. With a required lead thickness of $1/8$ in. or more, application is much easier and cheaper in multiple layers of 1/16 in. because this thickness can be cut with suitable shears and can be lifted more readily. One-eighth inch lead must be chiseled and is difficult to lift because of its weight. Furthermore, it is much easier to overlap 1/16-in. Pb at seams and joints.

3. *Megavoltage Therapy* (1 to 25 million volt range). Concrete with a density of 2.35 g/cc (147 lb/cu ft) is an economical wall material here because it provides both adequate shielding and structural strength. Only approximate values of thickness will be given—accurate planning in advance by a qualified expert is imperative. In the average cobalt 60 installation about 1 meter (3 ft) or more of concrete of the above density may serve as the primary barrier, and about 0.6 meter (2 ft) as the secondary barrier. This will vary, of course, with the energy and direction of the beam, size of the source, and other protective factors. Thus, for 6-MV x rays (linear accelerator) about two meters (7 ft) of high density concrete is needed for the primary barrier. *Leakage radiation* is important, since the housing for cobalt 60 provides only relative protection and the radioactive source radiates continuously. The exposure rate from leakage radiation must be added to that from scattered radiation (ie, the *stray radiation*) in calculating wall thickness for the secondary barrier. Radiation that has been scattered twice is usually reduced to a permissible level by a barrier of 1/4 in. Pb, but this needs verification. The best method of watching the patient during megavoltage therapy is closed circuit television.

WORKING CONDITIONS

Certain general rules govern personnel safety. These should be impressed repeatedly on all Radiology Department personnel, since their cooperation is mandatory.

1. Never expose a human for demonstration purposes alone.
2. Never remain in a radiographic or radiotherapy room while an exposure is in progress. In general, approximately 0.1 percent of the useful beam is scattered perpendicular to the beam at a distance of 1 meter from the patient.
3. Never hold a patient for therapy, because of the high inten-

sity of the scattered radiation. Patients should *rarely* be held for radiography, since many efficient devices are available, in addition to the technologist's ingenuity. However, if a patient must be held for radiography, this should preferably be done by a person not habitually exposed to ionizing radiation; in any case, protection by a lead apron and lead gloves is mandatory.

4. Give yourself the same protection as a loaded cassette!

5. In *fluoroscopy*, personnel protection is extremely important and you should be sure that the following items are available and in use:

a. A *protective drape* having a lead (Pb) equivalent of at least 0.25 mm, or preferably 0.5 mm, situated between the fluoroscopic assembly and the fluoroscopist to block scattered radiation, mainly from the patient.

b. A *protective apron* to be worn by personnel in the fluoroscopy room. This apron must have a Pb equivalent of at least 0.25 mm, or preferably 0.5 mm. When not actually assisting the radiologist, stand either in the control booth or behind the radiologist.

c. A *lead shield* at least 0.25 mm thick covering the *Bucky slot* to give additional protection to the personnels' gonads from scattered radiation.

d. Special precautions against the increased scattered radiation engendered by large format image intensifiers (12 in. × 12 in. or larger).

6. Check *lead-protective gloves* (same Pb requirements as for aprons) periodically for cracks by means of a radiographic test using medium speed intensifying screens and exposure factors of 100 kV and 10 mAs at a 40-in. (100 cm) distance. With 400-speed film-screen combinations the mAs should be reduced to 2.5.

7. When on duty, always wear a film badge or TLD monitor as explained on pages 547–548.

PROTECTION SURVEYS

The evaluation of actual or potential exposure hazards in radiology requires periodic protection surveys. A complete survey must be made *initially* by a *qualified expert*, then repeated after any change in conditions that might affect exposure of personnel. If more shielding is indicated, the area should be resurveyed after installation of the additional barrier. This situation may arise, for example, in replacing a cobalt 60 source by one of higher activity, or by a linear accelerator.

If, in the opinion of the qualified expert, there is reasonable probability that a person in a controlled or uncontrolled area may receive more than 10 mR (0.01 R) in one week, then one or more of the following steps should be taken:

1. Determine the cumulative dose in the area in question.

2. Use personnel monitoring in the area in question.

3. Add barrier material to comply with authoritative recommendations in *NCRP Report #34*.

4. Impose restrictions on the use of the equipment, or on the direction of the beam.

5. Impose restrictions on the occupancy of the area if this is controlled.

A tissue-equivalent phantom such as piled sheets of Masonite™ or plastic must be used as a source of scattered radiation to check the safety of the secondary barrier.

All "on-off" control mechanisms (control panel, entrance door, emergency cutoff switch) should be checked semiannually and repaired if necessary.

Warning signs must be posted in a prominent place in the appropriate areas as follows:

a. **CAUTION RADIATION AREA** sign in area where prevailing exposure rate is more than 5 mR/hr but less than 100 mR/hr.

b. **CAUTION HIGH RADIATION AREA** sign at entrance to any area in which the exposure rate is 100 mR/hr.

c. **CAUTION RADIOACTIVE MATERIAL** where the activity exceeds a specified level— ^{131}I, 10 μCi; ^{32}P, 100 μCi; ^{60}Co, 10 μCi.

Whenever any restriction has been placed on the equipment, such as limitation of beam angulation to prevent penetration of a secondary barrier by the useful beam, the specified restriction must be enforced.

All reports of calibrations and surveys should be made in writing, signed by the qualified expert, and filed **permanently.** The report should indicate whether a resurvey is needed, and when.

Electrical power to megavoltage equipment must be **locked in the "off" position** when equipment is not in use.

Instructions must be posted conspicuously in the control area describing the steps to be taken in the event equipment cannot be turned off.

The name, address, and phone number of the Radiation Safety Officer should be posted in a conspicuous place in the control area for prompt service in the event of an emergency. A responsible substitute should be available, on call, if the Radiation Safety Officer cannot be reached.

PROTECTION OF THE PATIENT IN DIAGNOSTIC RADIOLOGY

All x-ray exposures, regardless of how small they may be, entail some degree of risk to the patient. In other words, there is no threshold dose for radiation injury. However, this should not deter us from using x rays for diagnostic purposes when medically indicated; you must keep in mind the benefit/risk ratio in each case, although as a technologist you have no control over the ordering of x-ray examinations. At the same time, you should continually strive to minimize patient exposure; this is especially important in fertile women who may unknowingly be in the first trimester of pregnancy.

Because of the urgency of protecting the general public from unnecessary radiation, the U.S. Congress in 1968 passed the Radiation Control for Health and Safety Act which set up the Bureau of Radiological Health (BRH) under the Food and Drug Administration (FDA). The BRH has the responsibility, through its five divisions, of (1) establishing manufacturing standards for all x-ray-producing electronic equipment, (2) following up on compliance with these standards, (3) studying the biologic effects of radiation, (4) developing programs for training and medical applications, and (5) overseeing the field of radioactive materials and nuclear medicine.

In 1964, and again in 1970, the BRH surveyed a number of

installations to find possible trends in the exposure of patients
during diagnostic radiologic procedures. The results of these surveys are summarized in Table 23.3. Note the 20 percent increase
in the utilization of diagnostic x rays during the six-year interval.
Also, while the mean ratio of the beam area to the film area has
shown a significant decrease of 30 percent, the average skin
exposure for a plain radiograph of the abdomen has increased by
25 percent! According to the later survey, the average skin exposure for a posteroanterior radiograph of the chest is about 30 mR
(0.03 R), and for an anteroposterior radiograph of the abdomen
about 600 mR (0.6 R).

TABLE 23.3
SELECTED RESULTS OF THE X-RAY EXPOSURE STUDIES
OF THE BUREAU OF RADIOLOGICAL HEALTH

	1964	*1970*	*Change*
# having 1 or more examinations	108×10^6	130×10^6	+20%
# radiographs per examination	2.2	2.4	+10%
mean ratio of beam area to film area	1.9	1.2	−30%
av. skin exposure per film (AP or PA abdomen)	480 mR	620 mR	+25%
av. skin exposure per film (PA chest)	28 mR	27 mR	0
genetically significant dose per year	16 mrads	20 mrads	+25%

Because of possible genetic damage, gonadal exposure must be
minimized by appropriate beam limitation (collimation), filtration,
protective Pb shielding, and high speed film-screen imaging systems.
Rare earth screens have contributed much the the reduction of
gonadal as well as whole-body exposure of patients.

The last line in Table 23.3 shows that the genetically significant
dose (GSD) has increased about 25 percent, to 20 mrads per year,
between the two surveys. The GSD is the quotient of the total
gonadal dose received in diagnostic radiology by all fertile individuals in the population, divided by the total population, and corrected
by the average number of expected offspring.

Under the Radiation Control for Health and Safety Act, standards for medical x-ray equipment went into effect on August 1, 1974. Of major importance is the recommendation that the components of a diagnostic x-ray unit must, together, make up an integrated system. Furthermore, the manufacturer must test and adjust the equipment at the factory as the final step in the production line. Finally, the installers of the equipment must follow closely the manufacturers' instructions. Some of the more significant of the numerous specifications include:

1. Ability of the equipment to reproduce an exposure for any permissible combination of kV, mA, and time.

2. Proportionality between exposure and time.

3. Provision of automatic collimation for each film size in stationary equipment.

4. Automatic collimation of the fluoroscopic beam at the patient's entrance port, for spotfilm radiography.

5. Built-in filtration to remove radiation that is too soft to be radiographically useful.

Patient Protection in Radiography

We must emphasize that every effort should be directed toward minimizing exposure of the patient during radiologic examinations, especially to the gonads and the pregnant uterus, because of the danger of inducing injury to the genetic material or embryo. Protection can be achieved by lead shielding and by tight collimation whenever these do not hamper the examination. At the same time, unnecessary exposure to other parts of the body should be avoided because of possible somatic injury by radiation, especially to the blood-forming bone marrow.

Table 23.4 shows the estimated average skin exposure per film, according to the BRH report of 1970.

Of greater importance are the estimated absorbed doses in the **gonads** during various radiographic examinations according to the same BRH report. These values are shown in Table 23.5. They are based on medium-speed screen-film combinations.

While the data in Tables 23.4 and 23.5 may suffice in general, it is actually preferable to measure the x-ray output of each radiographic unit and determine gonadal doses from appropriate tables

TABLE 23.4
ESTIMATED AVERAGE EXPOSURE PER FILM AT SKIN ENTRANCE,
BASED ON ALL TYPES OF FACILITIES*

Examination	*Entrance Exposure per Film*
	mR
Skull	330
Chest	44
Chest (PA view)	27
Shoulder	260
Thoracic and Cervical Spine	980
Abdomen—KUB	670
Cholecystography and Cholangiography	620
Lumbar Spine	1,920
Lumbosacral Spine	2,180
Upper G.I. Series	710
Barium Enema	1,320
Pelvis	610
Hip	560
Femur	120
Tibia and Fibula	40
Ankle	140
Foot, Toes, Heel	120
Forearm and Elbow	60
Hand and Wrist	100

*From *Population Exposure to X Rays, U.S. 1970.* Bureau of Radiological Health, U.S. Department of Health, Education, and Welfare. Unless otherwise stated, these are mean exposures for various views. Compare these data with those in Table 23.5 which gives exposures using the best possible protective measures in 1957.

in *Handbook of Selected Organ Doses for Projections Common in Diagnostic Radiology* by M. Rosenstein (HEW/FDA 76-8031). Table 23.6 has been adapted from Table 7 in that publication to show in particular the absorbed doses in the ovaries, uterus (no larger than 2-month's pregnant), and testes, resulting from an anteroposterior view of the abdomen.

Note that the basic data include the organ dose per 1000 mR (1 R) in air exposure at the skin, for a focus-film distance of 40 in. (100 cm), film size 14 in. × 17 in. (35.6 cm × 43.2 cm), and a variety of x-ray beam HVLs (mm Al). X-ray output in mR/mAs having been measured at 40 in. using the selected kVp, this value is recorded and kept in an accessible place.

To find the ovarian or uterine (normal size) dose for an anteroposterior view of the abdomen in a particular patient, suppose that

TABLE 23.5
ESTIMATED AVERAGE GONADAL DOSE PER EXAMINATION
FROM RADIOGRAPHY BY TYPE OF EXAMINATION
BY SEX IN THE UNITED STATES
IN 1970 SURVEY (REVISED).*

Type of Examination	Male	Female
	mrads	mrads
Skull	—	—
Cervical Spine	—	—
Chest	—	1
Thoracic Spine	3	10
Upper G.I. Series	1	170
Barium Enema	175	900
Cholecystography	—	80
Excretory Urography	200	600
Abdomen (KUB)	100	220
Lumbar Spine	220	720
Pelvis	360	210
Hip	600	125
Upper Limbs	—	—
Lower Limbs	15	—

*Data rounded off, based on X-ray Exposure Study (XES), new dose model, Bureau of Radiological Health. The published data include a standard error for each average, amounting to about ±8 to 15 percent.

with exposure factors 90 kVp, 100 mAs, 40-in. FFD, and 2.5 mm Al filter, the output is 5 mR/mAs, then for 100 mAs the exposure at the skin (entrance exposure) would be

$$5 \text{ mR/mAs} \times 100 \text{ mAs} = 500 \text{ mR}$$

In Table 22.6 we see that for a radiographic beam having a HVL of 2.5 mm Al, the uterine dose is 265 mrads for an entrance exposure of 1000 mR. Since we have just found that the required skin exposure in this case is 500 mR, the uterine dose for a KUB would be

$$500 \text{ mR}/1000 \text{ mR} \times 265 \text{ mrads} = 123 \text{ mrads}$$

On the assumption that this dose results from a medium-speed film-screen system, we can state that with a 400-speed system, the uterine dose can be reduced to

$$100/400 \times 123 \text{ mrads} = 31 \text{ mrads}$$

TABLE 23.6
ABDOMINAL-ORGAN DOSE (mrad) FOR 1,000 mR
ENTRANCE SKIN EXPOSURE IN AIR
AP ABDOMEN, 40-IN FFD, 14 in. X 17 IN. FILM

	Organ Dose in mrads				
Beam Quality HVL (mm Al)	*1.5*	*2.0*	*2.5*	*3.0*	*3.5*
Ovaries	97	149	203	258	313
Embryo (uterus)	133	199	265	330	392
Testes	<0.01	<0.01	<0.01	<0.01	<0.01

Data abbreviated from Table 7 in *Handbook of Selected Organ Doses for Projections Common in Diagnostic Radiology*, by M. Rosenstein (HEW/FDA 76-8031), 1976.

Dose Reduction in Radiography. We have at least six ways to minimize patient exposure during radiography. They are extremely important and should be learned and used by every technologist. We shall now discuss them individually.

1. *Beam Filtration.* Patient exposure can be greatly reduced by the insertion of an aluminum (Al) filter in the beam to remove the lower energy photons which would otherwise be absorbed by the patient and not contribute to the radiographic image. In other words, a suitable aluminum filter decreases unnecessary exposure of the patient. Naturally, this requires a filter of the proper thickness. Recommendations for filter thickness have been expressed either as (a) minimum total thickness in mm aluminum equivalent (Al eq), including inherent filtration by the glass window of the x-ray tube and the cooling oil in the tube housing, or as (b) half-value layer (HVL) of the x-ray beam in mm Al.

Table 23.7 shows the minimum Al eq filtration needed for each of three useful kVp ranges according to NCRP Report No. 33 (1968). You can see that above 70 kVp, the *total* filtration must be no less than *2.5 mm Al eq.* It is common practice to use this amount of filtration for beams generated at potentials below 70 kVp as well.

However, we prefer to state beam quality in terms of HVL because this can be measured by a qualified person. Furthermore, the inherent filtration of an x-ray tube is not always known, so there is uncertainty as to how much additional filter is required. The HVL is usually determined at 80 kVp and must have a

TABLE 23.7
REQUIREMENTS FOR FILTRATION IN RADIOGRAPHY*

Operating kVp	Minimum Total Filter (inherent plus added) in mm Al eq
Below 50	0.5
50–70	1.5
Above 70	2.5

*From NCRP Report No. 33 (1968).

minimum value of 3 mm Al at this kVp level. (The *U.S. Code of Federal Regulations — 21 CFR 800.10, April 1983* — specifies minimum HVLs for various kVp ranges on all new equipment manufactured after December 1, 1983.)

How much dose reduction can we expect from beam filtration? Table 23.8 shows that a 3 mm Al filter (added) reduces exposure to the testes to about 1/3 to 1/2 that with an unfiltered beam at 65 to 68 kV (Ardran and Crooks). Another study with a pelvic phantom showed that a 3 mm Al filter reduces skin exposure to about 1/5 that without filtration at 60 kV, other exposure factors (mAs) being adjusted to maintain equal radiographic density (Trout and others). Furthermore, in this latter study it was found that at 60 kV the mAs had to be increased to compensate for the removal of x-ray photons by the filter, but this did not increase the actual exposure of the patient. At 130 kV, filters up to 3 mm thick did not require an increase in mAs.

2. *Beam Limitation ("Collimation").* As we have already explained (see pages 411–417), a decrease in the cross-sectional area of the beam not only avoids unnecessary exposure of the patient outside the area of interest, but it also reduces the amount of scattered radiation generated within the patient. We achieve this most efficiently by means of beam-limiting devices that are loosely called collimators. The variable shutter type is preferred. Federal regulations require that all new equipment must have *positive variable beam-limiting devices* interlocked with the bucky tray so that the beam size is automatically restricted to the particular

TABLE 23.8
REDUCTION IN EXPOSURE OF MALE GONADS (TESTES)
WHEN 3 mm Al FILTER IS ADDED*

Examination	Added Filtration	kV	Testes Uncovered	Testes Covered 1 mm Sheet Lead
			mR	mR
Pelvis, AP	0	65	2,000	42
15 × 12 in. film	3 mm Al	65	670	24
Lumbar Spine, AP	0	68	24	5
10 × 12 in. film	3 mm Al	68	6	2

*Data of Ardran, G. M., and Crooks, H. E. (Courtesy of authors and *British Journal of Radiology*.)

cassette size. A manual override may be provided for use, with certain limitations, in the event of system failure. Neither the length nor the width of the x-ray field in the plane of the film (or other image receptor) may differ from the corresponding film dimension by more than 3 percent of the FFD. Thus, at a 40-in. (100-cm) FFD, the x-ray field dimension at the film must be within 3 cm of the corresponding film dimension.

3. *Gonadal Shielding.* Although the beam should be so restricted that direct exposure of the gonads does not occur unnecessarily, additional precautions should be taken to use specific gonadal shields when these do not obscure the area of interest. In the majority of radiographic examinations, specific shielding of the testes should be used when they lie within the beam, or within 5 cm beyond the edge of the beam. The shield must have a lead equivalent of at least 0.5 mm. Ovaries should be shielded whenever possible, although this is limited by uncertainty as to their exact location.

4. *High-speed Image Receptors.* A great reduction in patient exposure results from the use of the highest speed intensifying screens and films consistent with satisfactory image quality. Rare earth screens having a speed of 400, that is, four times that of medium speed screens, decrease patient exposure to about one-fourth relative to medium speed without significantly impairing recorded detail. Therefore, high-speed film-screen systems should

prevail in routine radiography, although slower systems still play an important role in special situations where fine recorded detail is needed.

5. ***Optimum Film Processing.*** Automated film processing has become universal in modern radiology departments. Processors require careful maintenance for optimal function. This assures consistently high radiographic quality in properly exposed films and helps avoid repeat examinations.

6. ***High Kilovoltage.*** As we pointed out earlier (see pages 251–252), higher kV entails more efficient tube operation. Also, for equal radiographic density, higher kV with lower mAs delivers a smaller absorbed dose to the patient. Therefore, we should use the highest kV consistent with optimum image quality. With modern equipment capable of a wide range of mAs values, an optimum kV can be selected for a particular anatomic part. The most modern radiographic equipment is provided with automatic exposure control (phototiming) which selects optimum kV and mAs for various anatomic regions

7. ***Careful technic*** to minimize repeat examinations.

Based on the preceding discussion, we may summarize as follows the important factors in reducing patient exposure during radiography—so-called ***minimum dose radiography:***

1. ***Beam filtration*** to provide an ***HVL of at least 3 mm Al at 80 kVp.*** Or we may express the required filtration in terms of the ***total minimum*** (inherent plus added); this is ***2.5 mm Al eq*** for beams generated at potentials above 70 kVp, although the same filtration is used at 70 kVp and below.
2. ***Beam limitation ("collimation")*** to the smallest possible dimensions by a variable beam-limiting device. Equipment of the most modern type is provided with positive (automatic) variable beam-limiting devices with manual override.
3. ***Lead shielding of the gonads*** by at least 0.5 mm lead equivalent (see NCRP Report No. 68). However, it may be omitted if it hides the area of interest.
4. ***Highest speed screen-film systems*** consistent with good image quality; 400-speed systems using rare earth screens and

appropriate films in general radiography.

5. *Optimum film processing* for consistent results.
6. *Highest practicable kV* that still yields good image quality.
7. *Careful technic* to minimize repeat examinations.

In any procedure using ionizing radiation, whether radiography, fluoroscopy, or nuclear medicine, the patient should be questioned about previous exposures. The total exposure, especially to gonads, embryo, and bone marrow, should be kept at the lowest level consistent with medical needs.

Radiographic examinations that expose the gonads or uterus in fertile women should be performed only when absolutely necessary, since the patient may not be aware that she is pregnant. It is during the first few months that the embryo is most susceptible to fatal injury or the induction of serious congenital anomalies. Some authorities recommend the so-called *10-day rule:* such examinations should be performed only during the first 10 days following the onset of a menstrual period (ie, the "safe" period) because ovulation and pregnancy are much less apt to occur during this time than later in the menstrual cycle. However, if a radiographic examination is medically necessary, it should be carried out with strict adherence to all available protective measures as described above.

Patient Protection in Fluoroscopy

Fluoroscopy presents a considerable hazard, so before a patient is subjected to this type of examination, a careful history should be taken to ascertain the recency and number of previous fluoroscopic studies. X-ray exposures produce cumulative effects, and further exposures must be governed by what has gone before.

Several precautions should be observed to reduce exposure during fluoroscopy:

1. *Intermittent Fluoroscopy.* It is good practice to use intermittent activation of the fluoroscopic tube to decrease patient exposure and prolong tube life.

2. *Restriction of Field Size.* The size of the fluoroscopic field must be limited by suitably collimating lead shutters placed between the tube and the patient. As we have seen, the skin and depth

doses, as well as the scattered radiation into the surroundings, decrease as the area of the radiation field is decreased. Therefore, the fluoroscopic beam should be restricted to the smallest field that includes the area of interest, to reduce exposure of both the patient and personnel. According to the Federal Register Code *21 CFR 800.10,* neither the length nor the width of the useful beam at the image receptor shall exceed that of the visible image area by more than three percent of the source-image receptor distance. In this case, the image receptor is the input screen of the image intensifier.

3. *Correct Operating Factors.* An increase in kV produces an increase in fluoroscopic image brightness. If this is accompanied by an increase in filtration and a compensating decrease in mA, exposure rate to the patient is actually decreased with no change in image brightness. In other words, for a given image brightness, x-ray exposure of the patient decreases as kV is raised and mA is lowered. Since further improvement becomes insignificant above 100 kV, the recommended operating factors are 90 to 100 kV, 2 to 3 mA, and 2.5 mm Al equivalent filter (or beam HVL 3 mm Al) for bright (image intensified) fluoroscopy. Image resolution can be improved by increasing the exposure rate, but this is strictly limited by maximum permissible exposure of the patient. For children the kV should be reduced to a value depending on body thickness, just as in radiography. The source-skin distance must be at least 15 in. (38 cm) with stationary and 12 in. (30 cm) with mobile fluoroscopic equipment according to the federal code cited above. Distances longer than these, with compensating increase in exposure factors, do not significantly reduce patient exposure.

4. *Filtration.* We can increase the hardness of an x-ray beam by using a suitable filter. This removes relatively more soft than hard x rays, thereby removing a large portion of non-image-producing radiation which would otherwise be absorbed in the patient's skin. In fluoroscopy, the same filtration is required as in radiography: total of 2.5 mm Al equivalent, or HVL of 3 mm Al.

5. *Maximum Permissible Exposure.* Although there is the hazard of cumulative small doses of radiation during one's lifetime, there is as yet no official limit to x-ray exposure of patients in diagnostic radiology. Obviously, this should be reduced to a mini-

mum consistent with medical needs. According to the federal code cited above, the exposure rate at the table top (ie, patient's entrance exposure rate) must be no greater than 10 R/min for fluoroscopic equipment with automatic exposure rate control and no greater than 5 R/min without automatic exposure rate control. This does not apply to the exposure rate in the radiographic spotfilm mode. In addition, a timer must be provided to preset the on-time of the fluoroscopic tube for a cumulative total of no more than 5 min. At the end of this time, an audible signal must indicate that the time limit has been reached and must continue to sound as long as fluoroscopy continues until the timer is reset.

6. *Primary Protective Barrier.* This must be provided to protect the fluoroscopist by intercepting the entire cross section of the useful beam at any SID (ie, distance between x-ray source and input screen). The fluoroscopic tube must not produce x rays unless the barrier is in its proper position. This barrier must limit the fluoroscopist's exposure from transmitted radiation, essentially, to no more than 2 mR/hr for each R/min of the patient's entrance exposure rate.

Patient Protection in Therapy

The problem of patient protection in therapy differs from that in diagnosis. Depending on the lesion to be treated, a radiation therapist varies the radiation dose to obtain the desired effect. In some instances this dose is so small that little or no skin reaction ensues. At the other extreme lies the treatment of certain cancers that require doses large enough to produce significant changes in normal tissues.

Various size cones serve to restrict the treatment field in *orthovoltage* radiotherapy. Frequently, the field is further delimited by lead shields, which are arranged to protect the surrounding normal tissues. The thickness of such lead barriers depends on the kV and filtration (ie, HVL) of the x-ray beam. Table 23.9, based on the data of Trout and Gager, summarizes the lead thickness required for beams of various half-value layers to reduce the exposure rate to 0.5 percent of the initial value. The last column in the table indicates the nearest lead thicknesses that are ordinarily available

TABLE 23.9
THICKNESS OF LEAD REQUIRED TO REDUCE
THE INCIDENT RADIATION TO 0.5 PERCENT
OF THE INITIAL EXPOSURE RATE,
WITH BEAMS OF VARIOUS DEGREES OF HARDNESS*

kV	Half Value Layer	Thickness of Lead for 0.5% Transmission		Usual Thickness of Lead Available
		mm	in.	in.
60	0.5 mm Al	0.21	0.008	1/100
100	1.0 mm Al	0.68	0.026	3/100
140	0.5 mm Cu	1.52	0.06	1/16
200	1.0 mm Cu	1.97	0.08	5/64
220	2.0 mm Cu	2.77	0.11	1/8
250	3.0 mm Cu	3.45	0.14	5/32

*Data of Trout, E. D. and Gager, R. M. (Courtesy of *American Journal of Roentgenology.*)

and may safely be used with the beam of a given half-value layer.

In irradiation therapy in the one to two million volt range a lead block 5 cm (2 in.) thick is required to shape the beam. The block should be at least 38 cm (15 in.) from the skin to avoid contamination of the beam with Compton electrons which intensify the skin reaction.

ELECTRICAL PROTECTION

It is noteworthy that the introduction of shockproof equipment in therapy and radiography has made nonshockproof equipment obsolete. With modern equipment, the shock hazard has been eliminated, provided the ground connections are intact, grounding is adequate, and the cables are in satisfactory condition. These should be inspected periodically.

Oddly enough, one of the commonest sources of electrical danger exists in the darkroom. All exposed electric outlets must be **grounded.** The technologist should always observe the **one-hand rule:** never reach for an electric fixture while the other hand is submerged in the processing tanks or is touching a conductor.

High-voltage, low-amperage shock tends to "throw," whereas low-voltage, high-amperage shocks tends to "hold" the victim. In the latter instance, do not grasp the victim directly, but first either open the main switch or remove him/her by means of a dry board, a dry wad of newspaper, or a dry rope. Immediately call for medical aid, in the meanwhile applying cardiopulmonary resuscitation (CPR).

Closely allied to the electric hazard is the *danger of explosion.* When certain gas anesthetics reach a sufficiently high concentration in the atmosphere, they may ignite explosively if a spark occurs either in the electrical contacts of the equipment or from a static electric discharge. Fortunately, explosive gases are no longer used in modern operating rooms.

PERSONNEL PROTECTION IN BRACHYTHERAPY

By *brachytherapy* we mean treatment at short distances (interstitial, intracavitary, or surface) with sealed sources of radium or one of its substitutes such as gold 198, cesium 137, iridium 192, or tantalum 182. Just as with x rays, inadvertent exposure of personnel during brachytherapy involves general body radiation as well as local radiation. These two aspects of protection will now be discussed separately. Sealed sources must be tested every six months if they are subject to leakage as is true with radium (see *NCRP Report #40,* pp. 12 to 14).

Protection from Whole-body Exposure in Brachytherapy

Whole-body exposure from brachytherapy occurs during:
1. Storage
2. Manipulation
3. Transportation

Storage of radionuclides requires *lead* and *distance,* the two best available means of protection for this purpose. However, large thicknesses of lead are needed because of the great penetrating power of gamma rays (see pages 553–555 for method of computing adequate distances and barriers, and *NCRP Report #40*).

Table 23.10 shows the thickness of lead shielding required to reduce to the MPD, the exposure from various quantities of radium stored at different distances. In this table, note that 100 mg radium should be stored in a container with a wall thickness of 7.2 cm lead at 1 meter (3 ft). At 2 meters (6 ft) the thickness is reduced to 4.4 cm lead. With these factors, the MPD (0.1 R per week) will not be exceeded during a forty-hour work-week. In general, more lead is required for larger quantities of radium, but this is not proportional, as shown in the table; the half value layer of radium gamma rays is 1.4 cm lead (Pb). Note that if the amount of stored radium is doubled, one additional HVL (1.4 cm Pb) is needed for protection. As the distance is halved, 2 HVL (2.8 cm Pb) must be added (why?). Different lead thicknesses are required for radium substitutes such as [137]cesium, depending on their gamma-ray energy.

TABLE 23.10
THICKNESS OF LEAD STORAGE CONTAINER
NEEDED FOR PROTECTION FROM RADIUM GAMMA RAYS,
REDUCING EXPOSURE TO 100 MR/WK (40-HR WORK WEEK)*

	Distance	
	1 Meter	*2 Meters*
Radium		
mg	*cm Lead*	*cm Lead*
50	5.8	3.0
100	7.2	4.4
200	8.6	5.8

*Based on *NCRP Report #40*.

Manipulation of sources, as in loading needles, capsules, or other applicators would subject the body to a large exposure. This can be reduced to the permissible level by a wide, L-shaped lead block *at least 5 cm (2 in.) thick* placed between the source and the operator. It should have, at the top, an inclined lead glass visor, equivalent to at least 6 mm lead (see Figure 23.2).

Figure 23.2. Front view of L-shaped lead protective block for loading applicators with radioactive sources such as radium or [137]cesium. The operator stands in front of the block so that the upright section protects the body and the inclined lead visor protects the face. Even more adequate protection of the face, neck, and upper part of the chest can be achieved by use of a higher upright lead section with visibility provided by a wall-mounted mirror.

Protection from Local Exposure to Radium or Its Substitutes

For protection of the hands from *local injury,* the above general measures should first be carefully observed. Then, the additional precaution of handling sources only with long forceps should be strictly observed. *Speed of handling* is as important as distance since both reduce the exposure of the skin. *Never, under any circumstances, should a source be picked up directly with the fingers.* Long forceps or some similar instrument should be used. Leaded gloves and aprons offer no protection from gamma rays because it is impracticable to use sufficient lead thickness; even more important, secondary radiation induced in lead of this thickness would actually increase exposure. In fact, lead foil is used as an intensifying screen with megavoltage radiation for port radiographs in teletherapy and in industrial radiography of metals.

Local injury may not appear for a number of years, depending, of course, on the exposure. It consists, in the early stages, of reddening and dryness of the skin. Later, this gives way to brittleness and splitting of the nails, followed by keratoses, atrophy, and ulceration of the skin. Finally, cancer may develop in the ulcerated areas.

Transportation of sources requires long-handled containers lined with sufficient lead. For example, 100 mg radium should be carried in a container lined with 2 cm lead suspended by a handle 45 cm long; or, the container may have a 1 cm lead thickness and a handle 60 cm long. Transportation should be as fast as possible, preferably by someone who does not regularly handle radioactive sources if they are to be carried frequently.

PROTECTION IN NUCLEAR MEDICINE

The handling of radionuclides requires certain percautions because of the harmful effects of chronic exposure to ionizing radiation, as already described. But the problems associated with radionuclides differ in some respects from those prevailing in the diagnostic x-ray department; hence, the need of a separate section dealing with health physics in nuclear medicine. Medical compounds containing radionuclides are called ***radiopharmaceuticals.***

Types of Radiation. Before discussing the harmful effects of radiation emitted by radionuclides and the methods of protection, let us review the types of radiation involved. In general, radioactive substances give off three types of radiation: alpha particles, beta particles, and gamma rays. Figure 23.3 shows their respective half-value layers as an indication of their penetrating abilities. Since radiopharmaceuticals emit only gamma or beta rays, our discussion will be limited to them. Not only do gamma rays have much greater penetrating ability than beta particles, but they also differ from them in character. Thus, gamma rays are electromagnetic waves or photons, whereas beta particles consist of high-speed electrons. Consequently, protection must differ for these two kinds of radiation.

Harmful Effects. These have already been described in detail on pages 548–552. The same effects are produced by beta and gamma

Figure 23.3. Comparative absorption of alpha, beta, and gamma rays in various materials. Also shown are the half-value layers (HVL) of 1 MeV gamma rays in lead, concrete, and body tissues.

radiation as by x radiation, for equal absorbed doses. However, beta radiation is less penetrating than the others, its effects being limited to the skin with external exposure, or to its immediate vicinity with internally deposited beta-emitting sources. On the other hand, the effects of x and gamma rays are manifested deep within the body even with external exposure.

Maximum Permissible Dose Equivalent. Since the radiations from artificial radionuclides used in medicine include only beta and gamma rays, the maximum permissible dose can be stated in rads, as already described on pages 545–546. The same equation applies:

$$MPD = 5(N - 18) \text{ rads}$$

where N is the age. It must be emphasized again that this equation applies to *chronic whole body exposure of professional radiation workers,* including technologists. The same limit applies to exposure of the gonads and the eyes. The MPD to the hands, forearms, feet, and ankles is fifteen times that to the whole body. For more specific data on MPD, see Figure 23.1 and *NCRP Report #39* and *#40.*

Principles of Radiation Protection. There are basically four factors, suitable combinations of which are used to reduce or eliminate radiation hazards in nuclear medicine. These include: (1) *distance,*

(2) *shielding*, (3) *time of exposure*, and (4) *limitation of activity* of source to smallest required amount. In this section, we shall assume that the radioactive sources are sealed in the form of capsules or needles. Liquid preparations of radionuclides, except for the hazard of spill, ingestion, or inhalation, may also be regarded as sealed sources insofar as external protection is concerned.

1. *Distance.* This is often the easiest and least expensive method of reducing the exposure rate to the permissible level. In the case of gamma rays, the inverse square law applies with reasonable accuracy for the purpose of protection in storage and handling. Long forceps for picking up capsules or needles (^{131}I or ^{60}Co), and removing ^{131}I solutions and other radionuclides from shipping containers, will reduce significantly the exposure of the hands and forearms. With highly active sources, remote handling equipment is necessary to keep the exposure down to the permissible level.

The *storage* of radiopharmaceuticals that emit *gamma rays* should be as remote as possible from areas habitually occupied by personnel and patients. The following equation gives the *shortest permissible distance* (*SPD*) for *gamma-ray emitters*, that is, the distance at which the exposure rate approximates the MPD in a forty-hour work week:

$$D = 20\sqrt{A\Gamma} \; cm \qquad (3)$$

where D is the *SPD*, A is the activity of the radionuclide in mCi, and Γ (Greek capital *gamma*) is the specific gamma-ray constant (defined as the exposure rate in R/hr at a distance of 1 cm from a point source of a radionuclide having an activity of 1 mCi). For example, what is the *SPD* from a capsule of ^{131}I containing 10 mCi? The value of Γ for ^{131}I is 2.18 R/hr at 1 cm. Therefore,

$$D = 20\sqrt{10 \times 2.18} = 20\sqrt{21.8}$$
$$= 20 \times 4.7 = 94 \; cm \; or \; 3 \; feet$$

The values of Γ for several of the more commonly used radionuclides are shown in Table 23.11. In actual practice, distance alone is usually impracticable, so shielding is needed to provide adequate protection.

2. *Shielding.* Protective materials placed between a radioactive source and its surroundings to reduce the exposure rate are called

TABLE 23.11
SPECIFIC GAMMA-RAY CONSTANTS
(Γ) OF SOME RADIONUCLIDES*

Nuclide	Γ
	R/mCi-hr at 1 cm
^{198}Au	2.3
^{60}Co	13.0
^{131}I	2.18
^{137}Cs	3.3
^{226}Ra	8.25 (0.5 mm Pt capsule)

*Based on *ICRU Handbook 86* (experimental values).

shields or *barriers.* Proper shielding contributes materially to the reduction of *gamma-ray exposure rate,* especially when combined with distance. The shield may be incorporated in the container itself, or it may be placed as a barrier around the source in the storage or working area. *Lead* of proper thickness serves as the most satisfactory barrier material for storage of radiopharmaceuticals because of its efficiency as an absorber of gamma rays.

The fraction of radiation (of given quality) absorbed by a barrier depends on its *atomic number* and *thickness.* We ordinarily specify barrier thickness in HVL because one HVL of any particular material is equivalent in shielding ability to one HVL of any other material. The HVL, it may be recalled, designates that thickness of any material that reduces the exposure rate of radiation by one-half. The number of HVL's, *n,* required to decrease the exposure rate from a gamma-ray source with an activity A mCi to the permissible level (forty-hour week) at a given distance d cm from the source is given by the following equation:

$$2^n = \frac{400A\Gamma}{d^2} \tag{4}$$

For example, what is the thickness of lead barrier in HVL needed to reduce the gamma radiation from 100 mCi of ^{131}I to the permissible level at a distance of 2 meters (200 cm)? Substituting in equation (4),

$$2^n = \frac{400 \times 100 \times 2.18}{200 \times 200}$$

$$2^n = 2.18$$

$$n \log 2 = \log 2.18$$

$$n = \frac{\log 2.18}{\log 2} = \pm \frac{0.3385}{0.3010} = 1.1 \text{ HVL}$$

Since the HVL of the ^{131}I gamma radiation is 0.3 cm lead,

$$1.1 \text{ HVL} = 1.1 \times 0.3 = 0.33 \text{ cm lead}$$

As a general rule, gamma-ray emitting radiopharmaceuticals should be stored in their shipping container and surrounded with lead bricks 5 cm (2 in.) in thickness, on all sides that might constitute radiation hazard. Routine monitor surveys should then establish the adequacy of the barrier.

Shielding of **beta radiation** differs from that of gamma rays. Since the range of beta particles in soft tissues is usually limited to several mm, the external hazard can be readily controlled. The range of a beta particle depends on its energy; therefore low energy beta particles (ie, less than 0.3 MeV) are absorbed by the container, by the cornified layer of the skin, or by several feet of air. On the other hand, the medical radionuclides ^{32}P (maximum beta energy 1.7 MeV) and ^{90}Sr-^{90}Y (maximum beta energy 2.18 MeV) require special shielding to protect against brems radiation produced when the beta particles interact with atoms. Plastic materials such as Lucite or polystyrene are preferred because they are light-transparent and because their low atomic number reduces the intensity of brems radiation production. About ¼ in. plastic suffices for ^{32}P, and about ⅜ in. for ^{90}Sr. Since air contributes significantly to the protective barrier, the handling of these beta emitters, especially when sealed, poses no difficult problem if a sufficient thickness and area of plastic shielding are used.

3. *Time of Exposure.* Since the total exposure is equal to the exposure rate times the time, it is obvious that the faster a given procedure is carried out, the smaller is the exposure incurred by the operator. Each different procedure should first be practiced with blank (nonradioactive) materials until adequate speed has

been attained. Only then should the procedure be conducted with radioactive material.

4. *Limitation of Activity of Stored Radiopharmaceuticals.* The exposure rate is directly proportional to the activity of the source. Furthermore, the exposure rates from all sources must be added to obtain the total exposure rate. Hence, the quantities stored should be kept at a minimum consistent with the requirements of the department.

Radiation Monitoring. Besides requiring that all personnel wear film badges (see page 547–548), every Nuclear Medicine Department should conduct periodic surveys to determine the exposure rates from stored radionuclides (radium as well as artificial radionuclides); from possibly contaminated work areas and waste receptacles, especially when liquid preparations are used; and from possibly contaminated clothing, shoes, instruments, and hands. Such surveys are advisable at least weekly, and even more often when deemed necessary. Whenever patients receive radionuclides in quantities other than tracer doses, clothing, sputum cups, bedpans, urinals, and other utensils that may have become contaminated must be surveyed before they can be declared "safe." All contaminated articles must be stored in special bins with appropriate lead shielding and at a permissible distance until the activity has decreased to a level a few times that of background.

The two most popular survey instruments include (1) the *survey meter*, a portable battery operated *GM counter* with a ratemeter, and (2) the *cutie pie*, a direct-reading *ionization chamber* (see Figures 23.4 and 23.5). Both are calibrated to read in mR/hr (milliroentgens per hour). In addition, the survey meter can indicate counts per minute and is usually provided with earphones for audible detection of counts. A survey meter operating continuously as a GM counter should be placed at the exit of any laboratory where high level activity prevails, so that a constant check can be maintained on personnel leaving the laboratory.

Special Precautions—Nursing Procedures. Complete details for every possible radionuclide procedure are beyond the intent of this book. Reference should be made to publications of the Atomic Energy Commission, or the appropriate State Agency or local Health Department. However, certain principles are exemplified

Figure 23.4. Battery-operated portable survey meter with GM counter. A phone jack is included for audible detection. (*Based on Nuclear-Chicago Model.*)

Figure 23.5. Battery-operated radiation meter known popularly as the "cutie pie." Ionization chamber type.

by the more commonly used radiopharmaceuticals. In any event, children and pregnant women should be kept out of the room of any patient receiving internal gamma-ray therapy.

1. *Waste Disposal.* All radioactive wastes must be disposed of according to the regulations of the State Health Department, especially where high activity is concerned. With ^{131}I in quantities used for tracer studies and in treatment of hyperthyroidism, and

with ³²P used in diagnosis and treatment, no special precautions are necessary for waste disposal. But with the amount of ¹³¹I used in the treatment of thyroid cancer and heart disease the high activity in the urine demands monitoring of contaminated linens by the radiation safety officer. Patients receiving radiopharmaceuticals internally may freely use the regular toilet facilities regardless of the dose, but hospitalization is required if the activity of ¹³¹I within the body exceeds 30 mCi. Even at this level, close contact may be hazardous to a small infant or child.

2. **Nursing Procedures.** Hazard to nursing personnel can be minimized (see *NCRP Report #37* for details):

a. *¹³¹I in Hyperthyroidism.* For the first three days, rubber gloves should be worn in handling emesis basins, bedpans, and urinals; linens should be handled in the same way if the patient is incontinent, but should not be changed unless soiled. All linens should be placed in a special hamper and surveyed. The gloves should be washed for two minutes with soap and running water before being removed from the hands, and then set aside for surveying; the hands should then be thoroughly washed. Ambulatory patients should use the bathroom.

b. *¹³¹I in Thyroid Cancer or Heart Disease.* Activity in the urine and sweat is very high, but the external hazard is small (actually, much less than in radium therapy). The nurse should wear rubber gloves as above. No baths are to be given during the first forty-eight hours. Linens should be surveyed. The patient should also be surveyed and permissible distances and exposure times posted. Children and pregnant women must not be allowed to visit, a cautionary radioactivity sign being posted on the door of the patient's room. The patient may have bathroom privileges, but contaminated linens require surveying by the radiation safety officer, and disposal according to regulations.

c. *³²P in Therapy.* No precautions are needed other than rubber gloves if the patient is incontinent or vomits within the first twenty-four hours. A responsible member of the Nuclear Medicine Department should be notified of such occurrence.

d. *¹⁹⁸Au, Ra and ⁶⁰Co (internal) Therapy.* Radioactive gold in pleural or peritoneal effusions requires monitoring the patient and posting safe distances and exposure times. As for *¹⁹⁸Au,* rubber gloves should be used during the first forty-eight hours; dressings from contaminated wounds must not be changed during the first three days and must be surveyed.

Precautions with ^{198}Au are generally the same as for ^{131}I. Table 23.12 gives the shortest permissible distances and the longest permissible daily exposure times for personnel attending patients harboring radionuclides of various activities. These assume no shielding by the patient's body. However, such **personnel** are in a restricted area whenever they are attending a patient containing a gamma-emitting radionuclide and should be monitored on the basis of the occupational MPD.

TABLE 23.12

MINIMUM PERMISSIBLE WORKING DISTANCES AND
DAILY EXPOSURE TIMES FOR PERSONNEL
ATTENDING PATIENTS RECEIVING
VARIOUS ACTIVITIES OF RADIONUCLIDES

^{131}I or ^{198}Au (first 2 days)	Ra	Maximum Permissible Daily Exposure Times in Minutes for Various Distances			
mCi	mCi	30 cm (1 ft)	60 cm (2 ft)	1 m (3 ft)	2 m (6 ft)
25	—	20	90	200	800
50	—	10	45	100	400
150	50	4	15	30	120
200	—	2½	12	25	100
300	100	2	7½	15	60

Children and pregnant women should not be allowed to visit patients undergoing internal therapy with gamma-emitting radionuclides. The same applies to women in the child-bearing age, within the first ten days of the last menstrual period, unless they are on contraceptive medication. With any of the gamma-ray emitters, appropriate warning signs must be posted on the door of the patient's room.

The following list of unsafe practices serves as a useful check list of the safety of one's own nuclear medicine department.

1. Inadequate planning—excessive time required for carrying out procedures.
2. Improper monitoring.
3. Inadequate shielding.

4. Inadequate use of trays and paper covering of work areas when radioactive liquids are used.

5. Pipetting solutions by mouth instead of remote apparatus.

6. Poor work habits, such as smoking or eating in the laboratory.

7. Inadequate use of proper outer garments, such as rubber gloves and laboratory coats, when handling high level radioactive liquids.

8. Improper waste disposal.

9. Improperly designed fume hoods in high-level laboratories.

10. Changing levels of activity without modifying procedures to maintain low hazard.

11. Failure to keep adequate radiation safety records of radionuclides received, waste disposal, and personnel exposure.

12. Failure to post special signs to mark storage and disposal areas.

RADIATION HYGIENE

Assuming that all of the above safety factors have been followed and the technologist has been most conscientious in observing the rules, can we be certain that hazards have been completely removed? As far as we know, there have been no harmful effects from exposures approximating the MPD. Periodic blood counts, although of value in detecting early radiation injury, are a poor substitute for preventive monitoring of radiation by means of film badges or other devices. Film badges are readily available through commercial radiation laboratories. If the permissible dose is exceeded, the situation must be corrected without delay.

Upon accepting a new job, radiologic technologists should have a complete blood count and physical examination. In addition, radionuclide technologists should wear finger film badges or, preferably, TLD rings to monitor hand exposure. Upon terminating employment, the technologist must be given a complete summary of the incurred radiation exposure.

The danger from ionizing radiation in the well-controlled Radiology Department is virtually nil provided all personnel make full use of all protective devices and equipment and take care to avoid exposure. This is confirmed by the fact that there have been no reports of radiation injury to radiologic technologists in well-controlled Radiology Departments.

QUESTIONS AND PROBLEMS

1. State the causes of background radiation. What is the average individual background exposure per year from natural and from artificial sources?
2. Define maximum permissible dose equivalent. What is the whole-body MPD for an eight-hour day? For one week? For one year?
3. Describe two methods by which one may determine the amount of whole-body radiation being received in the Radiology Department.
4. Discuss the effects of excessive whole-body exposure to ionizing radiation. What are the locally damaging effects of over-exposure to ionizing radiation?
5. Name the materials widely used in protective barriers. What material (and thickness) is required for the walls of ordinary radiographic rooms? For 250-kV x rays? For cobalt 60 gamma rays? For 6-MV x rays?
6. How can one avoid the local deleterious effects of x rays? Of radium and artificial radionuclides.
7. Define dose equivalent; quality factor. What is the unit of *DE?* Of what importance are these concepts?
8. Discuss minimum exposure radiography in (1) fluoroscopy and (2) radiography, including the important factors in each.
9. Assume that the conditions of your x-ray department are "safe," from the standpoint of ionizing radiation. State three rules of conduct on your part that will help keep your exposure below the MPD.
10. Discuss the best means of protection from radium gamma rays.
11. Name and describe the four main protective measures with radionuclides.
12. Find the shortest permissible distance from 100 mCi of ^{131}I. Suppose this source is to be stored at a distance of 1 meter from an occupied area; what thickness of lead would be

required to reduce the exposure to the MPD at the same distance?

13. Why should x-ray equipment be grounded? Does an ordinary steam-heating pipe afford a satisfactory ground connection? A gas pipe? A water pipe?

14. What is the one-hand rule? Why should it always be observed?

15. Discuss the basic precautions of nursing personnel in attending patients undergoing internal radium and artificial radionuclide therapy. Why should children and pregnant women not be permitted to visit patients undergoing internal therapy with gamma-emitting radionuclides?

16. A patient has a 60-mg radium implant, and the survey meter reads 50 mR/hr at one meter from the patient.
    A. Find the maximum allowable time of exposure at a distance of one meter from the patient during an 8-hour working day for (1) radiologic personnel and (2) for nonradiologic nursing personnel.
    B. What would the maximum allowable times be in each instance at a distance of two meters?

APPENDIX–ANSWERS TO PROBLEMS

Chapter 1.

1. (a) $\frac{1}{2}$ (b) $\frac{3}{4}$ (c) $\frac{2}{3}$ (d) $\frac{4}{5}$
2. (a) $1\frac{4}{5}$ (b) $1^{71}/_{84}$ (c) $1^{29}/_{30}$
3. 25 bu
4. (a) $1\frac{1}{3}$ (b) $1\frac{1}{63}$ (c) $1^{13}/_{27}$
5. $b = ac$ $c = b/a$
6. (a) 8   (b) -3 (c) $2\frac{1}{3}$ (d) $4\frac{4}{9}$ (e) 44
7. (a) $\frac{2}{3}$ (b) 5   (c) $10\frac{1}{2}$ (d) 15
8. 20 cm
9. tripled
10. 12.56 cm^2
11. 600 sq ft
12. about $3\frac{3}{4}$ min
13. 3,600,000
14. 4.24×10^5
15. 1.6×10^6

Chapter 2.

11. 20 C
12. 104 F

Chapter 4.

7. 12
8. At. no. 6
   Mass no. 8

Chapter 6.

8. 2 amps
9. 150 volts
11. $1.8\ \Omega$; 4, 2, and $\frac{2}{3}$ amps in branches; $6\frac{2}{3}$ amps in main lines.

13. 24 watts

Chapter 10.

3. 110,000 volts = 110 kV
10. 100/240 or 5/12

Chapter 13.

11. 1/10 sec

Chapter 16.

9. 10 gal (38 liters).

Chapter 18.

13. 80 R/min   5R/min
14. 300 mA
16. 20 mAs
31. Image diameter 10 in. (25.4 cm). Percentage magnification 11% Magnification factor 1.11

Chapter 19.

18. 16 in. (40.6 cm)
20. 8 in. × 10 in. (20.3 cm × 25.4 cm)

Chapter 22.

9. Total counting time 5.3 min; background counting time 2.6 min. Total count 1060, background count 130.
10. 435 cps, corrected, with GM counter. No correction needed for scintillation counter.

Chapter 23.

12. 9.7 ft; 0.94 cm lead.
16. A. (1) 24 min/day
        (2) 2.4 min/day
      B. (1) 96 min/day
        (2) 9.6 min/day

BIBLIOGRAPHY

Batson OV, Carpentier VE. Stereoscopic depth perception. *Am J Roentgenol* *51*:202, 1944.

Bergeron RT. Manufacturers' designation of diagnostic x-ray tube focal spots. *Radiology 111*:421, 1974.

Bernstein H, Bergeron RT, Klein DJ. Routine evaluation of focal spots. *Radiology 111*:427, 1974.

Bloom WL, Jr, Hollenbach JL, Morgan JA. *Medical Radiographic Technic,* 3rd ed. Springfield, Thomas, 1969.

Bookstein JJ, Voegeli E. A critical analysis of magnification radiography. *Radiology 98*:23, 1971.

Bucky GP. A grating-diaphragm to cut off secondary rays from the object. *Archives of the Roentgen Ray,* June 1913.

Bureau of Radiological Health. *Population Exposure to X rays U.S. 1970.* Washington, D.C., U.S. Department of Health, Education, and Welfare, 1973.

Bureau of Radiological Health. *Pre-release Report: X-ray Exposure Study (XES) Revised Estimates of 1964 and 1970 Genetically Significant Dose.* Washington, D.C., U.S. Department of Health, Education, and Welfare, 1975.

Bushong SC. *Radiologic science for technologists. Physics, Biology, and Protection,* 2nd ed. St Louis, Mosby, 1980.

Chamberlain WE. Fluoroscopes and fluoroscopy. *Radiology 38*:383, 1942.

Christensen EE, Curry TS III, Nunnally J. *An Introduction to the Physics of Diagnostic Radiology,* 2nd ed. Philadelphia, Lea & Febiger, 1978.

Cullinan JE. *Illustrated Guide to X-ray Technics,* 2nd ed. Philadelphia, Lippincott, 1980.

Dalrymple GV, Gaulden ME, Kollmorgen GM, Vogel HH Jr. *Medical Radiation Biology.* Philadelphia, Saunders, 1973.

Doi K, Rossman K. Effect of focal spot distribution on blood vessel imaging in magnification radiography. *Radiology 114*:435, 1975.

Dyke WP. Advances in field emission. *Sci Am 210*:108, 1964.

Eastman Kodak Company, Rochester, N. Y.:
   The Fundamentals of Radiography, 1980.
   Radiography in Modern Industry.
   Sensitometric Properties of X-ray Films.

Egan RL. *Technologist Guide to Mammography.* Baltimore, Williams & Wilkins, 1968.

Ettinger A, Fainsinger MH. Zonography in daily radiological practice. *Radiology 87:*82, 1966.

Federal Register *Code of Federal Regulations (21 CFR 800. 10)* U.S. Government Printing Office. April 1, 1983.

Field T, Seed L. *Clinical Use of Radioisotopes.* Chicago, Year Bk Med, 1961.

Fuchs WC. *Principles of Radiographic Exposure and Processing.* Springfield, Thomas, 1969.

Gaulden ME. Possible effects of diagnostic X-rays on the human embryo and fetus. *J Arkansas Med Soc, 70:*424, 1974.

Gould RG, Hale J. Control of scattered radiation by air gap techniques: application to chest radiography. *Am J Roentgenol 122:*109, 1974.

Graham BJ, Thomas WN. *An Introduction to Physics for Radiologic Technologists.* Philadelphia, Saunders, 1975.

Grigg ERN. *The Trail of the Invisible Light.* Springfield, Thomas, 1965.

Handbooks, U. S. Department of Commerce, National Bureau of Standards, Superintendent of Documents, Washington, DC.

   84. *Radiation Quantities and Units. International Commission on Radiologic Units and Measurements (ICRU Report 10a).*

   85. *Physical Aspects of Radiation (ICRU Report 10b).*

   86. *Radioactivity (ICRU Report 10c).*

   87. *Clinical Dosimetry (ICRU Report 10d).*

   88. *Radiobiologic Dosimetry (ICRU Report 10e).*

   89. *Methods of Evaluating Radiological Equipment and Materials (ICRU Report 10f).*

Hendee WR. *Medical Radiation Physics,* 2nd ed. Chicago, Year Bk Med, 1979.

Humphries RE. Personal communication.

Jaffe C, Webster EW. Radiographic contrast improvement by means of slit radiography. *Radiology 116:*631, 1975.

Jans RG, Butler PF, McCrohan JL, Thompson WE. The status of film-screen mammography: results of the BENT study. *Radiology 132:*197, 1979.

Johns HE, Cunningham JR. The Physics of Radiology, 4th ed. Springfield, Thomas, 1983.

Kieffer J. Analysis of laminographic motions and their values. *Radiology 33:*560, 1939.

Liebel-Flarsheim Company. *Characteristics and Applications of X-ray Grids.* Cincinnati, 1968.

Littleton JT, Rumbaugh CL, Winter FS. Polydirectional body section roentgenography: a new diagnostic method. *Am J Roentgenol 89:*1179, 1963.

McGann MJ. Plesiosectional tomography of the temporal bone. *Am J Roentgenol 88:*1183, 1963.

Milne ENC. Characterizing focal spot performance. *Radiology 111:*483, 1974.

National Council on Radiation Protection and Measurements (NCRP) Reports: NCRP, P. O. 7910 Woodmont Ave. Bethesda MD 20814.

   30. *Safe Handling of Radioactive Materials (1964).*

33. *Medical X-ray and Gamma-ray Protection for Energies up to 10 MeV—Equipment Design and Use (1968).*
34. *Medical X-ray and Gamma-ray Protection for Energies up to 10 MeV—Structural Shielding Design and Evaluation (1970).*
37. *Precautions in the Management of Patients Who Have Received Therapeutic Amounts of Radionuclides (1970).*
39. *Basic Radiation Protection Criteria (1971).*
40. *Protection Against Radiation from Brachytherapy Sources (1972).*
45. *Natural Background Radiation in the United States (1975).*
66. *Mammography (1980).*
68. *Radiation Protection in Pediatric Radiology (1981).*

O'Mara RE, Ruzicka FF Jr, Osborne A, Connell J Jr. Xeromammography and film mammography: completion of a comparative study. *Radiology 88:*1121, 1967.

Paul JE, Razzak MA, Sodee DB. *Textbook of Nuclear Medicine Technology.* St Louis, Mosby, 1969.

Pfalzner PM. Attenuation coefficient: finite or infinitesmal? *Physics in Med & Biol 11:*132, 1966.

Potter HE. The Bucky diaphragm principle applied to roentgenology. *Am J Roentgenol 7:*292, 1920.

Potter HE. History of diaphragming roentgen rays by the use of the Bucky principle. *Am J Roentgenol 25:*396, 1931.

Quimby EH, Feitelberg S, Silver S. *Radioactive Isotopes in Clinical Practice.* Philadelphia, Lea & Febiger, 1968.

Rao GUV, Clark RL. Radiographic magnification versus optical magnification. *Radiology 94:*196, 1970.

Rao GUV, Clark RL, Gayer BW. Radiographic magnification: a critical, theoretical, and practical analysis. *Appl Radiol* Part I, 2(1):37, Jan–Feb 1973; 2(2):25, Mar–Apr 1973.

Ridway A, Thumm W. *The Physics of Medical Radiography.* Reading, A-W, 1968.

Rosenstein M. *Handbook of Selected Organ Doses for Projections Common in Radiology.* HEW/FDA 76-8031, 1976.

Rossmann K, Lubberts G. Some characteristics of line spread-function and modulation transfer function of radiographic films and screen-film systems. *Radiology 86:*235, 1966.

Rossman K. Point spread-function, line spread-function, and modulation transfer function. *Radiology 93:*257, 1969.

Scheele RV, Wakley J. *Elements of Radiation Protection.* Springfield, Thomas, 1975.

Schulz RJ. *Primer of Radiation Protection.* New York, GAF Corporation, 1969.

Seemann HE. *Physical and Photographic Principles of Medical Radiography.* New York, John Wiley & Sons, Inc., 1968.

Selman J. *The Basic Physics of Radiation Therapy,* 2nd ed. Springfield, Thomas, 1976.

Selman J. *Elements of Radiobiology.* Springfield, Thomas, 1983.

Shapiro J. *Radiation Protection. A Guide for Scientists and Physicians.* Cambridge, Harvard U Pr, 1972.

Spiegler P, Breckenridge WC. Imaging of focal spots by means of the star test pattern. *Radiology 102:*679, 1972.

Sprawls P Jr. *The Physical Principles of Diagnostic Radiology.* Baltimore, University Park Press, 1977.

Statkiewicz MA, Ritenour ER. *Radiation Protection for Student Radiographers.* Denver, Multi-Media, 1983.

Ter-Pogossian M. *The Physical Aspects of Diagnostic Radiology.* New York, Hoeber, 1967.

Theron WO, Moore R, Amplatz K. The evaluation of high-speed screen-film combinations in angiography. *Radiology 114:*449, 1975.

Trout ED, Gager RM. Protective materials for field definition in radiation therapy. *Am J Roentgenol 63:*396, 1950.

Trout ED, Kelley JP, Cathey GA. The use of filters to control radiation exposure to the patient in diagnostic radiology. *Am J Roentgenol 63:*946, 1952.

Trout ED, Kelley JP, Larson VL. A comparison of an air gap and a grid in roentgenography of the chest. *Am J Roentgenol 124:*404, 1975.

INDEX